Theory of Optimal Control and Mathematical Programming

McGRAW-HILL SERIES IN SYSTEMS SCIENCE

Berlekamp *Algebraic Coding Theory*
Canon, Cullum, and Polak *Theory of Optimal Control and Mathematical Programming*
Gill *Linear Sequential Circuits*
Harrison *Introduction to Switching and Automata Theory*
Jelinek *Probabilistic Information Theory: Discrete and Memoryless Models*
Mangasarian *Nonlinear Programming*
Nilsson *Learning Machines: Foundations of Trainable Pattern-classifying Systems*
Papoulis *Probability, Random Variables, and Stochastic Processes*
Papoulis *Systems and Transforms with Applications in Optics*
Viterbi *Principles of Coherent Communication*
Weber *Elements of Detection and Signal Design*
Zadeh and Desoer *Linear System Theory: The State Space Approach*

Theory of Optimal Control and Mathematical Programming

MICHAEL D. CANON
Research Staff
San Jose Research Laboratory
IBM Corporation
San Jose, California

CLIFTON D. CULLUM, JR.
Research Staff
Thomas J. Watson Research Center
IBM Corporation
Yorktown Heights, New York

ELIJAH POLAK
Professor of Electrical Engineering and Computer Sciences
University of California, Berkeley

McGRAW-HILL BOOK COMPANY

New York San Francisco St. Louis Toronto
London Sydney Mexico Panama

This book was set in Monotype Modern 8A, printed on permanent paper, and bound by The Maple Press Company. The designer was Janet Bollow; the drawings were done by David Strassman. The editors were Basil G. Dandison, Jr., Alice S. Goehring, and Stuart A. Kenter. Charles A. Goehring supervised production.

Theory of Optimal Control and Mathematical Programming

Printed in the United States of America.

Library of Congress catalog card number: 73-78954

234567890 MAMM 787654321

09760

Preface

Until recently, optimal control and nonlinear programming were considered to be distinct disciplines. In the late 1960s, however, it became apparent that a unified approach was not only feasible, but also highly desirable. This volume started out as a research monograph, presenting the authors' original work on a unified theory of constrained optimization in finite-dimensional spaces. This theory deals with conditions of optimality and with their utilization in algorithms. While this volume was being developed, the material to be used was presented in graduate courses on optimization in the department of Electrical Engineering and Computer Sciences, University of California, Berkeley, and in the department of Industrial Engineering, Columbia University. As a result, the scope of the book was enlarged, and a number of examples and exercises were added to provide the reader with a means for testing his understanding of the material. Also, two appendixes were added: one to provide the necessary mathematical background in convexity and one to derive the Pontryagin maximum principle as an illustration of how results are extended from finite-dimensional spaces to infinite-dimensional spaces.

This book has three basic aims: to present a unified theory of optimization, to introduce nonlinear programming algorithms to the control engineer, and to introduce the nonlinear programming expert to optimal control. This volume can be used either as a graduate text or as a reference text. As a basis for a graduate course, the book can be used on several levels. An advanced two-quarter sequence should cover the entire material. Alternatively, to lower the level of the course and reduce the time required, particularly difficult material may be omitted without loss of continuity: Sections 2.3, 2.4, 4.1, and some of the convergence proofs in Chapters 6 and 7, and Appendix B. Furthermore, the course may be biased toward optimal control by omitting Chapter 3, or toward nonlinear programming by omitting Chapter 4 and the optimal control applications in the other chapters. Thus in effect, this book offers several options.

At the end of each chapter is a short list of references, chosen either because they serve as a source for the material of that chapter or because they present an alternative, or complementary, point of view. Thus the references listed constitute a representative sample and not a comprehensive bibliography.

Basically, this book consists of two parts. In the first part, optimal control and nonlinear programming problems are shown to be equivalent to a simple canonical form of a mathematical programming problem. Necessary and sufficient conditions of optimality are derived for this canonical problem and are then specialized to obtain a number of specific results for nonlinear programming and optimal control problems. Much of this material is original. In the second part, a selection of linear and nonlinear programming algorithms is presented, and it is shown how these can be used for the solution of discrete optimal control problems. These algorithms were also chosen to illustrate how optimality conditions are used either as stopping rules in an algorithm, or conceivably, to suggest certain major features of an algorithm. To highlight these applications of optimality conditions, it is necessary to present the algorithms in a somewhat unorthodox manner. This will cause no difficulty to the person unfamiliar with the algorithms, while to the expert it will offer an alternative point of view.

The reader will observe that dynamic programming, stochastic optimal control, and stochastic mathematical programming have been omitted. Dynamic programming is omitted because the theory presented here adds little to its understanding and because it is covered extensively in other books. Stochastic problems are omitted chiefly because their inclusion would have increased this volume considerably beyond its projected size.

The authors are grateful to Dr. E. J. Messerli for a number of examples, exercises, and specialized optimality conditions; to Drs. J. Cullum, H. Halkin, S. Winograd, and Mr. L. P. Kalfon for their critical comments and suggestions; and to the graduate students who took the course EECS 226 at the University of California, Berkeley for their assistance in eliminating errors and ambiguities from the manuscript. Last, but not least, we wish to thank Mrs. Billie Vrtiak for the great care she took in typing the manuscript.

The preparation of this volume involved a great amount of research which would have been impossible without the generous support received from the International Business Machine Corporation; from the National Aeronautics and Space Administration, under grant NsG 354 and supplements 1, 2, 3, 4; from the National Science Foundation under grant GK 716; and from the University of California. This support is gratefully acknowledged.

Michael D. Canon
Clifton D. Cullum, Jr.
Elijah Polak

NOTE TO THE READER

The system of numbering and cross referencing used in this book is described as follows. The top of the right-hand page carries the section number and an abbreviated title of the section to which the page belongs. The top of the left-hand page carries the title of the chapter to which the page belongs. For example, SEC. 5.2 LINEAR CONTROL PROBLEMS appears on the right-hand page in Section 2 of Chapter 5, whose title OPTIMAL CONTROL AND LINEAR PROGRAMMING appears on the left-hand pages. Within each section, definitions, theorems, equations, remarks, and so forth, are numbered consecutively by means of boldface numerals appearing in the left-hand margin. In reference to a section within the same chapter, the section number only is used; in reference to a section in another chapter, both the chapter number and the section number are used. For example, "it was shown in Section 3" refers to Section 3 of the same chapter, while "it was shown in Section 2.3" refers to Section 3 of Chapter 2. Similarly, "substituting from (3)" refers to item 3 in the same section, "substituting from (2.3)" refers to item 3 in Section 2 of the same chapter, and "substituting from (3.2.3)" refers to item 3 in Section 2 of Chapter 3. The two appendixes are lettered A and B, and in references the letters A and B are used in the position of chapter numbers.

Preceding the index is a glossary of symbols which describes notational conventions and contains brief definitions and references to the principal symbols used in this book. The reader is advised to examine this glossary before reading the book.

Contents

1
Problem formulation

1.1 INTRODUCTION

With the exception of Appendix B, the sections of this book which deal with optimal control consider discrete optimal control problems only. In addition, optimal control problems are treated as special cases of mathematical programming problems.

There are essentially two reasons for stressing discrete optimal control. The first reason is pedagogical; the second, and more important one is technical. Discrete optimal control problems are optimization problems in finite-dimensional spaces and, as such, require considerably less mathematical sophistication in their treatment than continuous optimal control problems. In addition, as we shall see in Appendix B, the extension of results from finite-dimensional spaces to infinite-dimensional spaces, and hence to continuous optimal control problems, is conceptually straightforward. It therefore seems to be pedagogically efficient to study discrete optimal control in depth and then to learn about continuous optimal control through natural extensions.

Our main reason for attaching so much importance to discrete optimal control is technical and stems from the constantly increasing use of digital computers in the control of dynamical systems. In any computation carried out on a digital computer, we can do no better than to obtain a finite set of real numbers. Thus in solving a continuous optimal control problem of the form:

1 Minimize $\int_0^{t_f} f^0(x(t),u(t),t)\, dt$ subject to the constraints that for $t \in [0,t_f]$

2 $$\frac{d}{dt}x(t) = f(x(t),u(t),t) \qquad x(t) \in E^n,\ u(t) \in E^m$$

3 $$x(0) \in X_0 \qquad x(t_f) \in X_f$$

4 $$u(t) \in U,$$

we are forced to resort to some form of discretization.

If the discretization is governed only by the nature of the integration formulas to be used in solving (2) and in computing (1), then, in any iterative scheme, we must compute and store a very large number of points $x(t_i)$ and $u(t_i)$, with $t_i \in [0,t_f]$, at each iteration. Thus a straightforward discretization requires large memory capacity and usually results in long computation times, both of which are unacceptable if relatively small computers are to be used to control relatively fast dynamics.

The discretization favored by the authors is the one resulting from the restriction of the inputs $u(\cdot)$ to a class of functions representable by a finite set of parameters. The choice of the class of functions to which $u(\cdot)$ is to belong and of the number of parameters to be computed can be used by the designer to gain a great amount of freedom in controlling the dimension, and hence also the computational complexity of the resulting optimization problem. The price of such a simplification is a reduction in performance. However, without additional restrictions, problem (1) may not be solvable at all (within a prescribed time on the computer we must use), and there may be no choice but to further restrict the problem to make it tractable.

We shall now consider a few simple examples of commonly used discretizations of the inputs $u(\cdot)$. Suppose that in addition to (4) we require that the inputs be piecewise constant. In particular, we may require that

5 $$u(t) = u_i \qquad t \in [iT, (i+1)T),\ u_i \in U,\ i = 0, 1, 2\ \ldots, k-1,$$

where $t_f = kT$ and k is an integer design parameter. The resulting discrete-time optimal control problem has the form:

6 Minimize $\sum_{i=0}^{k-1} f_i^0(x_i,u_i)$ subject to the constraints

7 $$x_{i+1} - x_i = f_i(x_i,u_i) \qquad i = 0, 1, 2, \ldots, k-1$$

8 $$x_0 \in X_0 \qquad x_k \in X_f \qquad u_i \in U,$$

where $f_i(x_i,u_i)$ and $f_i^0(x_i,u_i)$ are computed as follows. For $t \in [iT, (i+1)T)$ let $x_i(t)$ be the solution of (2) corresponding to $u(t) \equiv u_i$ for $t \in [iT, (i+1)T)$ and satisfying $x_i(iT) = x_i$. In addition, we must have that for $i = 0, 1, 2, \ldots, k-1$, $x_{i+1} = x_i((i+1)T)$. Consequently,

9 $$x_{i+1} - x_i = \int_{iT}^{(i+1)T} f(x_i(t),u_i,t)\, dt,$$

and since $x_i(t)$ is uniquely determined by x_i and u_i, the functions in (6) and (7) are properly defined, as follows:

10 $$f_i^0(x_i,u_i) = \int_{iT}^{(i+1)T} f^0(x_i(t),u_i,t)\, dt.$$

11 $$f_i(x_i,u_i) = \int_{iT}^{(i+1)T} f(x_i(t),u_i,t)\, dt.$$

Other useful discretizations of the input that might be considered are

12 $$u(t) = \sum_{j=0}^{s} u_i^j t^j \qquad t \in I_i,\ u_i^j \in A_j \subset E^m,$$

where $\bigcup_i I_i = [0,t_f]$ and the A_j are suitably related to the original constraint set U. Note that when this particular discretization is interpreted in terms of a discrete dynamical system such as (7), we we find that the vector $u_i = (u_i^0,u_i^1, \ldots ,u_i^s) \in E^m \times E^m \times E^m \times \cdots \times E^m$ and therefore has different dimension from the vector $u(t)$.

Once a discretization of the above type has been performed, the original optimal control problem becomes a finite-dimensional mathematical programming problem. This will be demonstrated in detail in the following sections of this chapter. It should be noted at this point, however, that a continuous optimal control problem may generate a finite-dimensional mathematical programming problem without simultaneously giving rise to a discrete optimal control problem. For example, this would be the case if we found it necessary to restrict the inputs $u(\cdot)$ as follows: for $t \in [0,t_f]$

13 $$u(t) = \sum_{i=1}^{s} u_i \varphi_i(t) \qquad u_i \in U_i \subset E^1,$$

where $\varphi_i: E^1 \to E^m$.

The realization that optimal control and mathematical programming problems are essentially one and the same thing, has led the authors [1] (as well as Neustadt [2], and Halkin and Neustadt [3]) to the construction of a unified theory of optimization. As we shall see later, this theory results in substantial conceptual simplifications and facilitates the transcription of highly sophisticated nonlinear programming algorithms for use in discrete optimal control.

1.2 STATEMENT OF THE DISCRETE OPTIMAL CONTROL PROBLEM

To define an optimal control problem we must specify the dynamics of the system, the constraints on the controls and on the trajectories, and in addition, we must specify a cost function. In this book we shall consider finite-dimensional systems whose dynamics satisfy a difference equation of the form

1 $$x_{i+1} - x_i = f_i(x_i,u_i) \qquad i = 0, 1, 2, \ldots,$$

where $x_i \in E^n$ is the system state at time $i = 0, 1, 2, \ldots$; $u_i \in E^m$ is the system input, or control, at time $i = 0, 1, 2, \ldots$; and the $f_i(\cdot,\cdot)$ for $i = 0, 1, 2, \ldots$ are functions mapping $E^n \times E^m$ into E^n, assumed to be continuously differentiable always in x, but not always in u.

The duration of an optimal control process may be either preassigned or not; i.e., it is either fixed or free. It is necessary to emphasize this distinction at the very outset, because considerably more results, both qualitative and algorithmic, are available for fixed-time problems than for free-time problems. Indeed, we shall confine ourselves almost exclusively to fixed-time optimal control problems, and we shall later see how free-time problems can often be solved by solving a sequence of fixed-time problems of increasing duration. In any event, we shall always assume that the duration of the optimal process is finite, since otherwise the optimization might have to be carried out in an infinite-dimensional space, which is outside the scope of this text.

Now let us turn our attention to the type of constraints we shall encounter in fixed-time processes, *which we assume to be of k steps duration*. We assume that we are given k subsets of E^m, which we shall designate by U_i for $i = 0, 1, \ldots, k-1$; $k+1$ subsets of E^n, which we shall designate by X_i for $i = 0, 1, \ldots, k$; a function $h(\cdot,\cdot)$ from $E^{n(k+1)} \times E^{km}$ into E^s, where s is some positive integer; and a subset $D \subset E^s$. Depending on the result desired, we shall later impose various conditions on the sets U_i, X_i, and D and the function $h(\cdot,\cdot)$.

Now let $\mathcal{U} = (u_0,u_1, \ldots ,u_{k-1})$ be a control sequence, and let $\mathcal{X} = (x_0,x_1, \ldots ,x_k)$ be a corresponding trajectory determined by system (1).† We shall say a control sequence $\mathcal{U}$ and a corresponding

† Note that the trajectory $\mathcal{X}$ is not defined uniquely by the control sequence $\mathcal{U}$, since it also depends on the initial state x_0.

trajectory $\mathcal{X}$ are *admissible*[1] if they satisfy the *control constraints*

2 $$u_i \in U_i \qquad i = 0, 1, \ldots, k-1,$$

the *state-space constraints*

3 $$x_i \in X_i \qquad i = 0, 1, \ldots, k,$$

and the *trajectory constraints*

4 $$h(\mathcal{X},\mathcal{U}) \in D.$$

In a typical boundary-value problem, the sets U_i may be intervals of the form $U_i = \{u: |u| \leqq 1\}$ for $i = 0, 1, \ldots, k-1$; the sets X_0 and X_k may be manifolds of the form $X_i = \{x: g_i(x) = 0\}$ for $i = 0, k$ where $g_i: E^n \to E^{l_i}$ for $i = 0, k$; and the other constraints may be nonexistent; that is, $X_i = E^n$ for $i = 1, 2, \ldots, k-1$ and $h \equiv 0$. The function h is commonly used to express limitations imposed by the total quantity of available resources, such as energy or fuel, in which case (4) may assume the form

5 $$\sum_{i=0}^{k-1} \|u_i\|^2 \leqq d \qquad \text{or} \qquad \sum_{i=0}^{k-1}\sum_{j=1}^{m} |u_i^j| \leqq d,$$

where $\|\cdot\|$ is the euclidean norm.

Finally, we assume that we are given a *real-valued cost function*

6 $$f(\cdot\,,\cdot)$$

defined on $E^{n(k+1)} \times E^{mk}$.† As a typical example of the function $f(\cdot,\cdot)$, consider the one defined by

7 $$f(\mathcal{X},\mathcal{U}) = \|x_k - x_d\|^2 + \sum_{i=0}^{k-1} \|u_i\|^2,$$

which expresses the deviation of the terminal state x_k from a given point $x_d \notin X_k$, summed with the energy expended by taking system (1) from an initial state $x_0 \in X_0$ to the terminal state $x_k \in X_k$.

We can now combine the dynamical system (1) with the constraints (2) to (4) and the cost function (6) to obtain a precise formulation of the most general fixed-time optimal control problem that we can consider in this framework.

8 **The fixed-time optimal control problem.** Given a dynamical system

9 $$x_{i+1} - x_i = f_i(x_i,u_i) \qquad i = 0, 1, \ldots, k-1$$

(where the states $x_i \in E^n$ for $i = 0, 1, \ldots, k$, the controls $u_i \in E^m$

[1] Later on, the words *admissible* and *feasible* will be used synonymously.

† We shall always consider a control sequence $\mathcal{U} = (u_0,u_1, \ldots, u_{k-1})$ to be a vector in E^{mk} and a trajectory $\mathcal{X} = (x_0,x_1, \ldots, x_k)$ to be a vector in $E^{n(k+1)}$.

for $i = 0, 1, \ldots, k-1$, and k is the specified duration for the process), together with subsets $X_i \subset E^n$ for $i = 0, 1, \ldots, k$, subsets $U_i \subset E^m$ for $i = 0, 1, \ldots, k-1$, a subset $D \subset E^s$, a constraint function $h(\cdot,\cdot)$ from $E^{n(k+1)} \times E^{mk}$ into E^s, and a real-valued cost function $f(\cdot,\cdot)$ defined on $E^{n(k+1)} \times E^{mk}$, find a control sequence $\hat{\mathfrak{U}} = (\hat{u}_0, \hat{u}_1, \ldots, \hat{u}_{k-1})$ and a corresponding trajectory $\hat{\mathfrak{X}} = (\hat{x}_0, \hat{x}_1, \ldots, \hat{x}_k)$ satisfying (9), with

10 $$\hat{u}_i \in U_i \qquad i = 0, 1, \ldots, k-1$$
11 $$\hat{x}_i \in X_i \qquad i = 0, 1, \ldots, k$$
12 $$h(\hat{\mathfrak{X}}, \hat{\mathfrak{U}}) \in D,$$

such that for every control sequence $\mathfrak{U} = (u_0, u_1, \ldots, u_{k-1})$ and every corresponding trajectory $\mathfrak{X} = (x_0, x_1, \ldots, x_k)$ satisfying (9) to (12)

13 $$f(\hat{\mathfrak{X}}, \hat{\mathfrak{U}}) \leq f(\mathfrak{X}, \mathfrak{U}). \quad \square$$

A free-time problem differs from a fixed-time problem in one important detail: the duration of the process, k, is not specified in advance. The easiest way to extend the definition of the fixed-time optimal control problem to free-time problems is by assuming that instead of having a fixed cost function f and constraint function h, we have a sequence of such functions, $f_{(k)}$ and $h_{(k)}$, parametrized by the duration k. Similarly, we have to assume that we have a sequence of subsets D_k. Thus we shall consider the free-time problem as a sequence of fixed-time problems.

14 **The free-time optimal control problem.** Given a dynamical system

15 $$x_{i+1} - x_i = f_i(x_i, u_i) \qquad i = 0, 1, 2, \ldots,$$

together with subsets $X_i \subset E^n$ for $i = 0, 1, 2, \ldots$, subsets $U_i \subset E^m$ for $i = 0, 1, 2, \ldots$, subsets $D_k \subset E^s$ for $k = 0, 1, 2, \ldots$, a sequence of constraint functions $h_{(k)}(\cdot,\cdot)$ mapping $E^{n(k+1)} \times E^{mk}$ into E^s for $k = 0, 1, 2, \ldots$, and a sequence of real-valued cost functions $f_{(k)}(\cdot,\cdot)$ defined on $E^{n(k+1)} \times E^{mk}$ for $k = 0, 1, 2, \ldots$, find an integer $\hat{k}$, a control sequence $\hat{\mathfrak{U}}_{\hat{k}} = (\hat{u}_0, \hat{u}_1, \ldots, \hat{u}_{\hat{k}-1})$, and a corresponding trajectory $\hat{\mathfrak{X}}_{\hat{k}} = (\hat{x}_0, \hat{x}_1, \ldots, \hat{x}_{\hat{k}})$ satisfying (15), with

16 $$\hat{u}_i \in U_i \qquad i = 0, 1, \ldots, \hat{k}-1$$
17 $$\hat{x}_i \in X_i \qquad i = 0, 1, \ldots, \hat{k}$$
18 $$h_{(\hat{k})}(\hat{\mathfrak{X}}_{\hat{k}}, \hat{\mathfrak{U}}_{\hat{k}}) \in D_{(\hat{k})},$$

such that for every $k = 0, 1, \ldots$, for every control sequence $\mathfrak{U}_k = (u_0, u_1, \ldots, u_{k-1})$, and for every corresponding trajectory $\mathfrak{X}_k = (x_0, x_1, \ldots, x_{k-1})$ satisfying (15) to (18), with k taking the place of $\hat{k}$,

19 $$f_{(\hat{k})}(\hat{\mathcal{X}}_{\hat{k}},\hat{\mathcal{U}}_{\hat{k}}) \leqq f_{(k)}(\mathcal{X}_k,\mathcal{U}_k). \quad \square$$

1.3 A CANONICAL FORM OF THE DISCRETE OPTIMAL CONTROL PROBLEM

There are various ways of associating a cost with a fixed-time control process $(\mathcal{X},\mathcal{U})$, that is, a control sequence $\mathcal{U}$ and a corresponding trajectory $\mathcal{X}$. The most common one is to assign a cost to each state transition, in which case the total cost is the sum of these individual costs, and we therefore have

1 $$f(\mathcal{X},\mathcal{U}) = \sum_{i=0}^{k-1} f_i^0(x_i,u_i),$$

where the $f_i^0(\cdot,\cdot)$ for $i = 0, 1, \ldots, k-1$ are real-valued functions defined on $E^n \times E^m$. As an example, consider a minimum-energy problem for which

2 $$f(\mathcal{X},\mathcal{U}) = \sum_{i=0}^{k-1} \|u_i\|^2,$$

where $\|\cdot\|$ denotes the euclidean norm. As another example, suppose that we wish to minimize the value $\varphi(x_k)$ of a real-valued function φ of the terminal state, that is,

3 $$f(\mathcal{X},\mathcal{U}) = \varphi(x_k).$$

If we now examine (3) and (1), we find that by letting $f_i^0(\cdot,\cdot) \equiv 0$ for $i = 0, 1, \ldots, k-2$ and $f_{k-1}^0(x_{k-1},u_{k-1}) = \varphi(x_{k-1} + f_{k-1}(x_{k-1},u_{k-1}))$, we can convert (3) to the form of (1).

It should be clear from these examples that many optimal control problems have cost functions which can be written in form (1). However, there are also a number of optimal control problems for which the cost associated with a control process $(\mathcal{X},\mathcal{U})$ cannot be decomposed into a sum. A simple example of this occurs when the cost function $f(\cdot,\cdot)$ has the form

4 $$f(\mathcal{X},\mathcal{U}) = \max_{i=0,1,\ldots,k-1} \varphi^i(x_i,u_i),$$

that is, when we wish to minimize the maximum "deviation" from a desired control process.

Since fixed-time optimal control problems with costs of form (1) are by far the most common, they have received the lion's share of the attention. It is sometimes convenient to combine the dynamic equations (2.1) with the cost expression (1) into a single augmented dynamical system as follows. Let the scalars x_i^0 for $i = 0, 1, \ldots, k$ be determined by the difference equation

5 $$x_{i+1}^0 - x_i^0 = f_i^0(x_i,u_i) \qquad i = 0, 1, \ldots, k-1,$$

with $x_0{}^0 = 0$, where $((x_0,x_1, \ldots ,x_k),(u_0,u_1, \ldots ,u_{k-1}))$ is any control process of the system (2.1). We now let $\mathbf{x} = (x^0,x) \in E^{n+1}$, where $x^0 \in E^1$ and $x \in E^n$ [that is, $\mathbf{x} = (x^0,x^1, \ldots ,x^n)$], and for $i = 0, 1, \ldots , k - 1$ we define the functions $\mathbf{f}_i$: $E^{n+1} \times E^m \to E^{n+1}$ by $\mathbf{f}_i(\mathbf{x},u) = (f_i{}^0(x,u),f_i(x,u))$. Finally, we combine equations (2.1) and (5) into the augmented system

6 $$\mathbf{x}_{i+1} - \mathbf{x}_i = \mathbf{f}_i(\mathbf{x}_i,u_i) \qquad i = 0, 1, \ldots , k - 1.$$

With the introduction of the augmented system (6), we are led to the following important special case of the fixed-time optimal control problem (2.8).

7 **The canonical optimal control problem (fixed-time).** Given a dynamical system

8 $$\mathbf{x}_{i+1} - \mathbf{x}_i = \mathbf{f}_i(\mathbf{x}_i,u_i) \qquad i = 0, 1, \ldots , k - 1$$

(where the states $\mathbf{x}_i \in E^{n+1}$ for $i = 0, 1, \ldots , k$, the controls $u_i \in E^m$ for $i = 0, 1, \ldots , k - 1$, and k is the specified duration of the process), together with subsets $\mathbf{X}_i \subset E^{n+1}$ for $i = 0, 1, \ldots , k$, subsets $U_i \subset E^m$ for $i = 0, 1, \ldots , k - 1$, a subset $\mathbf{D} \subset E^s$, and a constraint function $\mathbf{h}(\cdot,\cdot)$ mapping $E^{(n+1)(k+1)} \times E^{km} \to E^s$, find a control sequence $\hat{\mathfrak{U}} = (\hat{u}_0,\hat{u}_1, \ldots ,\hat{u}_{k-1})$ and a corresponding trajectory $\hat{\mathfrak{X}} = (\hat{\mathbf{x}}_0,\hat{\mathbf{x}}_1, \ldots ,\hat{\mathbf{x}}_k)$ satisfying (8), with

9 $$\hat{u}_i \in U_i \qquad i = 0, 1, \ldots , k - 1$$
10 $$\hat{\mathbf{x}}_i \in \mathbf{X}_i \qquad i = 0, 1, \ldots , k$$
11 $$\mathbf{h}(\hat{\mathfrak{X}},\hat{\mathfrak{U}}) \in \mathbf{D},$$

such that for every control sequence $\mathfrak{U}$ and every corresponding trajectory $\mathfrak{X}$ satisfying (8) to (11)

12 $$\hat{x}_k{}^0 \leq x_k{}^0,$$

where $x_k{}^0$ is the first component of $\mathbf{x}_k$. □

13 **Remark.** Observe that in the above definition we have *not* made the assumption implied by (6) that the functions $\mathbf{f}_i$ for $i = 0, 1, \ldots , k - 1$ and $\mathbf{h}$ do not depend on the cost variable x^0. As will be seen from example (16) below, the removal of this assumption enables us to treat an important class of problems without increasing the dimension of the dynamical system. □

When the system (8) is indeed an augmented system, then the functions $\mathbf{f}_i$ and $\mathbf{h}$ do not depend on x^0, that is, $\mathbf{f}_i$: $E^n \times E^m \to E^{n+1}$ and $\mathbf{h}$: $E^{n(k+1)} \times E^m \to E^s$, and the sets $\mathbf{X}_i$ assume the form

14 $$\mathbf{X}_0 = \{0\} \times X_0$$
$$\mathbf{X}_i = E^1 \times X_i \qquad i = 1, 2, \ldots , k.$$

The effect of transcribing an optimal control problem into the canonical form is to make the problem completely geometric, as will be seen in Section 2.4.

15 **Exercise.** Obtain a canonical formulation for free-time optimal control problems analogous to (7) above. □

16 **Example.** It is not always necessary to augment the dynamic equations (2.1) in order to cast the problem into canonical form. This is clearly the case when the cost is of the form

17 $$f(\mathfrak{X},\mathfrak{U}) = x_k^1.$$

Thus consider the case when we wish to take an object constrained to move on a line from some initial position x_0 to a position as far as possible from the initial point (for example, a ballistics problem). In this case we may care little about the terminal values of the other state variables. Then if for $i = 0, 1, \ldots, k$ we let $x_i^0 = -(x_i^1 - x_0^1)$ and renumber the other state variables $x_i^2, x_i^3, \ldots, x_i^n$ as $x_i^1, x_i^2, \ldots, x_i^{n-1}$, we find that the original problem has been transcribed into canonical form without our having augmented the state space. □

1.4 THE MATHEMATICAL PROGRAMMING PROBLEM

For the purpose of this book it will be convenient to adopt a canonical form for the mathematical programming problem. We shall call this form the *Basic Problem* because all the optimization problems which we shall consider can be transcribed into this form and it will play a central role in the following chapters.

1 **The Basic Problem.** Given a real-valued continuously differentiable function $f(\cdot)$ defined on E^n, a continuously differentiable function $r(\cdot)$ from E^n into E^m, and a subset $\Omega \subset E^n$, find a vector $\hat{z} \in E^n$ satisfying

2 $$\hat{z} \in \Omega$$

3 $$r(\hat{z}) = 0$$

such that

4 $$f(\hat{z}) \leqq f(z)$$

for all $z \in E^n$ satisfying (2) and (3). □

Note that we have refrained from saying how the set Ω is characterized and that we have chosen to highlight the presence of equality constraints on the minimization of $f(z)$. The reason for breaking up the constraints on the minimization of $f(z)$ into equality constraints and other constraints is that it is often impossible to obtain meaningful necessary conditions of optimality without imposing this much additional structure. This fact will become increasingly clear in Chapters 2 and 3.

5 **Remark.** The formulation of the Basic Problem does *not* imply that equality constraints *cannot* enter into the characterization of the set Ω. The set Ω may well be of the form $\Omega = \{z: s(z) = 0, q(z) \leqq 0\}$, where $s: E^n \to E^l$ and $q: E^n \to E^m$. We simply choose to highlight *some* of the equality constraints. □

Finally, in the chapters to follow it will often be necessary to refer to vectors z which satisfy (2) and (3) as well as to vectors $\hat{z}$ which are solutions to the Basic Problem. We shall therefore give these vectors special names. These names are commonly used in mathematical programming literature.

6 **Definition.** A vector $z \in E^n$ will be said to be *feasible* (or a *feasible solution*) for the Basic Problem if it satisfies (2) and (3). A vector $\hat{z} \in E^n$ will be said to be *optimal* (or an *optimal solution*) for the Basic Problem if it is feasible and satisfies (4) for all feasible vectors $z \in E^n$. □

1.5 EQUIVALENCE OF THE OPTIMIZATION PROBLEMS

We shall now show that the fixed-time optimal control problems (2.8)† and (3.7) can be transcribed into the form of the Basic Problem (4.1), and similarly, that the Basic Problem (4.1) can be transcribed into a one-step two-point-boundary-value optimal control problem of form (2.8) or (3.7). The fact that these transformations are possible is important, since it enables us to interpret results obtained for either one of these problems in the light of the other.

Thus consider again the fixed-time optimal control problem (2.8), and let $z = (x_0,x_1, \ldots ,x_k,u_0,u_1, \ldots ,u_{k-1})$, where $\mathcal{U} = (u_0,u_1, \ldots ,u_{k-1})$ and $\mathcal{X} = (x_0,x_1, \ldots ,x_k)$ are a control sequence and a corresponding trajectory of the system (2.9).

† When the cost function $f(\mathcal{X},\mathcal{U}) \triangleq \max \varphi^i(x_i,u_i)$ for $i = 0, 1, \ldots , k-1$, as in (3.4), it becomes necessary to introduce a new variable, ζ, and to consider instead the equivalent problem: minimize ζ subject to $\zeta - \varphi^i(x_i,u_i) \geq 0$ for $i = 0, 1, \ldots , k-1$ and the constraints in (2.8). This transcription is necessary to make the cost function differentiable in the final form (4.1) of the problem.

Suppose that for $i = 0, 1, \ldots, k$ the subsets X_i of E^n [see (2.3)] are of the form

1 $$X_i = \{x: g_i(x) = 0,\ x \in X_i'\},$$

where $g_i(\cdot)$ is a continuously differentiable function mapping E^n into E^{l_i} and X_i' is a subset of E^n which cannot be described by a system of equations. Also suppose that for $i = 0, 1, \ldots, k$ the subsets U_i [see (2.2)] of E^m are of the form

2 $$U_i = \{u_i: \psi_i(u_i) = 0,\ u_i \in U_i'\},$$

where ψ_i is a continuously differentiable function mapping E^m into E^{s_i} and U_i' is a subset of E^m which, again, cannot be described by a system of equations. Finally, let $V = h^{-1}(D)$ [see (2.4)]. Then, to convert the fixed-time optimal control problems (2.8) or (3.7) into the Basic Problem (4.1), we may let[1]

3 $$\Omega = (X_0' \times X_1' \times \cdots \times X_k' \times U_0' \times U_1' \times \cdots \times U_{k-1}') \cap V$$

and define the function $r(\cdot)$ by

4 $$r(z) = \begin{bmatrix} x_1 - x_0 - f_0(x_0,u_0) \\ x_2 - x_1 - f_1(x_1,u_1) \\ \cdot \\ \cdot \\ \cdot \\ x_k - x_{k-1} - f_{k-1}(x_{k-1},u_{k-1}) \\ g_0(x_0) \\ g_1(x_1) \\ \cdot \\ \cdot \\ \cdot \\ g_k(x_k) \\ \psi_0(u_0) \\ \psi_1(u_1) \\ \cdot \\ \cdot \\ \cdot \\ \psi_{k-1}(u_{k-1}) \end{bmatrix}.$$

The cost function, of course, remains the same, $f(z) = f(\mathfrak{X},\mathfrak{U})$. □

[1] As we shall see in Section 2.4, the transcription of problem (2.8) or (3.7) into the form of the Basic Problem (4.1) can be carried out in more ways than one. By and large, the transcription given here is more convenient for the purpose of analysis, while the transcription given in Section 2.4 is more suitable for computation when the sets $X_i = E^n$ for $i = 1, 2, \ldots, n - 1$, since it results in a lower-dimensional function $r(\cdot)$.

We transcribe the Basic Problem (4.1) into a one-step optimal control problem of form (2.8) by treating the variable z as a control and by constructing the fictitious dynamical system given by the difference equation

5 $$x_{i+1} - x_i = f_i(x_i,z) \qquad i = 0,$$

where $x_i = (x_i^1,x_i^2, \ldots ,x_i^m) \in E^m$ for $i = 0, 1$ and $f_0(x_0,z) \triangleq r(z)$.

The constraints now become $X_0 = \{0\}$, $X_1 = \{0\}$, and $U_0 = \Omega$. The cost of this one-step transition is given by $f_0^0(x_0,z) \triangleq f(z)$. To obtain (3.7), we simply proceed as in Section 3. □

We have thus seen that for the purpose of analysis the fixed-time optimal control problem (2.8) and the Basic Problem (4.1) are equivalent, and we shall therefore choose the form to be used in the analysis of any particular problem simply on the basis of convenience.

REFERENCES

1. M. D. Canon, C. D. Cullum, and E. Polak: Constrained Minimization Problems in Finite Dimensional Spaces, *SIAM J. Control*, **4**:528–547 (1966).
2. L. W. Neustadt: An Abstract Variational Theory with Applications to a Broad Class of Optimization Problems, I. General Theory, II. Applications, *SIAM J. Control*, **4**:505–527 (1966), **5**:90–137 (1967).
3. H. Halkin and L. W. Neustadt: General Necessary Conditions for Optimization Problems, *Proc. Natl. Acad. Sci.*, **56**(4):1066–1071 (1966).

2
Conditions of optimality for the basic problem

2.1 INTRODUCTION

We have already seen in Section 1.5 that fixed-time discrete optimal control problems, with very general constraints, are transcribable into the form of the Basic Problem (1.4.1). We observe at this point that the standard nonlinear programming problem is simply the Basic Problem with the set Ω described by a system of inequalities. We also saw in Section 1.5 that the Basic Problem is transcribable into a one-step two-point-boundary-value optimal control problem.[1] Thus we could adopt either the Basic Problem or the two-point-boundary-value discrete optimal control problem as our canonical constrained optimization problem. However, since it contains no dynamic equations, the Basic Problem has less structure, and it is therefore the simpler, and in a sense the more general, of the two candidates for a canonical form. We shall therefore adopt it as our standard problem from now on.

[1] A two-point-boundary-value optimal control problem is the particular case of the control problem (1.2.7) in which $X_0 = \{\hat{x}_0\}$ and $X_k = \{\hat{x}_k\}$, that is, the initial and terminal states are given, and there are no other trajectory constraints, that is, $h \equiv 0$ and $X_i = E^n$ for $i = 2, 3, \ldots, k - 1$.

One of our major goals is a unified theory of constrained optimization. We propose to achieve this goal in two steps. The first step will consist of obtaining conditions of optimality for the Basic Problem. The second step, which will be undertaken in the following chapters, will be to interpret these conditions of optimality in terms of specific optimization problems.

The reader might be perturbed by the fact that the unified approach we are about to present does not seem to relate to the perturbed-trajectory approach used in the past by Pontryagin et al. [7], Jordan and Polak [8], Halkin [9], and many others. We shall therefore demonstrate in Section 4 that the perturbed-trajectory approach actually can be recovered by transcribing optimal control problems into the form of the Basic Problem (1.4.1) in a manner somewhat more complicated than the one given in Section 1.5.

2.2 A FIRST APPROACH TO NECESSARY CONDITIONS

We propose to accomplish two objectives in this section. The first is to obtain a necessary condition of optimality for the Basic Problem (1.4.1) without differentiating between equality and other constraints. Such an approach readily yields a necessary condition, but unfortunately, as will be seen in Chapter 3, it cannot be applied meaningfully to a large class of nonlinear programming and optimal control problems. Since the difficulties are usually caused by the equality constraints, our next objective is a heuristic development of an "approximate" necessary condition of optimality which does take into account the fact that some of the constraints are equality constraints. This approximate condition will be refined into a rigorous necessary condition of optimality in the next section.

To avoid the need for excessive leafing back and forth, the Basic Problem (1.4.1) is restated here.

1 **The Basic Problem.** Given a real-valued continuously differentiable function $f(\cdot)$ defined on E^n, a continuously differentiable function $r(\cdot)$† mapping E^n into E^m, and a subset Ω of E^n, find a vector $\hat{z} \in E^n$ satisfying

2 $$\hat{z} \in \Omega$$
3 $$r(\hat{z}) = 0$$

such that for all $z \in E^n$ satisfying (2) and (3)

4 $$f(\hat{z}) \leqq f(z). \quad \square$$

† The vector $r(z) \in E^m$ will be assumed to be a column vector, so that $r(z) = (r^1(z), r^2(z), \ldots, r^m(z))^T$, where T denotes transposition.

Since for the time being we do not propose to differentiate between equality and other constraints, we combine them into a set Ω', defined by

5 $$\Omega' = \{z \colon z \in \Omega,\ r(z) = 0\}.$$

The Basic Problem now becomes:

6 **Basic Problem.** Find a $\hat{z} \in \Omega'$ so that $f(\hat{z}) \leqq f(z)$ for all $z \in \Omega'$. □

Also, in terms of (5), definition (1.4.6) can be rephrased as follows.

7 **Definition.** We shall say that a vector $\hat{z} \in E^n$ is a *feasible solution* to the Basic Problem if $\hat{z} \in \Omega'$, and we shall say that $\hat{z}$ is an *optimal solution* to the Basic Problem if $\hat{z}$ solves problem (6). □

Suppose that $\hat{z}$ is an optimal solution. We now define a cone of directions which are tangent to all the "smooth" paths in Ω' which originate at $\hat{z}$.

8 **Definition.** The *tangent cone* to the set Ω' at $\hat{z} \in \Omega'$, denoted by $TC(\hat{z},\Omega')$, is the set of all vectors $\delta z \in E^n$ with the property that for every $\delta z \in TC(\hat{z},\Omega')$ there exists a $t_1 > 0$ and a continuous function $o(\cdot)$ from the reals into E^n, satisfying $\|o(t)\|/t \to 0$ as $t \to 0$, such that

9 $$z(t) \triangleq [\hat{z} + t\,\delta z + o(t)] \in \Omega' \qquad 0 \leqq t \leqq t_1,$$

where t_1 and $o(\cdot)$ may depend on $\hat{z}$ and δz. □

10 **Remark.** Thus if $\delta z \in TC(\hat{z},\Omega')$, then there is in Ω' a finite arc, emanating from $\hat{z}$ and defined by (9), which is differentiable at $\hat{z}$ and to which δz is a tangent at $\hat{z}$. □

11 **Exercise.** Use scaling to show from (9) that if $\delta z \in TC(\hat{z},\Omega')$, then so does $\lambda\, \delta z$ for all $\lambda \geq 0$, thus establishing that $TC(\hat{z},\Omega')$ *is indeed a cone.* □

We are now ready to prove our first necessary condition of optimality.

12 **Theorem.**[1] If $\hat{z}$ is an optimal solution to the Basic Problem (1) and $TC(\hat{z},\Omega')$ is the tangent cone to Ω' at $\hat{z}$, where Ω' is as defined in (5), then

[1] A form of this theorem was first presented by Kuhn and Tucker [5].

13 $$\langle -\nabla f(\hat{z}),\delta z\rangle \leqq 0 \qquad \text{for all } \delta z \in \overline{\text{co}}\; TC(\hat{z},\Omega').\dagger$$

Proof. Suppose that there is a $\delta z^* \in TC(\hat{z},\Omega')$ which does not satisfy (13), that is,

14 $$\langle -\nabla f(\hat{z}),\delta z^*\rangle > 0.$$

Then, by definition (8), there is a $t_1^* > 0$ and a continuous function $o^*(\cdot)$ such that

15 $$[\hat{z} + t\,\delta z^* + o^*(t)] \in \Omega' \qquad 0 \leqq t \leqq t_1^*.$$

Expanding the cost function $f(\cdot)$ along the arc defined by (15), we get

16 $$f(\hat{z} + t\,\delta z^* + o^*(t)) = f(\hat{z}) + t\langle \nabla f(\hat{z}),\delta z^*\rangle + o(t) \qquad 0 \leqq t \leqq t_1^*,$$

where $o(\cdot)$ is a continuous function such that $o(t)/t \to 0$ as $t \to 0$. Since $\langle \nabla f(\hat{z}),\delta z^*\rangle < 0$, by (14), and in (16) the term linear in t dominates $o(t)$ for t sufficiently small, we conclude that there exists a t^* in the interval $(0,t_1^*]$ such that

17 $$f(\hat{z} + t^*\,\delta z^* + o^*(t)) < f(\hat{z}),$$

which contradicts the optimality of $\hat{z}$, since $z^* = \hat{z} + t^*\,\delta z^* + o(t^*)$ is a feasible solution; i.e., it is in Ω'. Consequently, for every $\delta z \in TC(\hat{z},\Omega')$

18 $$\langle -\nabla f(\hat{z}),\delta z\rangle \leqq 0.$$

Now let δz be an arbitrary vector in co $TC(\hat{z},\Omega')$; then for some integer s

19 $$\delta z = \sum_{i=1}^{s} \mu^i\,\delta z_i,$$

where $\delta z_i \in TC(\hat{z},\Omega')$, $\sum_{i=1}^{s} \mu^i = 1$, and $\mu^i \geqq 0$ for $i = 1, 2, \ldots, s$. But since each $\delta z_i \in TC(\hat{z},\Omega')$ satisfies (18) and the $\mu^i \geqq 0$, it is clear that every $\delta z \in$ co $TC(\hat{z},\Omega')$ must satisfy (18). Now, the function $\langle \nabla f(\hat{z}),\cdot\rangle$ is obviously continuous, and hence if (18) holds for all $\delta z \in$ co $TC(\hat{z},\Omega')$, it must also hold for all $\delta z \in \overline{\text{co}}\; TC(\hat{z},\Omega')$, the closure of this set. □

20 **Remark.** In anticipation of the fact that we shall have to rely heavily in the next section on the Brouwer fixed-point theorem, let us see how the first part of the proof of theorem (12) can be accom-

† The symbol co $TC(\hat{z},\Omega')$ denotes the convex hull of $TC(\hat{z},\Omega')$, while $\overline{\text{co}}\; TC(\hat{z},\Omega')$ denotes the closure of the convex hull of $TC(\hat{z},\Omega')$ [see (A.3.32)].

plished by showing that a certain map has a fixed point. Suppose that $\delta z^* \in TC(\hat{z},\Omega')$ satisfies (14). Let $t_0 = \frac{1}{2}t_1^*$, where t_1^* is as in (15), and let σ be a real variable satisfying $|\sigma| \leqq \rho \triangleq t_0$. Then for $t = \alpha(t_0 + \sigma)$, with $\alpha \in (0,1]$, (16) becomes

21 $$f(\hat{z} + \alpha(t_0 + \sigma)\,\delta z^* + o^*(\alpha(t_0 + \sigma))) = f(\hat{z}) + \alpha t_0\langle\nabla f(\hat{z}),\delta z^*\rangle + \alpha\sigma\langle\nabla f(\hat{z}),\delta z^*\rangle + o(\alpha(t_0 + \sigma)),$$

where $o(\alpha(t_0 + \sigma))/\alpha \to 0$ as $\alpha \to 0$ uniformly in all $\sigma \in [-\rho,+\rho]$. Now, $\alpha t_0\langle\nabla f(\hat{z}),\delta z^*\rangle < 0$ for all $\alpha > 0$; hence to establish (17) we need simply find an $\alpha^* \in (0,1]$ and a $\sigma^* \in [-\rho,+\rho]$ which satisfy the equation

22 $$\alpha\sigma\langle\nabla f(\hat{z}),\delta z^*\rangle + o(\alpha(t_0 + \sigma)) = 0.$$

We let $x = \sigma\langle\nabla f(\hat{z}),\delta z^*\rangle$, $y_0 = t_0\langle\nabla f(\hat{z}),\delta z^*\rangle$, and $r = \rho|\langle\nabla f(\hat{z}),\delta z^*\rangle|$. If we substitute for σ and t_0 in (22), then (22) becomes

23 $$G_\alpha(\alpha x) \triangleq \alpha x + o\left(\frac{\alpha}{\langle\nabla f(\hat{z}),\delta z^*\rangle}(y_0 + x)\right) = 0.$$

Now let $\bar{o}(z) = o(z/\langle\nabla f(\hat{z}),\delta z^*\rangle)$, with $o(\cdot)$ as in (23). Then (23) becomes

24 $$G_\alpha(\alpha x) = \alpha x + \bar{o}(\alpha(y_0 + x)) = 0,$$

where $\bar{o}(\alpha(y_0 + x))/\alpha \to 0$ as $\alpha \to 0$ uniformly in $x \in [-r,+r]$. Hence there exists an $\alpha^* \in (0,1]$ such that

25 $$\alpha^* r > |\bar{o}(\alpha^* y_0 \pm r)|.$$

Referring to Figure 1, we see immediately that there must be a point $\alpha^* x^*$ in the interval $[-\alpha^* r,+\alpha^* r]$ such that $G_{\alpha^*}(\alpha^* x^*) = 0$, that is,

26 $$-\bar{o}(\alpha^*(y_0 + x^*)) = \alpha^* x^*,$$

which shows that $\alpha^* x^*$ is a fixed point of the map $-\bar{o}(\alpha^*(y_0 + \cdot))$ from the interval $[-\alpha^* r,+\alpha^* r]$ into the reals, and at the same time that (22) [and hence (17)] has a solution. □

Obviously, as far as theorem (12) is concerned, this is a long-winded approach to take, but we shall see in the next section that it cannot always be avoided in conjunction with other theorems.

27 **Exercise.** Let $\hat{z}$ be an optimal solution to the Basic Problem (1). Show that theorem (12) [that is, inequality (13)] remains valid for all $\delta z \in \overline{\text{co}}\; TC_s(\hat{z},\Omega')$, where $TC_s(\hat{z},\Omega')$ is as defined in (28). □

28 **Definition.** The *sequential tangent cone* to the set Ω' at $\hat{z} \in \Omega'$, denoted by $TC_s(\hat{z},\Omega')$, is the set consisting of the origin together with

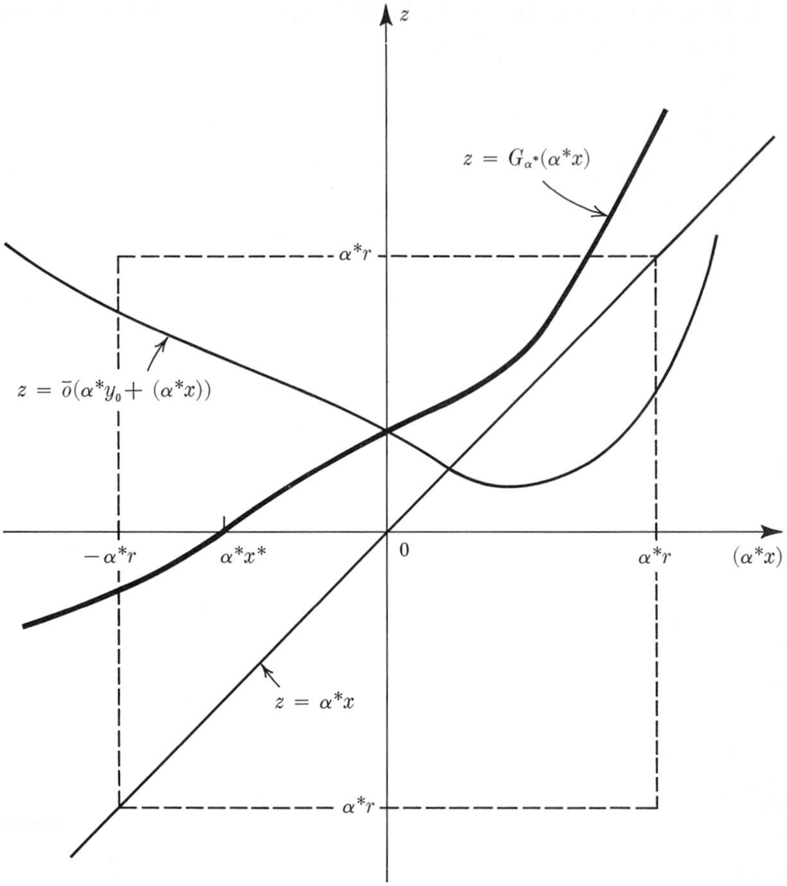

Figure 1

all nonzero vectors δz which have the property that there exists a sequence of vectors $\{\delta z_i\}$ such that $(\hat{z} + \delta z_i) \in \Omega'$ for $i = 1, 2, 3, \ldots,$ $\delta z_i \to 0$ as $i \to \infty$ and $\delta z_i / \|\delta z_i\| \to \alpha\, \delta z$ as $i \to \infty$ for some $\alpha > 0$. The sequence $\{\delta z_i\}$ may depend on $\hat{z}$ and δz. □

29 **Exercise.** Show that $TC_s(\hat{z},\Omega')$ is a closed cone. Show that $TC_s(\hat{z},\Omega') \supset TC(\hat{z},\Omega')$. Show that $TC_s(\hat{z},\Omega') = TC(\hat{z},\Omega')$ when Ω' is convex. □

Let us now return to theorem (12). Statement (13) is very simple, but it cannot be applied meaningfully unless we have the tangent cone $TC(\hat{z},\Omega')$, or at least a subset of $TC(\hat{z},\Omega')$. Thus the utility of theorem (12) depends entirely on our ability to obtain a characterization for the tangent cone. A detailed discussion of tangent cones is postponed until Chapter 3, and we shall see there that when the jacobian matrix $\partial r(\hat{z})/\partial z = \partial r^i(\hat{z})/\partial z^j$ has rank less than m, the tangent cone to Ω' at $\hat{z}$ cannot be constructed by standard methods. However, we shall also see that it is not exceptionally difficult to construct either tangent cones or subsets of tangent cones to the set Ω in a large number of interesting cases. We therefore proceed to construct a necessary condition of optimality which depends only on tangent cones or subsets of tangent cones to the set Ω.

Our first step is to combine the *cost function* $f(\cdot)$ with the *equality-constraint function* $r(\cdot)$, appearing in the statement of the Basic Problem (1), to define a continuously differentiable function $F(\cdot)$ mapping E^n into E^{m+1}:

30 $$F(z) = \begin{bmatrix} f(z) \\ r(z) \end{bmatrix}.$$

For the sake of convenience, we shall always write $F(z) = (f(z),r(z))$, although we mean a column vector, as in (30). We shall also number the components of E^{m+1} from 0 to m, rather than the usual 1 to $m + 1$, so that $y \in E^{m+1}$ has the form $y = (y^0,y^1, \ldots ,y^m)$; again we mean a column vector, but we omit the transposition sign. Consequently, $F(z) = (F^0(z),F^1(z), \ldots , F^m(z))$, where, by (30), $F^0(z) = f(z), F^1(z) = r^1(z), \ldots , F^m(z) = r^m(z)$. The jacobian matrix of $F(\cdot)$ evaluated at z will be denoted by $\partial F(z)/\partial z$; its first row is $\nabla F^0(z) = \nabla f(z)$, its second row is $\nabla F^1(z) = \nabla r^1(z)$, and so forth. Thus it is an $(m + 1) \times n$ rectangular matrix whose ijth element is $\partial F^i(z)/\partial z^j$.

Now, suppose that $\hat{z}$ is an optimal solution to the Basic Problem (1) and that δz is some small perturbation vector. Then, since $F(\cdot)$ is assumed to be continuously differentiable, we can expand it about $\hat{z}$ to obtain

31 $$F(\hat{z} + \delta z) = F(\hat{z}) + \frac{\partial F(\hat{z})}{\partial z}\,\delta z + o(\delta z),$$

where $o(\cdot)$ is a continuous function from E^n into E^{m+1} with the property that $\|o(\delta z)\|/\|\delta z\| \to 0$ as $\|\delta z\| \to 0$.

To avoid having to evaluate (31) with δz moving along a curve, as was done in (16), we assume that the entire tangent cone to Ω at $\hat{z}$, or at least a large subset of it, is made up of tangents to linear segments l of the form $l = \{z\colon z = \hat{z} + t\,\delta z,\ 0 \leqq t \leqq 1\}$ contained in Ω. We shall call such a subset a *radial cone*, which we now define formally.

32 **Definition.** The *radial cone* to Ω at $\hat{z} \in \Omega$, denoted by $RC(\hat{z},\Omega)$, is the set of all vectors δz for which there exists an $\epsilon > 0$ such that $(\hat{z} + \alpha\, \delta z) \in \Omega$ for all $\alpha \in [0,\epsilon]$. □

Thus the radial cone $RC(\hat{z},\Omega)$ is the cone generated by all the straight-line segments which emanate from $\hat{z}$ and are contained in Ω. When the set Ω is convex, the closure of the cone $\{\hat{z}\} + RC(\hat{z},\Omega)$, whose vertex is at $\hat{z}$, is the smallest closed cone with vertex at $\hat{z}$ which contains the set Ω.

33 **Exercise.** Let Ω be a convex subset of E^n. Show that the radial cone to Ω at $\hat{z} \in \Omega$ is the cone generated by the set Ω-$\{\hat{z}\}$ [see (A.4.7).] □

Example. Referring to Figure 2*a*, we see that when the point $\hat{z}$ is interior to the set Ω, the radial cone $RC(\hat{z},\Omega)$ is the whole space. When the set Ω is convex and $\hat{z}$ is a boundary point of Ω, $RC(\hat{z},\Omega)$ is as shown in Figure 2*b*, and when Ω is not convex but $\hat{z}$ is on the boundary of Ω, then $RC(\hat{z},\Omega)$ is as shown in Figure 2*c*. It is not difficult to show that when Ω is a closed polyhedral set, $RC(\hat{z},\Omega) = TC(\hat{z},\Omega) = TC_s(\hat{z},\Omega)$. □

It is rather clear that the major source of difficulty in deriving necessary conditions of optimality will be the term $o(\delta z)$ in (31). To reduce its effect, we begin by assuming that only the cost function $f(\cdot)$ is nonlinear. This enables us to obtain the following simple result.

34 **Theorem.** Let $\hat{z}$ be an optimal solution to the Basic Problem (1). If the function $r(\cdot)$ is affine, then the *negative cost ray*

35 $$R = \{y\colon y = \beta(-1,0,0, \ldots ,0) \in E^{m+1}, \beta > 0\}$$

cannot belong to the cone

36 $$K(\hat{z}) = \frac{\partial F(\hat{z})}{\partial z} RC(\hat{z},\Omega) = \left\{y\colon y = \frac{\partial F(\hat{z})}{\partial z}\, \delta z,\ \delta z \in RC(\hat{z},\Omega)\right\}.^{\dagger}$$

Proof. Suppose that R belongs to the cone $K(\hat{z})$; then there is a $\delta z^* \in RC(\hat{z},\Omega)$ such that

37 $$\frac{\partial F'(\hat{z})}{\partial z}\, \delta z^* \in R.$$

† Additional geometric insight into the nature of this theorem as well as theorem (3.12) can be obtained from the observation that $\hat{z}$ is an optimal solution to the Basic Problem (1) *if and only if* the ray R is disjoint from the set $F(\Omega) - \{\hat{y}\}$, where $\hat{y} = (f(\hat{z}),0,0, \ldots ,0)$. Theorem (34) states that if $\hat{z}$ is optimal, then the ray R must be disjoint from $K(\hat{z})$, which is a first-order approximation to $F(\Omega) - \{\hat{y}\}$; that is, (34) "approximates" the statement that R and $F(\Omega) - \hat{y}$ must be disjoint.

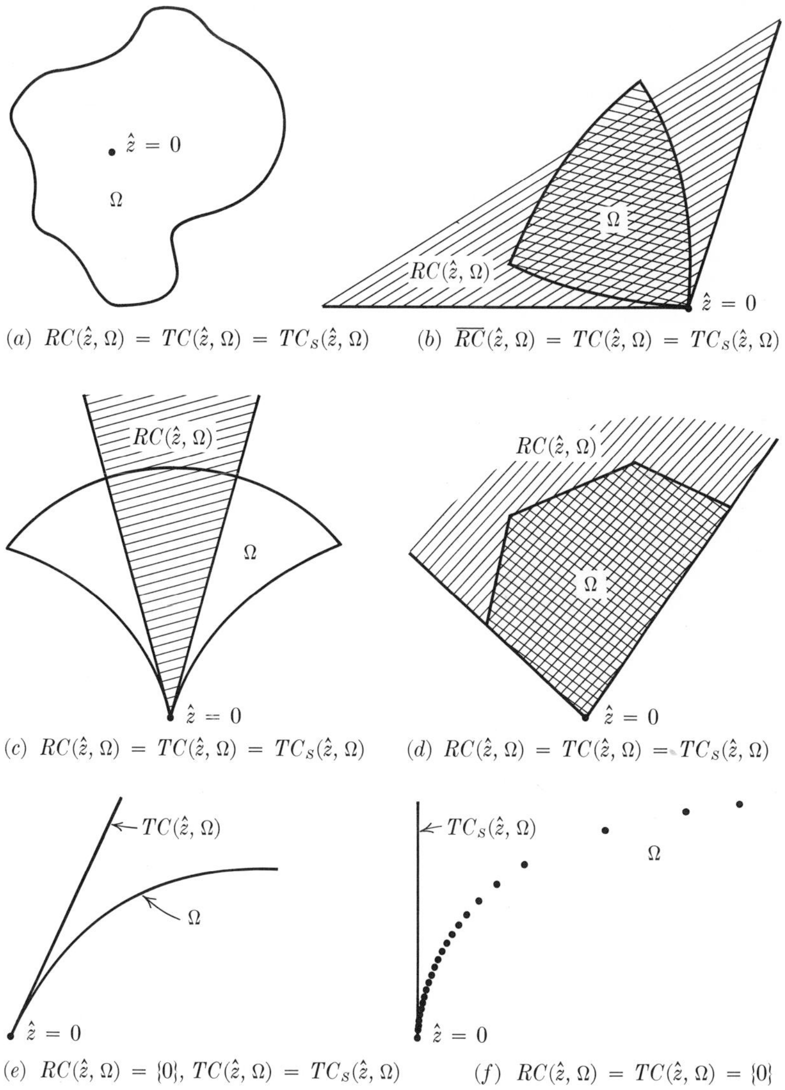

(*a*) $RC(\hat{z}, \Omega) = TC(\hat{z}, \Omega) = TC_S(\hat{z}, \Omega)$ (*b*) $\overline{RC}(\hat{z}, \Omega) = TC(\hat{z}, \Omega) = TC_S(\hat{z}, \Omega)$

(*c*) $RC(\hat{z}, \Omega) = TC(\hat{z}, \Omega) = TC_S(\hat{z}, \Omega)$ (*d*) $RC(\hat{z}, \Omega) = TC(\hat{z}, \Omega) = TC_S(\hat{z}, \Omega)$

(*e*) $RC(\hat{z}, \Omega) = \{0\}$, $TC(\hat{z}, \Omega) = TC_S(\hat{z}, \Omega)$ (*f*) $RC(\hat{z}, \Omega) = TC(\hat{z}, \Omega) = \{0\}$

Figure 2

Expanding (37) into component equations, we get

38 $$\langle \nabla f(\hat{z}), \delta z^* \rangle < 0$$

39 $$\langle \nabla r^i(\hat{z}), \delta z^* \rangle = 0 \qquad i = 1, 2, \ldots, m.$$

But $r(\cdot)$, by assumption, is affine, and hence [from (39)] we have

40 $$r^i(\hat{z} + \delta z^*) = r^i(\hat{z}) + \langle \nabla r^i(\hat{z}), \delta z^* \rangle = 0 \qquad i = 1, 2, \ldots, m.$$

Now,

41 $$f(\hat{z} + \alpha\, \delta z^*) = f(\hat{z}) + \alpha\langle \nabla f(\hat{z}), \delta z^*\rangle + o(\alpha),$$

where $o(\alpha)/\alpha \to 0$ as $\alpha \to 0$, and it follows from (38) and (41) that there exists an $\epsilon' > 0$ such that

42 $$f(\hat{z} + \alpha\, \delta z^*) < f(\hat{z}) \qquad \text{for all } \alpha \in (0,\epsilon'].$$

Furthermore, by definition (32), there is an $\epsilon(\hat{z},\delta z^*) > 0$ such that $\hat{z} + \alpha \delta z^* \in \Omega$ for all $\alpha \in [0,\epsilon(\hat{z},\delta z^*)]$. Let $\epsilon^* = \min\,[\epsilon',\epsilon(\hat{z},\delta z^*)]$; then $\hat{z} + \epsilon^*\, \delta z^*$ is a feasible solution; that is,

43 $$r(\hat{z} + \epsilon^*\, \delta z^*) = 0 \qquad \text{and} \qquad (\hat{z} + \epsilon^*\, \delta z^*) \in \Omega,$$

and

44 $$f(\hat{z} + \epsilon^*\, \delta z^*) < f(\hat{z}),$$

which contradicts the optimality of $\hat{z}$. □

45 **Corollary.** Suppose that the assumptions of theorem (34) are satisfied and, in addition, the cone $RC(\hat{z},\Omega)$ is convex. Then the cone $K(\hat{z})$ and the ray R can be separated, that is, there exists a nonzero vector $\psi \in E^{m+1}$, with $\psi^0 \leqq 0$, such that

46 $$\left\langle \psi, \frac{\partial F(z)}{\partial z}\, \delta z \right\rangle \leqq 0 \qquad \text{for all } \delta z \in RC(\hat{z},\Omega)$$

and

47 $$\langle \psi, y\rangle \geqq 0 \qquad \text{for all } y \in R.$$

Proof. When $RC(\hat{z},\Omega)$ is convex, the cone $K(\hat{z})$ is also convex. Since $K(\hat{z})$ does not contain the ray R, it follows from theorem (A.5.5) that there exists a vector $\psi \in E^{m+1}$ such that (46) and (47) are satisfied and hence $\psi^0 \leqq 0$. □

48 **Corollary.** In addition to the hypothesis of corollary (45), suppose that the cone $K(\hat{z})$ is closed. Then there is a nonzero vector $\psi = (\psi^0,\psi^1, \ldots ,\psi^m)$, with $\psi^0 < 0$, such that

49 $$\left\langle \psi, \frac{\partial F(\hat{z})}{\partial z}\, \delta z \right\rangle \leqq 0 \qquad \text{for all } \delta z \in RC(\hat{z},\Omega).$$

Proof. Since $R \cap K(\hat{z}) = \phi$, the point $l = (-1,0,0, \ldots ,0) \in E^{m+1}$ does not belong to the closed convex cone $K(\hat{z})$. It follows from corollary (A.5.28) and exercise (A.5.27) that there exists a vector $\psi \in E^{m+1}$ satisfying (49) and such that $\langle \psi, l\rangle > 0$; that is, $-\psi^0 > 0$.

50 **Example.** In many instances the radial cone $RC(\hat{z},\Omega)$ can be given a very simple description. Consider the case when the set Ω is a polyhedron of the form

$$\Omega = \{z: \langle q^i,z\rangle \leqq d^i,\ i = 1, 2, \ldots, k\},$$

where $q^i \in E^n$ for $i = 1, 2, \ldots, k$. Let $I(\hat{z})$ be the index set identifying the *active constraints;* that is,

$$I(\hat{z}) = \{i: \langle q^i,\hat{z}\rangle = d^i,\ i \in \{1,2, \ldots ,k\}\}.$$

If $I(\hat{z})$ is the empty set, then $\hat{z}$ is in the interior of Ω, and hence $RC(\hat{z},\Omega)$ is the whole space. If $I(\hat{z})$ is not empty, then it is easy to see that

51 $$RC(\hat{z},\Omega) = \{\delta z: \langle q^i,\delta z\rangle \leqq 0,\ i \in I(\hat{z})\}. \ \Box$$

We can now easily guess the extent to which theorem (34) will have to be modified to include the case where $r(\cdot)$ is not necessarily affine.

52 **A heuristic condition of optimality.** Suppose that R is not just any ray of the cone $K(\hat{z})$, but that it is an interior ray of $K(\hat{z})$. Then the second-order term $o(\cdot)$ in (31) is not likely to dislodge all the points of $F(\hat{z}) + R$ from the set $F(\{\hat{z}\} + RC(\hat{z},\Omega))$ [the image of $\{\hat{z}\} + RC(\hat{z},\Omega)$ under F], and hence the set $F(\Omega)$ will contain admissible points $y \in F(\hat{z}) + R$ of lower cost $f(\hat{z})$. Thus we would expect that the statement of theorem (34) need only be modified to read " . . . then the negative cost ray R cannot be an *interior* ray of the cone $K(\hat{z})$ . . . ." $\Box$

We shall see in the next section that this guess is correct, and we shall also see what further modifications are necessary to accommodate the case when the radial cone $RC(\hat{z},\Omega)$ contains only the zero vector.

2.3 THE FUNDAMENTAL THEOREM

With the preliminary analysis of the Basic Problem completed, we are now ready to approach the question of necessary conditions in earnest. We begin by introducing two types of conical approximations to the set Ω. These conical approximations will define the class of *perturbations* about $\hat{z}$, an optimal solution to the Basic Problem, in terms of which we shall state our necessary condition of optimality for $\hat{z}$. Thus a salient feature of the theorem to be derived is that it is not valid with respect to arbitrary perturbations about an optimal point, but is valid only with respect to a specific subclass, which may or may not exhaust all the possible perturbations about the optimal solution in question.

1 **Definition.** A convex cone $C(\hat{z},\Omega) \subset E^n$ will be called a *conical approximation of the first kind* to the constraint set Ω at the point $\hat{z} \in \Omega$ if for any collection $\{\delta z_1, \delta z_2, \ldots, \delta z_k\}$ of linearly independent vectors in $C(\hat{z},\Omega)$ there exists an $\epsilon > 0$, possibly depending on $\hat{z}$ and $\delta z_1, \delta z_2, \ldots, \delta z_k$, such that co $\{\hat{z}, \hat{z} + \epsilon\, \delta z_1, \hat{z} + \epsilon\, \delta z_2, \ldots, \hat{z} + \epsilon\, \delta z_k\} \subset \Omega$. □

If a cone $C(\hat{z},\Omega)$ is a conical approximation of the first kind to Ω at $\hat{z} \in \Omega$, then for every $\delta z \in C(\hat{z},\Omega)$ there exists, by definition, an $\epsilon > 0$ such that $(\hat{z} + \alpha\, \delta z) \in \Omega$ for all α satisfying $0 \leqq \alpha \leqq \epsilon$. Thus every conical approximation of the first kind to the set Ω at $\hat{z}$ is contained in the radial cone to Ω at $\hat{z}$, which was defined in (2.32).

2 **Lemma.** Suppose that Ω is a convex subset of E^n. Then the radial cone to Ω at any point $\hat{z} \in \Omega$ is a conical approximation of the first kind. Furthermore,

$$RC(\hat{z},\Omega) = \{\delta z\colon \delta z = \lambda(z - \hat{z}), \lambda \geqq 0, z \in \Omega\}.$$

Proof. From exercise (2.33), the radial cone to Ω at $\hat{z}$ is the cone generated by $\Omega - \{\hat{z}\}$; that is, $RC(\hat{z},\Omega)$ is as given above. Now, $RC(\hat{z},\Omega)$ is convex, since Ω is convex, and the cone generated by a convex set is a convex cone [see (A.4.8)].

Let $\{\delta z_1, \delta z_2, \ldots, \delta z_k\}$ be any set of vectors in $RC(\hat{z},\Omega)$. Then there are scalars $\lambda_i \geqq 0$ and vectors $z_i \in \Omega$ such that $\delta z_i = \lambda_i(z_i - \hat{z})$ for $i = 1, 2, \ldots, k$. Let $\epsilon > 0$ be chosen such that $0 \leqq \epsilon\lambda_i \leqq 1$ for every $i = 1, 2, \ldots, k$, and let $\xi_i = \epsilon\lambda_i$. Then $\hat{z} + \epsilon\, \delta z_i = \xi_i z_i + (1 - \xi_i)\hat{z} \in \Omega$, since Ω is convex. Therefore, by theorem (A.3.16), co $\{\hat{z}, \hat{z} + \epsilon\, \delta z_1, \ldots, \hat{z} + \epsilon\, \delta z_k\} \subset \Omega$. □

For most problems of interest we can derive necessary conditions of optimality in terms of perturbations δz belonging to a conical approximation of the first kind. However, there are a few important exceptions for which conical approximations of the first kind are either unavailable or else unsuitable. To provide for these situations we now introduce a somewhat more complex conical approximation to the set Ω at a point $\hat{z} \in \Omega$.

3 **Definition.** A convex cone $C(\hat{z},\Omega) \subset E^n$ will be called a *conical approximation of the second kind* to the set Ω at $\hat{z} \in \Omega$ if for any collection $\{\delta z_1, \delta z_2, \ldots, \delta z_k\}$ of linearly independent vectors in $C(\hat{z},\Omega)$ there exist an $\epsilon > 0$, possibly depending on $\hat{z}$, $\delta z_1, \delta z_2, \ldots, \delta z_k$, and a continuous map $\zeta(\cdot)$ from co $\{\hat{z}, \hat{z} + \epsilon\, \delta z_1, \hat{z} + \epsilon\, \delta z_2, \ldots,$

$\hat{z} + \epsilon\, \delta z_k\}$ into Ω such that $\zeta(\hat{z} + \delta z) = \hat{z} + \delta z + o(\delta z)$, where $\lim_{\|\delta z\| \to 0} \|o(\delta z)\|/\|\delta z\| = 0$.† □

4 **Remark.** Observe that if $C(\hat{z},\Omega)$ is a conical approximation of the first kind to Ω at $\hat{z} \in \Omega$, then it is also a conical approximation of the second kind to Ω at $\hat{z}$, with the map ζ being the identity map. However, while we can usually tell by inspection whether a set Ω has conical approximations of the first kind, it is often quite difficult to establish the existence of approximations of the second kind. This will become very clear in the next chapter. Consequently, the main reason for introducing conical approximations of the first kind is that they constitute a very important special class. *When we have no specific reason for indicating whether a cone $C(\hat{z},\Omega)$ is a conical approximation of the first kind or of the second kind, we shall refer to it simply as a conical approximation to Ω at $\hat{z} \in \Omega$, and we shall understand that it is a conical approximation of the second kind.* □

Let us consider a very simple example of a set Ω which has nontrivial conical approximations of the second kind but not of the first.

5 **Example.** Let $\Omega = \{z\colon z = z(\theta) = (r \cos \theta,\, r \sin \theta),\, 0 \leqq \theta \leqq \pi/2\}$; that is, Ω is a circular arc in the plane E^2. By inspection, the radial cone $RC(\hat{z},\Omega)$ to Ω at any point $\hat{z} \in \Omega$ is the singleton $\{0\}$, and hence there are no nontrivial conical approximations of the first kind to Ω. Now let $\hat{z} = (r \cos \hat{\theta},\, r \sin \hat{\theta})$ be any point in Ω; we shall show that when $\hat{\theta} < \pi/2$, the tangent ray $C(\hat{z},\Omega) = \{\delta z\colon \delta z = \alpha\, dz(\hat{\theta})/d\theta = \alpha(-r \sin \hat{\theta},\, r \cos \hat{\theta}),\, \alpha \geqq 0\}$ is a conical approximation of the second kind to Ω at $\hat{z}$.

Let $\delta z_1 = dz(\hat{\theta})/d\theta$; then, expanding the expression for $z(\theta)$ in the definition of Ω about $\hat{\theta}$, we get

6 $$z(\hat{\theta} + \alpha) = \hat{z} + \alpha\, \delta z_1 + o(\alpha) \qquad 0 \leqq \hat{\theta} + \alpha \leqq \frac{\pi}{2},$$

where o is a continuous function such that $\|o(\alpha)\|/\alpha \to 0$ as $\alpha \to 0$. Now let $\delta \tilde{z} \in C(\hat{z},\Omega)$ be arbitrary, but not zero. Then $\delta \tilde{z} = \tilde{\alpha}\, \delta z_1$ for some $\tilde{\alpha} > 0$. We now choose $\epsilon = [(\pi/2) - \hat{\theta}]/\tilde{\alpha}$ and define the map ζ

† When it is specifically known that the set Ω will be used with a *given* constraint function $r\colon E^n \to E^m$, it is convenient to make the definition of $C(\hat{z},\Omega)$ dependent on r in the following way: In definition (3), replace the phrase "any collection of linearly independent vectors" by the phrase "any collection of $(m + 1)$ linearly independent vectors." Furthermore, when $m = 0$, delete the requirement that $C(\hat{z},\Omega)$ be convex.

from co $\{\hat{z}, \hat{z} + [(\pi/2) - \hat{\theta}]\, \delta z_1\}$ into Ω by

7 $$\zeta(\hat{z} + \alpha\, \delta z_1) = \hat{z} + \alpha\, \delta z_1 + o(\alpha) \qquad 0 \leqq \alpha \leqq \frac{\pi}{2} - \hat{\theta}.$$

A comparison with (6) shows that ζ maps co $\{\hat{z},\hat{z} + [(\pi/2) - \hat{\theta}]\delta z_1\}$ into Ω, and consequently, the ray $C(\hat{z},\Omega)$ is a conical approximation of the second kind to Ω at $\hat{z}$. □

8 **Remark.** Comparing the definition of a conical approximation $C(\hat{z},\Omega)$ given in (3) with that of a tangent cone given in (2.8), we see that every vector in a conical approximation to a set Ω at a point $\hat{z} \in \Omega$ is also contained in the tangent cone $TC(\hat{z},\Omega)$. This is so because of the form of the map ζ. However, the tangent cone is not always convex, nor is it always possible to satisfy the condition of existence of a suitable map ζ. Hence the tangent cone to an arbitrary constraint set Ω will not always be a conical approximation. As we shall now see, an important exception arises when we know that the function $r(\cdot) \equiv 0$, that is, when we know that $m = 0$. This corresponds to the case of lumping all the constraints together into a single set Ω', as was done in (2.5). □

9 **Lemma.** Let $TC(\hat{z},\Omega')$ be the tangent cone to Ω' at $\hat{z} \in \Omega'$, with Ω' as defined in (2.5), containing all the constraints of the Basic Problem (2.1). Then $TC(\hat{z},\Omega')$ is a conical approximation to Ω' at $\hat{z}$ (in the sense indicated in the footnote on page 25).

Proof. Referring to definition (3) of a conical approximation we see that since $m = 0$, we need only show that for any $\delta z_1 \in TC(\hat{z},\Omega')$ there exist an $\epsilon > 0$ and a continuous map ζ from co $\{\hat{z}, \hat{z} + \epsilon\, \delta z_1\}$ into Ω' of the form $\zeta(\hat{z} + \delta z) = \hat{z} + \delta z + o(\delta z)$, where $\|o(\delta z)\|/\|\delta z\| \to 0$ as $\|\delta z\| \to 0$. Now, since $\delta z_1 \in TC(\hat{z},\Omega')$, there is in Ω' an arc of the form $c_1 = \{z\colon z = \hat{z} + t\, \delta z_1 + o_1(t),\ 0 \leqq t \leqq t_1,\ t_1 > 0\}$, where $o_1(\cdot)$ is a continuous function such that $\|o_1(t)\|/t \to 0$ as $t \to 0$. Let $\epsilon = t_1$; then for any $z = \hat{z} + t\, \delta z_1$ in co $\{\hat{z}, \hat{z} + \epsilon\, \delta z_1\}$, with $0 \leqq t \leqq \epsilon$, we define

10 $$\zeta(\hat{z} + t\, \delta z_1) = \hat{z} + t\, \delta z_1 + o_1(t).$$

Obviously, since $\delta z = t\, \delta z_1$ and δz_1 is a fixed vector, $\|o_1(t)\|/\|\delta z\| \to 0$ as $\|\delta z\| \to 0$. □

We now return to the Basic Problem (2.1). Recall that the continuously differentiable function F from E^n into E^{m+1} was defined in (2.30) as

11 $$F(z) = (f(z),r(z)),$$

where f is the cost function and r is the equality-constraint function of the Basic Problem (2.1). Recall also that we had agreed to denote the jacobian matrix $\partial F^i(z)/\partial z^j$ by $\partial F(z)/\partial z$ and to number the components of vectors in E^{m+1} from 0 to m; that is, $y \in E^{m+1}$ is given by $y = (y^0,y^1, \ldots ,y^m)$.

We now state and prove the most important result of the first half of the book: a necessary condition of optimality for the Basic Problem (2.1), from which all the necessary conditions given for specific problems in the following chapters will be derived.

12 **The fundamental theorem.** If $\hat{z}$ is an optimal solution to the Basic Problem (2.1) and $C(\hat{z},\Omega)$ is a conical approximation to Ω at $\hat{z}$, then there exists a nonzero vector $\psi = (\psi^0,\psi^1, \ldots ,\psi^m) \in E^{m+1}$, with $\psi^0 \leqq 0$, such that for all $\delta z \in \bar{C}(\hat{z},\Omega)$ [the closure of $C(\hat{z},\Omega)$ in E^n]

13 $$\left\langle \psi, \frac{\partial F(\hat{z})}{\partial z} \delta z \right\rangle \leqq 0.$$

Proof. Let $K(\hat{z}) \subset E^{m+1}$ be the cone defined by

14 $$K(\hat{z}) = \frac{\partial F(\hat{z})}{\partial z} C(\hat{z},\Omega) = \left\{\delta y \colon \delta y = \frac{\partial F(\hat{z})}{\partial z} \delta z,\ \delta z \in C(\hat{z},\Omega)\right\}.$$

The cone $K(\hat{z})$ is convex because the cone $C(\hat{z},\Omega)$ is convex, and the map $\partial F(\hat{z})/\partial z$ is linear (see Figure 1).

We shall now show that the optimality of $\hat{z}$ implies that the cone $K(\hat{z})$ must be separated from the ray

15 $$R = \{\delta y \colon \delta y = \beta(-1,0,0, \ldots ,0),\ \beta > 0\};$$

that is, there must exist a nonzero vector $\psi \in E^{m+1}$ such that (see Figure 1)

16 $$\langle \psi,\delta y\rangle \leqq 0 \qquad \text{for every } \delta y \in K(\hat{z})$$

and

17 $$\langle \psi,\delta y\rangle \geqq 0 \qquad \text{for every } \delta y \in R.$$

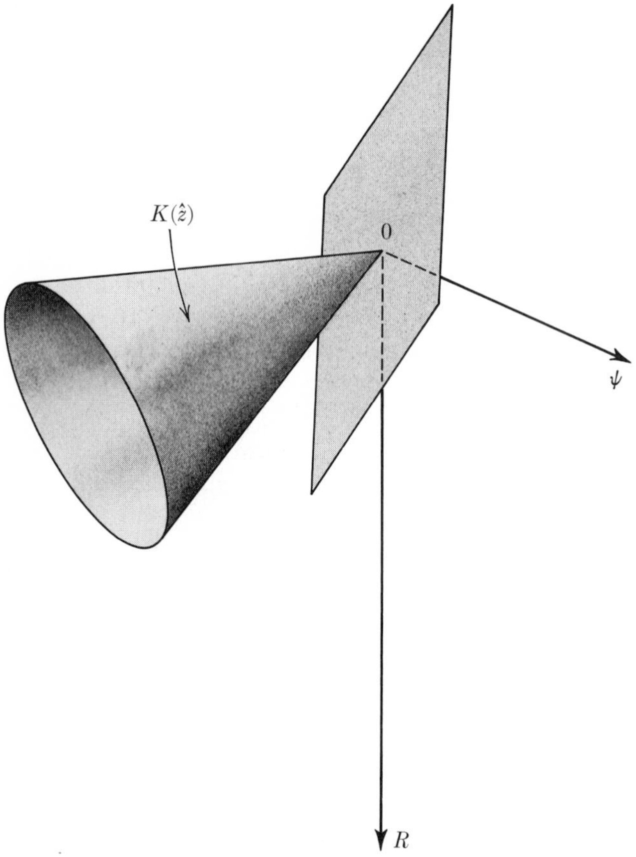

Figure 1

Note that (16) is only a slightly weaker statement than (13), and if (16) is true, then it must also be true that $\langle \psi, \delta y \rangle \leqq 0$ for every $y \in \bar{K}(\hat{z})$, the closure of $K(\hat{z})$, which is a slightly stronger statement than (13). Also note that (17) implies that $\psi^0 \leqq 0$. Thus to prove the theorem it is enough to establish the separation of $K(\hat{z})$ and R.

Suppose that the cone $K(\hat{z})$ and the ray R are not separated (see Figure 2). It then follows from theorem (A.5.5) that:

a. $K(\hat{z}) \cup R$ cannot be contained in an m-dimensional hyperplane.

b. $R \cap \text{rel int } K(\hat{z}) \neq \phi$.

Clearly, if one point of R belongs to the relative interior of $K(\hat{z})$, then every point of R belongs to the relative interior of $K(\hat{z})$. Thus, since $R \subset \text{rel int } K(\hat{z})$, it follows from (*a*) that $K(\hat{z})$ must be of dimension $m + 1$,† and hence that R is an interior ray of $K(\hat{z})$ [that is, all points of R are interior points of $K(\hat{z})$].

To obtain a contradiction we shall exhibit in $K(\hat{z})$ a vector δy^* which has in $C(\hat{z},\Omega)$ a corresponding vector δz^* with the following properties:

18 $$\frac{\partial F(\hat{z})}{\partial z}\,\delta z^* = \delta y^*.$$

19 $$\zeta(\hat{z} + \delta z^*) \in \Omega.$$

20 $$[F(\zeta(\hat{z} + \delta z^*)) - F(\hat{z})] \in R,$$

where ζ is a continuous map of the form $\zeta(\hat{z} + \delta z) = \hat{z} + \delta z + o(\delta z)$ $[\|o(\delta z)\|/\|\delta z\| \to 0$ as $\|\delta z\| \to 0]$. Obviously, if (18) to (20) hold, then the vector $z^* = \zeta(\hat{z} + \delta z^*)$ is in Ω, and since $F = (f,r)$, it follows

† Note that for the cone $K(\hat{z})$ to be of dimension $m + 1$, that is, for the cone $K(\hat{z})$ to have an interior, it is necessary that the columns of the matrix $\partial F(\hat{z})/\partial z$ span E^{m+1}, that is, that $\partial F(\hat{z})/\partial z$ have rank $m + 1$.

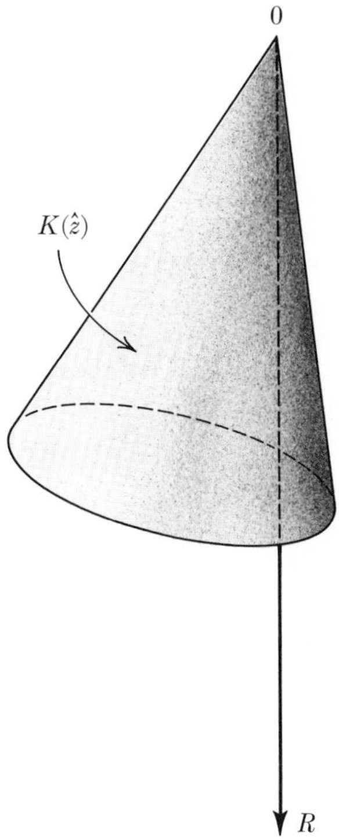

Figure 2

from (20) that $f(z^*) - f(\hat{z}) < 0$ and $r(z^*) - r(\hat{z}) = 0$. But $r(\hat{z}) = 0$, and therefore $z^* \in \Omega$, $r(z^*) = 0$ and $f(z^*) < f(\hat{z})$, contradicting the optimality of $\hat{z}$.

Our construction of the vectors δy^* and δz^* requires the use of the Brouwer fixed-point theorem[1] (see references [3, 4]). We begin by constructing in the cone $K(\hat{z})$ a simplex S (see Figure 3), with vertices 0 and $\delta y_1, \delta y_2, \ldots, \delta y_{m+1}$ and containing a segment $\Gamma = \{y: y = \beta(-1,0,0, \ldots ,0),\ 0 < \beta \leqq \nu\}$ of the ray R in its interior. Since R is assumed to be in the interior of $K(\hat{z})$, we can always construct such a simplex. We assume that we have made the lengths of the vectors δy_i for $i = 1, 2, \ldots, m + 1$ sufficiently small to ensure that for a set of vectors $\delta z_1\ \delta z_2, \ldots, \delta z_{m+1}$ in $C(\hat{z},\Omega)$ satisfying

21 $$\frac{\partial F(\hat{z})}{\partial z}\delta z_i = \delta y_i \qquad i = 1, 2, \ldots, m + 1$$

there exists a continuous map ζ from co $\{\hat{z}, \hat{z} + \delta z_1, \ldots, \hat{z} + \delta z_{m+1}\}$ into Ω of the form $\zeta(\hat{z} + \delta z) = \hat{z} + \delta z + o(\delta z)$, where $\|o(\delta z)\|/\|\delta z\| \to 0$ as $\|\delta z\| \to 0$.†

[1] The usual form of the Brouwer fixed-point theorem is as follows: *Brouwer fixed-point theorem.* If f is a continuous map from the closed unit ball $B = \{x \in E^n: \|x\| \leqq 1\}$, then f has a fixed point.

However, for the purpose of our proof we find it more convenient to work with the following alternative form.

Theorem. If f is a continuous map from the closed unit ball $B = \{x \in E^n: \|x\| \leqq 1\}$ into E^n, with $f(x) = x + g(x)$, where $\|g(x)\| \leqq 1$ for all x with $\|x\| = 1$, then the origin is contained in the range of f.

Proof. To say that the origin is contained in the range of f is equivalent to saying that the function $h(x) = -g(x)$ has a fixed point. Let us define the function h_1 by

$$h_1(x) = \begin{cases} -g(x) & \text{if } \|g(x)\| \leqq 1 \\ -g(x)/\|g(x)\| & \text{if } \|g(x)\| > 1. \end{cases}$$

Clearly, h_1 is a continuous function from the closed unit ball in E^n into the closed unit ball in E^n. Therefore, by the Brouwer fixed-point theorem, h_1 has a fixed point, say, x_1. If $\|h_1(x_1)\| < 1$, then $h_1(x_1) = -g(x_1)$, and x_1 is a fixed point of $-g$. Suppose $\|h_1(x_1)\| = 1$. Then $\|x_1\| = 1$, and consequently, $\|g(x_1)\| \leqq 1$. Again $h_1(x_1) = -g(x_1)$ and x_1 is a fixed point of $-g$. (Note that this result is true for any closed ball centered at the origin, not just for the unit ball.)

The Brouwer fixed-point theorem follows immediately from this theorem, so they are in fact equivalent.

† Since R has points in the interior of $K(\hat{z})$, there must exist some simplex S' in $K(\hat{z})$ with vertices $0, \delta y'_1, \ldots, \delta y'_{m+1}$ containing a segment Γ' of R in its interior. By definition of a simplex, the vectors $\delta y'_1, \ldots, \delta y'_{m+1}$ are linearly

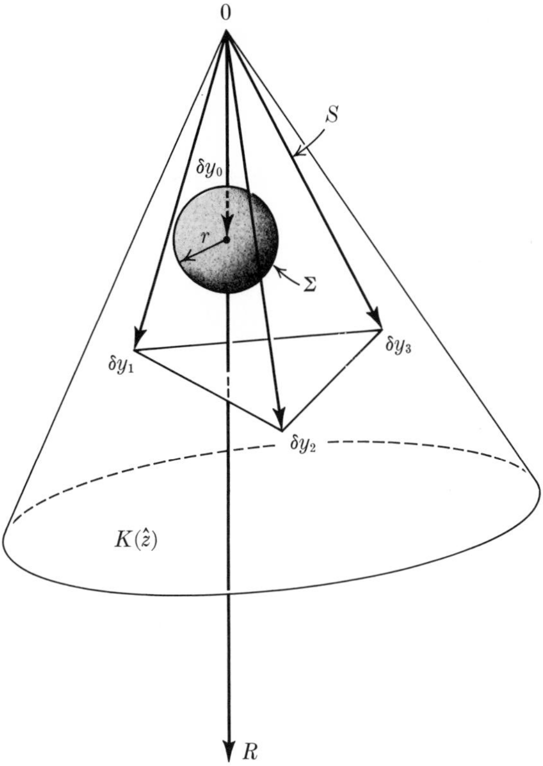

Figure 3

Let δy_0 be a point in the relative interior of $S \cap R$, and let $\Sigma \subset S$ be a closed ball with center δy_0 and radius r. For $0 < \alpha \leqq 1$, let $\Sigma_\alpha = \alpha\Sigma = \{\alpha\, \delta y \colon \delta y \in \Sigma\}$; that is, Σ_α is a closed ball with center at $\alpha\, \delta y_0$ and radius αr. Since for every vector $\delta y \in S$, $\alpha\, \delta y \in S$ for $0 \leqq \alpha \leqq 1$, it is clear that Σ_α is contained in the simplex S for $0 < \alpha \leqq 1$.

For a fixed α satisfying $0 < \alpha \leqq 1$ we now construct a map G_α from the ball $\Sigma_\alpha - \{\alpha\, \delta y_0\}$ (with center at the origin and radius αr)

---

independent, and so, as a result, are any $\delta z_i' \in C(\hat{z},\Omega)$ which satisfy

$$\delta y_i' = \frac{\partial F(\hat{z})}{\partial z}\, \delta z_i' \qquad \text{for} \qquad i = 1, 2, \ldots, m+1.$$

By definition (3) there exist an $\epsilon > 0$ and a continuous map $\zeta(\cdot)$ from co $\{\hat{z}, \hat{z} + \epsilon\delta z_1', \ldots, \hat{z} + \epsilon\delta z_{m+1}'\}$ into Ω. Setting $S = \epsilon S'$, so that $\delta y_i = \epsilon\delta y_i'$ and $\delta z_i = \epsilon\delta z_i'$ for $i = 1, 2, \ldots, m+1$, we obtain a simplex S with the desired properties.

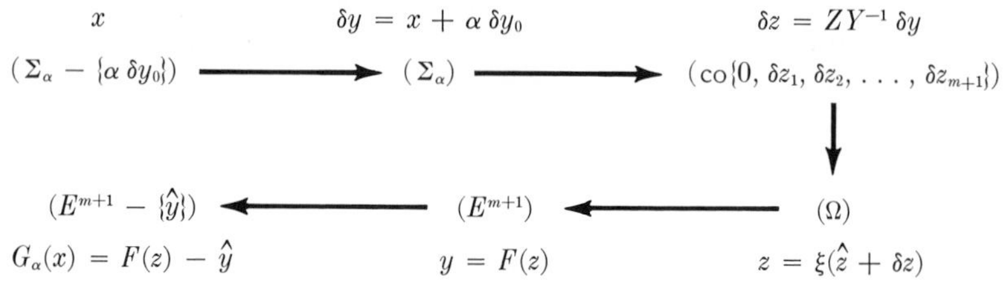

Figure 4 Construction of $G_\alpha(x)$.

into E^{m+1} as follows (see Figure 4). For any $x \in (\Sigma_\alpha - \{\alpha\,\delta y_0\})$ let

22 $$G_\alpha(x) = F(\zeta(\hat{z} + ZY^{-1}(\alpha\,\delta y_0 + x))) - (\hat{y} + \alpha\,\delta y_0),$$

where $\hat{y} = F(\hat{z})$, ζ is our map from co $\{\hat{z}, \hat{z} + \delta z_1, \ldots, \hat{z} + \delta z_{m+1}\}$ into Ω, Y is an $(m+1) \times (m+1)$ matrix whose ith column is δy_i, and Z is an $n \times (m+1)$ matrix whose ith column is δz_i. Since S is a simplex, the vectors δy_i are linearly independent, and therefore Y is nonsingular.

The composite map G_α can be seen to have been constructed for the purpose of finding a $\delta y^* \in K(\hat{z})$ and a $\delta z^* \in C(\hat{z},\Omega)$ satisfying (18) to (20) as follows. First, for any $x \in (\Sigma_\alpha - \{\alpha\,\delta y_0\})$ the vector $\delta y = (x + \alpha\,\delta y_0) \in \Sigma_\alpha \subset S$. Next, since $\delta y \in S$, $\delta y = \Sigma_{i=1}^{m+1} \mu^i\,\delta y_i = Y\mu$, where $\mu^i \geqq 0$ and $\Sigma_{i=1}^{m+1} \mu^i \leqq 1$, and therefore

$$z = \hat{z} + ZY^{-1}\,\delta y = \hat{z} + \Sigma_{i=1}^{m+1} \mu^i\,\delta z_i = (1 - \Sigma_{i=1}^{m+1} \mu^i)\,\hat{z} + \Sigma_{i=1}^{m+1} \mu^i\,(\hat{z} + \delta z_i)$$

is a point in co $\{\hat{z}, \hat{z} + \delta z_1, \ldots, \hat{z} + \delta z_{m+1}\}$. Consequently, since $(\partial F(\hat{z})/\partial z)\,Z = Y$, the vector $\delta z = z - \hat{z}$ satisfies $(\partial F(\hat{z})/\partial z)\,\delta z = \delta y$ [cf. (18)] and the vector z satisfies $\zeta(z) \in \Omega$ [cf. (19)]. If we can now show that for some α^* satisfying $0 < \alpha^* \leqq 1$ there is an x^* in $\Sigma_\alpha^* - \{\alpha^*\,\delta y_0\}$ such that $G_{\alpha^*}(x^*) = 0$, then the vector $\delta y^* = x^* + \alpha^*\,\delta y_0$ will satisfy not only (18) and (19), but also (20).

Recalling that

$$\zeta(\hat{z} + ZY^{-1}(\alpha\,\delta y_0 + x)) = \hat{z} + ZY^{-1}(\alpha\,\delta y_0 + x) + o(ZY^{-1}(\alpha\,\delta y_0 + x)),$$

we can expand the right-hand side of (22) about $\hat{z}$ as follows:

23 $$G_\alpha(x) = \hat{y} + \frac{\partial F(\hat{z})}{\partial z} ZY^{-1}(\alpha\,\delta y_0 + x) - (\hat{y} + \alpha\,\delta y_0) + o_G(ZY^{-1}(\alpha\,\delta y_0 + x)),$$

where o_G is a continuous function such that $\|o_G(y)\|/\|y\| \to 0$ as $\|y\| \to 0$. Since $Y = (\partial F(\hat{z})/\partial z)Z$, equation (23) simplifies out to

24 $$G_\alpha(x) = x + o_G(ZY^{-1}(\alpha\ \delta y_0 + x)).$$

Now, for $x \in \partial(\Sigma_\alpha - \{\alpha\ \delta y_0\})$, the boundary of the ball, $\|x\| = \alpha r$, and we may therefore write $x = \alpha\rho$, where ρ is a vector in E^{m+1} such that $\|\rho\| = r$. Hence for any $x \in \partial(\Sigma_\alpha - \{\alpha\ \delta y_0\})$

25 $$G_\alpha(x) = G_\alpha(\alpha\rho) = \alpha\rho + o_G(\alpha ZY^{-1}(\delta y_0 + \rho)),$$

and since $\|o_G(\alpha ZY^{-1}(\delta y_0 + \rho))\|/\alpha \to 0$ as $\alpha \to 0$ uniformly in ρ, with $\|\rho\| = r$, there exists an α^* satisfying $0 < \alpha^* \leqq 1$ such that

26 $$\|o_G(\alpha^*\ ZY^{-1}(\delta y_0 + \rho))\| < \alpha^* r$$

for all ρ satisfying $\|\rho\| = r$. Referring to Brouwer's fixed-point theorem (see the footnote on page 30), we find that the map $G_{\alpha*}$ satisfies its assumptions, and hence there is an x^* in $\Sigma_{\alpha*} - \{\alpha^*\delta y_0\}$ such that

27 $$G_{\alpha*}(x^*) = 0.$$

Now, $\delta y^* = \alpha^*\ \delta y_0 + x^*$ is in $\Sigma_{\alpha^*} \subset K(\hat{z})$, $\delta z^* = ZY^{-1}\ \delta y^*$ is in co $\{\delta z_1, \delta z_2, \ldots, \delta z_{m+1}\} \subset C(\hat{z},\Omega)$, $z^* = \zeta(\hat{z} + \delta z^*)$ is in Ω, and, by (22) and (27),

28 $$F(z^*) - F(\hat{z}) - \alpha^*\ \delta y_0 = 0.$$

But $\delta y_0 = (-\nu,0,0, \ldots ,0)$, with $\nu > 0$, so that $f(z^*) - f(\hat{z}) = -\alpha^*\nu < 0$ and $r(z^*) = 0$. Thus z^* satisfies the constraints of the Basic Problem and also results in a lower cost than the optimal solution $\hat{z}$, which is a contradiction.

We therefore conclude that $K(\hat{z})$ and R must be separated, which establishes (16) and (17). But then (16) must also be true for all $y \in \bar{K}(\hat{z})$, and since $[\partial F(z)/\partial z]\ \bar{C}(\hat{z},\Omega) \subset \bar{K}(\hat{z})$, the theorem is proved. □

The significance of the assumption of convexity on a conical approximation to the set Ω about a point $\hat{z} \in \Omega$ is quite clear, and the reader should have no difficulty finding cases for which the Fundamental Theorem (12) does not hold with respect to the radial cone $RC(\hat{z},\Omega)$ when $RC(\hat{z},\Omega)$ is not convex. We shall now see that the assumption concerning the existence of a map ζ is quite subtle and cannot be eliminated, even when the radial cone $RC(\hat{z},\Omega)$ is convex. Let us examine a case in which theorem (12) breaks down when this assumption is not satisfied.

29 **Example.** Suppose that for $z \in E^3$ we wish to minimize $f(z) = z^1$ subject to the constraints $r(z) = 0$ and $z \in \Omega$, where

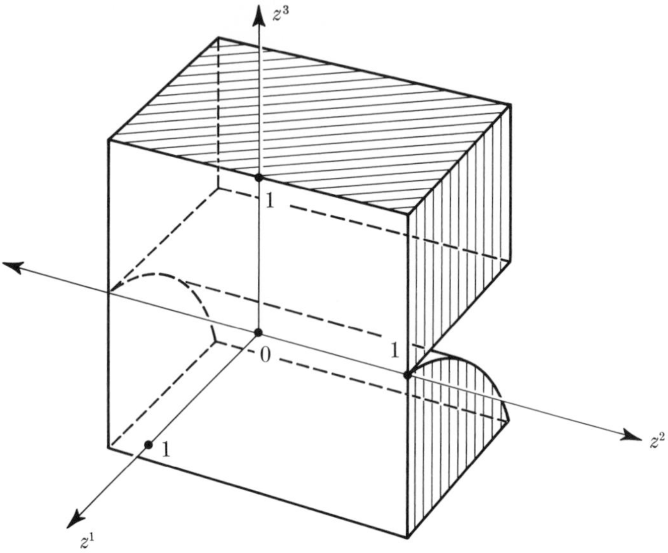

Figure 5

30 $$r(z) = \begin{bmatrix} z^2 \\ z^3 - \frac{1}{2}(z^1)^3 \end{bmatrix}$$

31 $$\Omega = \{z: -1 \leqq z^1 \leqq 0,\ -1 \leqq z^2 \leqq 1,\ 0 \leqq z^3 \leqq 1\} \cup \{z: -1 \leqq z^1 \leqq 0,\ -1 \leqq z^2 \leqq 1,\ -1 \leqq z^3 \leqq -(z^1)^2\}.$$

From (30) and (31) we see that $\hat{z} = (0,0,0)$ is the only vector which satisfies our constraints, and hence it is the optimal solution.

Now let us examine the radial cone $RC(\hat{z},\Omega)$, which is seen to be the set $\{z: z^1 \leqq 0\}$; that is, it is a half space. The reader may amuse himself by showing that although this cone is convex, there is no suitable map ζ for it. Hence it is not a conical approximation to the set Ω at $\hat{z}$, according to our definitions (1) and (3).

The jacobian matrix $\partial F(\hat{z})/\partial z$ is easily seen to be

$$\frac{\partial F(\hat{z})}{\partial z} = \begin{bmatrix} 1 & 0 & 0 \\ 0 & 1 & 0 \\ 0 & 0 & 1 \end{bmatrix},$$

and therefore the cone $K(\hat{z}) = [\partial F(z)/\partial z]\, RC(\hat{z},\Omega)$ is seen to be the set

$$K(\hat{z}) = \{y = (y^0,y^1,y^2): y^0 \leqq 0\}.$$

By inspection, the ray $R = \{y: y = \beta(-1,0,0),\ \beta \geqq 0\}$ belongs to the interior of the full-dimensional cone $K(\hat{z})$, in contradiction to the Fundamental Theorem (12). We therefore see that the requirement that there exist a suitable map ζ cannot be eliminated from definitions (1) and (3) of a conical approximation without invalidating our Fundamental Theorem (12). □

A Few Second-order Conditions of Optimality

Referring to the proof of the Fundamental Theorem (12), we see that this theorem degenerates, in the sense that it can be satisfied trivially, when the dimension of the cone $K(\hat{z})$ is less than $m + 1$. This is obviously the case when the vectors $\nabla f(\hat{z})$ and $\nabla r^i(\hat{z})$ for $i = 1, 2, \ldots, m$ are linearly dependent. To elaborate on this point, let us expand (13) into a sum of components: for all $\delta z \in \bar{C}(\hat{z},\Omega)$ we get

32
$$\left\langle \psi, \frac{\partial F(\hat{z})}{\partial z} \delta z \right\rangle = \left\langle \frac{\partial F(\hat{z})^T}{\partial z} \psi, \delta z \right\rangle = \left\langle \psi^0 \nabla f(\hat{z}) + \sum_{i=1}^{m} \psi^i \nabla r^i(\hat{z}), \delta z \right\rangle \leqq 0.$$

Now, if some of the vectors $\nabla f(\hat{z})$ and $\nabla r^i(\hat{z})$ for $i = 1, 2, \ldots, m$ are linearly dependent, then there exist multipliers $\psi^0, \psi^1, \ldots, \psi^m$, not all zero and with $\psi^0 \leqq 0$, such that

33
$$\psi^0 \nabla f(\hat{z}) + \sum_{i=1}^{m} \psi^i \nabla r^i(\hat{z}) = 0.$$

Clearly, these multipliers satisfy the conditions of the Fundamental Theorem (12), but apparently, their existence does not depend on, and therefore does not reflect, the optimality of the point $\hat{z}$.

Nevertheless, we cannot conclude automatically that whenever the vectors $\nabla f(\hat{z})$ and $\nabla r^i(\hat{z})$ for $i = 1, 2, \ldots, m$ are linearly dependent the Fundamental Theorem is useless, because a degeneracy of this type may occur without making (33) a trivial statement. For example, suppose that $\Omega = E^n$; then (32) must hold for every $\delta z \in E^n$, implying (33); that is, that these vectors must be linearly dependent at every optimal $\hat{z}$. Similarly, suppose the point $\hat{z}$ is in the interior of Ω; then again (33) is a meaningful condition of optimality [note that when $\hat{z}$ is in the interior of Ω, then $C(\hat{z},\Omega)$ is E^n]. Also, while it may be possible to satisfy (32) trivially by choosing multipliers which satisfy (33), it may also be possible to find a set of multipliers which satisfy (32) but not (33). This nontrivial set of multipliers may, possibly, give a nontrivial result.

When (33) can be satisfied trivially with $\psi^0 = -1$, $\psi^i = 0$ for $i = 1, 2, \ldots, m$ because $\nabla f(\hat{z}) = 0$, and the vectors $\nabla r^i(\hat{z})$ are linearly independent, we can strengthen the Fundamental Theorem (12) to some extent by introducing second-order effects, provided the function $f(\cdot)$ has continuous second-order partial derivatives.

34 **Definition.** Let the cost function $f(\cdot)$ be twice continuously differentiable. We define the *hessian* $H_{\hat{z}}(\cdot)$ mapping E^n into the reals to be the function

35 $$H_{\hat{z}}(\delta z) = \left\langle \delta z, \frac{\partial^2 f(\hat{z})}{\partial z^2} \delta z \right\rangle,$$

where $\partial^2 f(\hat{z})/\partial z^2$ is an $n \times n$ matrix whose ijth elements are $\partial^2 f(\hat{z})/\partial z^i \partial z^j$. □

Thus $\frac{1}{2}H_{\hat{z}}(\delta z)$ is the second term of the expansion of $f(\hat{z} + \delta z)$ about $\hat{z}$; that is,

36 $$f(\hat{z} + \delta z) = f(\hat{z}) + \langle \nabla f(\hat{z}), \delta z \rangle + \tfrac{1}{2}H_{\hat{z}}(\delta z) + \bar{o}(\delta z),$$

where $\bar{o}(\delta z)/\|\delta z\|^2 \to 0$ as $\|\delta z\| \to 0$.

37 **Exercise.** Prove the following theorems.

38 **Theorem.** If $\hat{z}$ is an optimal solution to the Basic Problem (2.1), with $\nabla f(\hat{z}) = 0$, and f is twice continuously differentiable, then

39 $$-H_{\hat{z}}(\delta z) \leqq 0 \qquad \text{for all } \delta z \in TC(\hat{z},\Omega'),$$

where $TC(\hat{z},\Omega')$ is the tangent cone to the constraint set Ω' defined in (2.5) and $H_{\hat{z}}(\cdot)$ is as defined in (35). □

Show that (39) also holds for all $\delta z \in TC_s(\hat{z},\Omega')$, the sequential tangent cone to Ω' at $\hat{z}$, defined in (2.28). [*Hint:* Proceed as for theorem (2.12)].

40 **Theorem.** If $\hat{z}$ is an optimal solution to the Basic Problem (2.1), with $\nabla f(\hat{z}) = 0$, and f is twice continuously differentiable, then the ray

41 $$R = \{y \in E^{m+1}: y = \beta(-1,0,0, \ldots ,0), \beta > 0\}$$

is not an interior ray of the set

42 $$L(\hat{z}) = \left\{y = (y^0,x) \in E^{m+1}: y^0 = H_{\hat{z}}(\delta z),\ x = \frac{\partial r(\hat{z})}{\partial z}\delta z,\ \delta z \in C(\hat{z},\Omega)\right\},$$

where $H_{\hat{z}}$ is as defined in (35), r and Ω are as in (2.1), and $C(\hat{z},\Omega)$ is any conical approximation to Ω at $\hat{z}$.

[*Hint:* This theorem is fairly difficult to prove. Show that if the theorem is false, then there must exist a simplex S in E^m, with vertices $x_1, x_2, \ldots, x_{m+1}$ and *containing the origin in its interior*, such that for $i = 1, 2, \ldots, m + 1$

43 $$x_i = \frac{\partial r(\hat{z})}{\partial z}\,\delta z_i \qquad \text{for some } \delta z_i \in C(\hat{z},\Omega),$$

with

44 $$H_{\hat{z}}(\delta z) < 0 \qquad \text{for all } \delta z \in \text{co}\,\{\delta z_1, \delta z_2, \ldots, \delta z_{m+1}\}$$

and

45 $$\zeta(\text{co}\,\{\hat{z} + \delta z_1, \hat{z} + \delta z_2, \ldots, \hat{z} + \delta z_{m+1}\}) \subset \Omega,$$

where ζ is the map in the definition of the conical approximation (3). Now construct a map G_α, as in the proof of the Fundamental Theorem (12), and complete the present proof.] □

A complete study of second-order conditions of optimality can be found in reference [6].

Conditions for $\psi^0 < 0$ in Theorem (12)

As will be seen in the next section and in subsequent chapters, it is much easier to make use of the Fundamental Theorem (12) when we are certain that ψ^0 may be taken to be nonzero, that is, $\psi^0 < 0$. The reader is now invited to prove some sufficient conditions which ensure that $\psi^0 < 0$.

46 **Exercise.** Consider the statement of theorem (12). Show that if $\langle \nabla f(\hat{z}), \delta z \rangle \geqq 0$ for every $\delta z \in \bar{C}(\hat{z},\Omega)$ such that $\langle \nabla r^i(\hat{z}), \delta z \rangle = 0$ for $i = 1, \ldots, m$, then there exists a vector ψ satisfying the conditions of theorem (12), with $\psi^0 < 0$. □

47 **Exercise.** Consider the statement of theorem (12) and suppose that

48 $$\overline{\text{co}}\; TC_s(\hat{z},\Omega') = \overline{\text{co}}\; TC_s(\hat{z},\Omega) \cap \{\delta z\colon \langle \nabla r^i(\hat{z}), \delta z \rangle = 0,\; i = 1, \ldots, m\},$$

where $\Omega' = \{z\colon r(z) = 0, z \in \Omega\}$. Show that under this assumption there exists a vector ψ satisfying the conditions of theorem (12), with $\psi^0 < 0$. [*Hint:* Recall that $\bar{C}(\hat{z},\Omega) \subset TC_s(\hat{z},\Omega)$; use exercises (46) and (2.27).] □

49 **Remark.** Assumption (48) is a condition involving *only* the constraints, which guarantees the existence of a vector ψ satisfying

theorem (12), with $\psi^0 < 0$. Conditions of this type are usually referred to as *constraint qualifications*, and it will be seen in Section 3.3 that both the *Kuhn-Tucker constraint qualification* and its weakened forms are equivalent to (48). □

50 **Exercise.** Consider the statement of theorem (12) and suppose that the origin in E^m is an interior point of the set

51 $$\tilde{K} = \{y\colon y^i = \langle \nabla r^i(\hat{z}), \delta z\rangle,\ i = 1, \ldots, m,\ \delta z \in C(\hat{z},\Omega)\}.$$

Show that under this assumption if ψ is a vector satisfying the conditions of theorem (12), then $\psi^0 < 0$. □

52 **Exercise.** Show that the origin in E^m is an interior point of the set $\tilde{K}$ [see (51)] if and only if the vectors $\nabla r^i(\hat{z})$ for $i = 1, \ldots, m$ are linearly independent and the subspace

53 $$P = \{\delta z\colon \langle \nabla r^i(\hat{z}), \delta z\rangle = 0,\ i = 1, \ldots, m\}$$

is not contained in a support hyperplane to the conical approximation $C(\hat{z},\Omega)$. □

54 **Exercise.** Show that the subspace P defined by (53) is not contained in a support hyperplane to the conical approximation $C(\hat{z},\Omega)$ if there is a δz^* in the *interior* of $C(\hat{z},\Omega)$ satisfying $\langle \nabla r^i(\hat{z}), \delta z^*\rangle = 0$ for $i = 1, \ldots, m$. □

Problems without Differentiability Assumptions

A question which may have crossed the mind of a reader familiar with such problems in optimal control as the minimum-fuel problem is what should be done when the cost function $f(\cdot)$ is not continuously differentiable. The following exercises should help clear up this point.

55 **Exercise.** Show that the original Basic Problem (2.1) is equivalent to the following augmented Basic Problem whose cost function is continuously differentiable:

56 Minimize $\langle e_1, \mathbf{z}\rangle$ subject to $\mathbf{r}(\mathbf{z}) = 0$ and $\mathbf{z} \in \Omega^*$, where $e_1 = (1,0,0, \ldots, 0) \in E^{n+1}$, $\mathbf{z} = (z^0, z) \in E^{n+1}$, with $z^0 \in E^1$ and $z \in E^n$, $\mathbf{r}(\mathbf{z}) = r(z)$, and $\Omega^* = \{\mathbf{z} = (z^0, z)\colon z \in \Omega,\ z^0 - f(z) \geq 0\}$.

Thus the nondifferentiable cost can be shifted into the constraint set by adding one component to z (we can obviously shift the nondifferentiable components of the function r into Ω without adding any new components to z). □

57 **Exercise.** Consider form (56) of the Basic Problem (2.1). Suppose that $f(\cdot)$ is a convex function and that $C(\hat{z},\Omega)$ is a conical approximation of the first kind to Ω at $\hat{z} \in \Omega$. Show that for $\hat{\mathbf{z}} = (f(\hat{z}),\hat{z})$

58 $$C(\hat{\mathbf{z}},\Omega^*) = \{\delta\mathbf{z} = \lambda(\delta z^0,\delta z)\colon \delta z \in C(\hat{z},\Omega),\ \lambda \geqq 0,\ \delta z^0 \geqq f(\hat{z} + \delta z) - f(\hat{z})\}$$

is a conical approximation of the first kind to Ω^* at $\hat{\mathbf{z}}$. □

59 **Exercise.** Suppose that the set Ω is convex and that the cost function $f(\cdot)$ is convex. Use the representation (56) of the Basic Problem and lemma (12) to show that condition (13) now takes on the form

60 $$\psi^0(f(z) - f(\hat{z})) + \sum_{i=1}^{m} \psi^i \nabla r^i(\hat{z})\,(z - \hat{z}) \leqq 0 \qquad \text{for all } z \in \Omega,$$

and that, in addition, when the functions r^i are affine, (60) becomes

61 $$\psi^0 f(\hat{z}) + \sum_{i=1}^{m} \psi^i r^i(\hat{z}) \geqq \psi^0 f(z) + \sum_{i=1}^{m} \psi^i r^i(z) \qquad \text{for all } z \in \Omega.$$

[This is a maximum-type condition and is true whether $f(\cdot)$ is differentiable or not.] □

62 **Exercise.** Let $F = (f,r)$, as before. Show that if the set $F(\Omega)$ is convex and $\hat{z}$ is an optimal solution to the Basic Problem, then there exist multipliers $\psi^0, \psi^1, \ldots, \psi^m$, not all zero, with $\psi^0 \leqq 0$, such that

63 $$\psi^0 f(\hat{z}) + \sum_{i=1}^{m} \psi^i r^i(\hat{z}) \geqq \psi^0 f(z) + \sum_{i=1}^{m} \psi^i r^i(z) \qquad \text{for all } z \in \Omega.$$

[This result is independent of whether $f(\cdot)$ and $r(\cdot)$ are differentiable or not.] □

2.4 THE TWO-POINT-BOUNDARY-VALUE OPTIMAL CONTROL PROBLEM

In the next chapter we shall use very efficient methods to deduce from Fundamental Theorem (3.12) almost all the presently known necessary conditions of optimality for a solution to an optimal control problem. Since most control engineers are accustomed to methods based on perturbations about optimal trajectories, which, incidentally, are less efficient than the techniques we use in Chapter 3, we shall now consider a treatment of the two-point-boundary-value optimal control problem in terms of perturbation techniques. This will serve the purpose of clarifying the similarities and the differences in the two approaches. The reader will have no difficulty in establishing the fact that the differences increase as the constraints on the optimal trajectory become more complicated.

In dealing with optimal control problems it is traditional to augment the system of dynamic equations as in (1.3.6) and to state the probems in the canonical form (1.3.7). We now proceed in this manner.

1 **The two-point-boundary-value optimal control problem.** We are given a fixed integer k and an augmented system of dynamic equations

2 $$\mathbf{x}_{i+1} - \mathbf{x}_i = \mathbf{f}_i(x_i,u_i) \qquad i = 0, 1, \ldots, k-1,$$

where $\mathbf{x}_i = (x_i^0,x_i^1, \ldots ,x_i^n)$ is the *augmented state*, or *phase*, of the system, $u_i = (u_i^1,u_i^2, \ldots ,u_i^m)$ is the *control*, or *input*, applied to the system, and the $\mathbf{f}_i(\cdot,\cdot)$ are differentiable functions from $E^{n+1} \times E^m$ into E^{n+1}. We are also given the boundary conditions

3 $$\mathbf{x}_0 = (0,\hat{x}_0^1,\hat{x}_0^2, \ldots ,\hat{x}_0^n)$$

4 $$\mathbf{x}_k \in \mathbf{X}_k = \{\mathbf{x}: \mathbf{x} = (x^0,\hat{x}_k^1,\hat{x}_k^2, \ldots ,\hat{x}_k^n)\},$$

where $\hat{x}_0^1, \hat{x}_0^2, \ldots, \hat{x}_0^n$ and $\hat{x}_k^1, \hat{x}_k^2, \ldots, \hat{x}_k^n$ are given and x^0 is an arbitrary scalar. Thus the initial phase is a fixed zero cost point, while the terminal phase lies on a fixed line which is parallel to the cost axis. Finally, we are given k sets $U_i \subset E^m$ for $i = 0, 1, \ldots, k-1$, to which the controls u_i are restricted. The radial cones $RC(u,U_i)$, with $u \in U_i$, arbitrary, are assumed to be conical approximations of the first kind for $i = 0, 1, \ldots, k-1$ [see (3.1)].

We are required to find a control sequence $\hat{\mathfrak{U}} = (\hat{u}_0,\hat{u}_1, \ldots, \hat{u}_{k-1})$, with $\hat{u}_i \in U_i$, whose corresponding phase trajectory $\hat{\mathfrak{X}} = (\hat{\mathbf{x}}_0,\hat{\mathbf{x}}_1, \ldots ,\hat{\mathbf{x}}_k)$ satisfies the given boundary conditions (3) and (4) such that for every other control sequence $\mathfrak{U} = (u_0,u_1, \ldots ,u_{k-1})$, with $u_i \in U_i$, whose corresponding phase trajectory $\mathfrak{X} = (\mathbf{x}_0,\mathbf{x}_1, \ldots ,\mathbf{x}_k)$ also satisfies (3) and (4) we have

5 $$\hat{x}_k^0 \leqq x_k^0. \quad \square$$

We shall call such a $\hat{\mathfrak{U}}$ an *optimal control sequence.*

6 **Remark.** Fortunately, the usual constraint sets U_i, such as $U_i = \{u: \max_j |u^j| \leqq \alpha^i\}$ or $U_i = \{u: \|u\| \leqq \beta^i\}$ are convex and their radial cones are conical approximations of the first kind, by lemma (3.2). $\square$

For the problem under consideration all the trajectories start at the same point $\hat{\mathbf{x}}_0 = (0,\hat{x}_0^1,\hat{x}_0^2, \ldots ,\hat{x}_0^n)$. Thus the solution of system (2) at time k, denoted by $\mathbf{x}_k(\hat{\mathbf{x}}_0,\mathfrak{U})$, which corresponds to an admissible control sequence $\mathcal{U}$, defines a map $\mathbf{F}$ with domain $U = U_0 \times U_1 \times \cdots \times U_{k-1} \subset E^{mk}$ and range in E^{n+1}, that is,

7
$$\mathbf{F}(\mathcal{U}) = (F^0(\mathcal{U}), F^1(\mathcal{U}), \ldots, F^n(\mathcal{U})) = \mathbf{x}_k(\hat{\mathbf{x}}_0, \mathcal{U}).$$

The map $\mathbf{F}$ is a composition map made up of the functions $\mathbf{f}_i(\cdot,\cdot)$ appearing in the difference equation (2). Since these functions are continuously differentiable, the map $\mathbf{F}$ is also continuously differentiable.

8 **Remark.** With the introduction of the map $\mathbf{F}$, the two-point-boundary-value optimal control problem (1) automatically assumes the form of the Basic Problem (2.1): minimize $F^0(\mathcal{U})$, subject to $F(\mathcal{U}) - \hat{x}_k = 0$ and $\mathcal{U} \in U$, where we define $F = (F^1, F^2, \ldots, F^n)$; that is, $\mathbf{F} = (F^0, F)$. □

The above rephrasing of the optimal control problem is implied in the proofs given by various writers and will therefore be familiar to the reader of control literature. Note that the function F above, which takes the place of the function r in the Basic Problem (2.1), is completely different in form from the function r constructed in Chapter 1 [see (1.5.4)]. For the purpose of obtaining necessary conditions form (1.5.4) is usually more convenient; however, there are many cases involving the construction of optimal control algorithms when the form F defined by (7) is preferred. These points will be clarified in later chapters.

We can now restate the Fundamental Theorem (3.12) in terms of control problem (1).

9 **Separation theorem.** If $\hat{\mathcal{U}}$ is an optimal control sequence for control problem (1) and the radial cone $RC(\hat{\mathcal{U}}, U)$ is a conical approximation of the first kind to U at $\hat{\mathcal{U}}$, then there exists a nonzero vector $\psi = (\psi^0, \psi^1, \ldots, \psi^n) \in E^{n+1}$, with $\psi^0 \leqq 0$, such that for all $\delta\mathcal{U} \in \overline{RC}(\hat{\mathcal{U}}, U)$, the closure of $RC(\hat{\mathcal{U}}, U)$ in E^{mk},

10
$$\left\langle \psi, \frac{\partial F(\hat{\mathcal{U}})}{\partial \mathcal{U}} \delta\mathcal{U} \right\rangle \leqq 0.$$

11 **Remark.** The radial cone to U at $\hat{\mathcal{U}}$ is the cross product of the radial cones to the sets U_i at $\hat{u}_i$; that is,

12
$$RC(\hat{\mathcal{U}}, U) = RC(\hat{u}_0, U_0) \times RC(\hat{u}_1, U_1) \times \cdots \times RC(\hat{u}_{k-1}, U_{k-1}).$$

It may therefore be easily verified that if the radial cones $RC(\hat{u}_i, U_i)$ are conical approximations of the first kind, as we have assumed

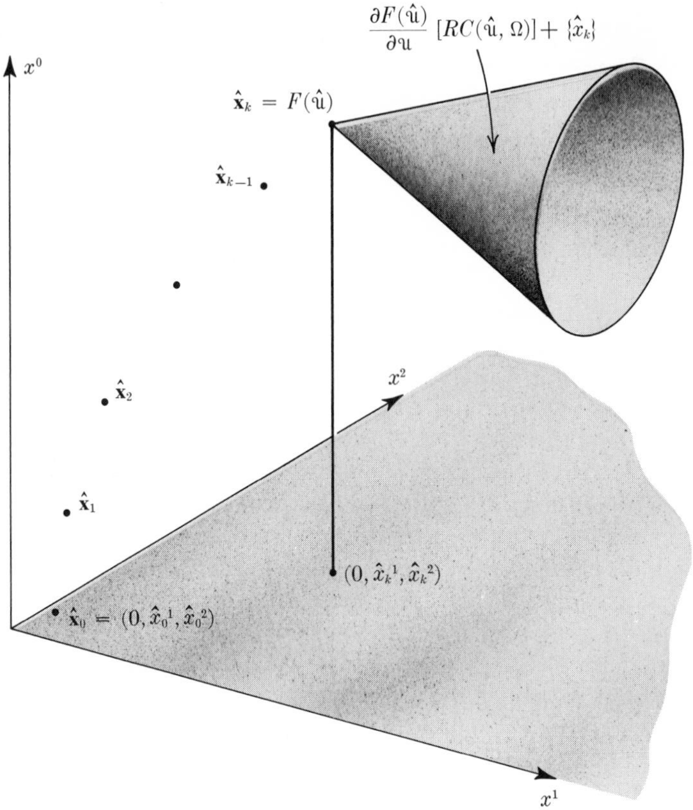

Figure 1

them to be, then their cross product $RC(\hat{\mathfrak{u}},U)$ is also a conical approximation the first kind. □

We must now interpret inequality (10) (see Figure 1). Let us begin by computing the jacobian matrix $\partial\mathbf{F}(\hat{\mathfrak{u}})/\partial\mathfrak{u}$. Let $\delta\mathfrak{u} = (\delta u_0, \delta u_1, \ldots, \delta u_{k-1})$ be any perturbation about the optimal control sequence $\hat{\mathfrak{u}}$; then, since $\mathbf{F}$ is continuously differentiable, the perturbed terminal phase is given by

13 $$\mathbf{F}(\hat{\mathfrak{u}} + \delta\mathfrak{u}) = \mathbf{F}(\hat{\mathfrak{u}}) + \frac{\partial\mathbf{F}(\hat{\mathfrak{u}})}{\partial\mathfrak{u}}\,\delta\mathfrak{u} + \mathbf{o}(\delta\mathfrak{u}),$$

where the $(n + 1) \times km$ jacobian matrix $\partial\mathbf{F}(\hat{\mathfrak{u}})/\partial\mathfrak{u}$ has as its $\alpha\beta$ element $\partial\mathbf{F}^\alpha(\hat{\mathfrak{u}})/\partial u_0{}^\beta$ for $\alpha = 0, 1, \ldots, n$, and $\beta = 1, 2, \ldots, m$, $\partial\mathbf{F}^\alpha(\hat{\mathfrak{u}})/\partial u_1^{\beta-m}$ for $\alpha = 0, 1, \ldots, n$ and $\beta = m + 1, m + 2, \ldots, 2m$, etc., and $\mathbf{o}(\delta\mathfrak{u})$ is a continuous function of $\delta\mathfrak{u}$ such that

$$\lim_{\|\delta\mathfrak{u}\|\to 0} \|\mathbf{o}(\delta\mathfrak{u})\|/\|\delta\mathfrak{u}\| = 0.$$

The most direct way to compute the linear term in (13) is to go back to the difference equation (2), which defines the map $\mathbf{F}$. Since the functions $\mathbf{f}_i(\cdot,\cdot)$ are continuously differentiable for $i = 0, 1, \ldots, k-1$, we may expand the right-hand side of (2) about the optimal control sequence $\hat{\mathfrak{u}} = (\hat{u}_0, \hat{u}_1, \ldots, \hat{u}_{k-1})$ and its corresponding optimal trajectory $\hat{\mathfrak{X}} = (\hat{\mathbf{x}}_0, \hat{\mathbf{x}}_1, \ldots, \hat{\mathbf{x}}_k)$ to obtain

14 $$(\hat{\mathbf{x}}_{i+1} + \delta\mathbf{x}_{i+1}) - (\hat{\mathbf{x}}_i + \delta\mathbf{x}_i) = \mathbf{f}_i(\hat{\mathbf{x}}_i,\hat{u}_i) + \frac{\partial}{\partial \mathbf{x}} \mathbf{f}_i(\hat{\mathbf{x}}_i,\hat{u}_i)\, \delta\mathbf{x}_i + \frac{\partial}{\partial u} \mathbf{f}_i(\hat{\mathbf{x}}_i,\hat{u}_i)\, \delta u_i + \mathbf{o}(\delta\mathbf{x}_i,\delta u_i) \qquad i = 0, 1, \ldots, k-1,$$

where $\delta\mathbf{x}_i \in E^{n+1}$ for $i = 0, 1, \ldots, k$, $\delta u \in_i E^m$ for $i = 0, 1, \ldots, k-1$ and we have used the obvious substitutions in (2)

15 $$\mathbf{x}_i = \hat{\mathbf{x}}_i + \delta\mathbf{x}_i \qquad \text{and} \qquad u_i = \hat{u}_i + \delta u_i.$$

The element in the α row and β column of the jacobian matrices $(\partial/\partial\mathbf{x})\mathbf{f}_i(\hat{\mathbf{x}}_i,\hat{u}_i)$ and $(\partial/\partial u)\mathbf{f}_i(\hat{\mathbf{x}}_i,\hat{u}_i)$ is $[(\partial/\partial\mathbf{x}^\beta)\mathbf{f}_i{}^\alpha(\mathbf{x},\hat{u}_i)]_{\mathbf{x}=\hat{\mathbf{x}}_i}$, with $\alpha, \beta = 0, 1, \ldots, n$, and $[(\partial/\partial u^\beta)\mathbf{f}_i{}^\alpha(\hat{\mathbf{x}}_i,u)]_{u=\hat{u}_i}$, with $\alpha = 0, 1, \ldots, n$ and $\beta = 1, 2, \ldots, m$, respectively; that is, $(\partial/\partial x)f_i(\hat{x}_i,\hat{u}_i)$ is an $(n+1) \times (n+1)$ matrix and $(\partial/\partial u)f_i(\hat{x}_i,\hat{u}_i)$ is an $(n+1) \times m$ matrix. The function $\mathbf{o}(\delta\mathbf{x}_i,\delta u_i)$ is continuous and has the property that $\lim_{(\delta\mathbf{x}_i,\delta u_i)\to 0} \|\mathbf{o}(\delta\mathbf{x}_i,\delta u_i)\|/\|(\delta\mathbf{x}_i,\delta u_i)\| = 0$, where $(\delta\mathbf{x}_i,\delta u_i)$ is a combined vector with $n + 1 + m$ components.

It is reasonably clear that the linear part of (13), $[\partial\mathbf{F}(\hat{\mathfrak{u}})/\partial\mathfrak{u}]\,\partial\mathfrak{u}$, can only be the result of the linear part of (14); i.e., it is the solution of the linear difference equation

16 $$\delta\mathbf{x}_{i+1} - \delta\mathbf{x}_i = \frac{\partial}{\partial \mathbf{x}} \mathbf{f}_i(\hat{\mathbf{x}}_i,\hat{u}_i)\, \delta\mathbf{x}_i + \frac{\partial}{\partial u} \mathbf{f}_i(\hat{\mathbf{x}}_i,\hat{u}_i)\, \delta u_i \qquad i = 0, 1, \ldots, k-1$$

with $\delta\mathbf{x}_0 = 0$ and $\delta\mathfrak{u} = (\delta u_0, \delta u_1, \ldots, \delta u_{k-1})$. Thus

17 $$\frac{\partial\mathbf{F}(\hat{\mathfrak{u}})}{\partial\mathfrak{u}}\, \delta\mathfrak{u} = \delta\mathbf{x}_k(0,\delta\mathfrak{u}).$$

Let $G_{i,j}$, where $i = j, j+1, \ldots, k$ and $j \in \{0,1, \ldots, k\}$, be the $(n+1) \times (n+1)$ matrix solution of

18 $$G_{i+1,j} - G_{i,j} = \frac{\partial}{\partial \mathbf{x}} \mathbf{f}_i(\hat{\mathbf{x}}_i,\hat{u}_i)\, G_{i,j} \qquad i = j, j+1, \ldots, k-1,$$

from the initial value $G_{j,j} = I$, the identity matrix; that is, $G_{i,j}$ is a state transition matrix. Hence $G_{j,j} = I$ and

19 $$G_{i,j} = \left[I + \frac{\partial}{\partial \mathbf{x}} \mathbf{f}_{i-1}(\hat{\mathbf{x}}_{i-1},\hat{u}_{i-1})\right]\left[I + \frac{\partial}{\partial \mathbf{x}} \mathbf{f}_{i-2}(\hat{x}_{i-2},\hat{u}_{i-2})\right] \cdots \left[I + \frac{\partial}{\partial \mathbf{x}} \mathbf{f}_j(\hat{\mathbf{x}}_j,\hat{u}_j)\right] \qquad i = j+1, j+2, \ldots, k$$

Now suppose that $\delta u_j \neq 0$ for some $j \in \{0, 1, \ldots, k-1\}$ and that $\delta u_i = 0$ for all other $i \in \{0, 1, \ldots, k-1\}$. Then $\delta \mathbf{x}_k$, the resulting solution of (16) at time k, is given by

20 $$\delta \mathbf{x}_k = G_{k,j+1} \frac{\partial}{\partial u} \mathbf{f}_j(\hat{\mathbf{x}}_j,\hat{u}_j)\ \delta u_j.$$

Since $\delta \mathbf{x}_0 = 0$, by assumption, we conclude from (17) and (20) that for an arbitrary $\delta \mathfrak{u} = (\delta u_0, \delta u_1, \ldots, \delta u_{k-1}) \in E^{km}$

21 $$\delta \mathbf{x}_k = \frac{\partial F(\hat{\mathfrak{u}})}{\partial \mathfrak{u}}\ \delta \mathfrak{u} = \sum_{j=0}^{k-1} G_{k,j+1} \frac{\partial}{\partial u} \mathbf{f}_j(\hat{\mathbf{x}}_j,\hat{u}_j)\ \delta u_j.$$

Thus we find that in partitioned form $\partial F(\hat{\mathfrak{u}})/\partial \mathfrak{u}$ can be expressed as

22 $$\frac{\partial F(\hat{\mathfrak{u}})}{\partial \mathfrak{u}} = \left(G_{k,1} \frac{\partial}{\partial u} f_0(\hat{\mathbf{x}}_0,\hat{u}_0) \,\vdots\, G_{k,2} \frac{\partial}{\partial u} f_1(\hat{\mathbf{x}}_1,\hat{u}_1) \,\vdots\, \cdots \,\vdots\, G_{kk} \frac{\partial}{\partial u} f_{k-1}(\hat{\mathbf{x}}_{k-1},\hat{u}_{k-1})\right).$$

If we substitute from (21) into (10), our necessary condition becomes

23 $$\left\langle \psi, \sum_{j=1}^{k-1} G_{k,j+1} \frac{\partial}{\partial u} \mathbf{f}_j(\hat{\mathbf{x}}_j\hat{u}_j)\ \delta u_j \right\rangle \leqq 0 \qquad \text{for all } \delta \mathfrak{u} \in \overline{RC}(\hat{\mathfrak{u}},U).$$

Now let us choose $\delta u_i \neq 0$ and $\delta u_j = 0$ for all $j \neq i$. Then (23) becomes

24 $$\left\langle \psi, G_{k,i+1} \frac{\partial}{\partial u} \mathbf{f}_i(\hat{\mathbf{x}}_i,u_i)\ \delta u_i \right\rangle \leqq 0 \qquad \text{for all } \delta u_i \in \overline{RC}(\hat{u}_i,U_i).$$

Finally, we introduce the $(n+1)$-dimensional *cophase vectors* $\mathbf{p}_0, \mathbf{p}_1, \ldots, \mathbf{p}_k$, defined by

25 $$\mathbf{p}_i = G_{k,i}^T\ \psi \qquad i = 0, 1, \ldots, k.$$

It can be verified by direct use of definition (19) of the matrices $G_{k,i}$ that the cophase vectors satisfy the adjoint difference equation

26
$$\mathbf{p}_i - \mathbf{p}_{i+1} = \left[\frac{\partial}{\partial \mathbf{x}} \mathbf{f}_i(\hat{\mathbf{x}}_i,\hat{u}_i)\right]^T \mathbf{p}_{i+1}$$
$$i = 0, 1, \ldots, k-1, \mathbf{p}_k = \psi.$$

In terms of the cophase variables, (24) becomes

27
$$\left\langle \mathbf{p}_{i+1}, \frac{\partial}{\partial u} \mathbf{f}_i(x_i,u_i)\, \delta u_i \right\rangle \leqq 0 \qquad \text{for all } \delta u_i \in \overline{RC}(u_i,U_i),$$
$$i = 0, 1, \ldots, k-1.$$

We can now summarize the above findings.

28 **Theorem.** If $\hat{\mathfrak{u}}$ is an optimal control sequence and $\hat{\mathfrak{X}}$ is the corresponding optimal trajectory for problem (1), and if for $i = 0, 1, \ldots, k-1$ the radial cones $RC(\hat{u}_i,U_i)$ are conical approximations to the sets U_i at $\hat{u}_i \in U_i$, then there exist vectors $\mathbf{p}_0, \mathbf{p}_1, \ldots, \mathbf{p}_k$ in E^{n+1}, not all zero, such that

29
$$\mathbf{p}_i - \mathbf{p}_{i+1} = \left[\frac{\partial}{\partial \mathbf{x}} \mathbf{f}_i(\hat{\mathbf{x}}_i,\hat{u}_i)\right]^T \mathbf{p}_{i+1} \qquad i = 0, 1, \ldots, k-1$$

30
$$p_k{}^0 \leqq 0$$

and for all $\delta u_i \in RC(\hat{u}_i,U_i)$, with $i = 0, 1, \ldots, k-1$,

31
$$\left\langle \frac{\partial}{\partial u} H(\hat{\mathbf{x}}_i,\hat{u}_i,\mathbf{p}_{i+1},i), \delta u_i \right\rangle \leqq 0,$$

where the hamiltonian $H(\cdot,\cdot,\cdot,\cdot)$ which maps $E^{n+1} \times E^m \times E^{n+1} \times \{0, 1, \ldots, k\}$ into the real line is defined by

32
$$H(\mathbf{x},u,\mathbf{p},i) = \langle \mathbf{p},\mathbf{f}_i(\mathbf{x},u)\rangle. \quad \square$$

33 **Corollary.** If the functions $\mathbf{f}_i(\mathbf{x},u)$ for $i = 0, 1, \ldots, k-1$ do not depend on the cost variable x^0, then the vectors $\mathbf{p}_0, \mathbf{p}_1, \ldots, \mathbf{p}_k$ satisfying (29) to (31) also satisfy $p_0{}^0 = p_1{}^0 = \cdots = p_k{}^0 \leqq 0$.

Proof. Since the functions $\mathbf{f}_i(\mathbf{x},u)$ do not depend on the cost variable x^0, the first column of the matrices $[(\partial/\partial\mathbf{x})\mathbf{f}_i(\hat{\mathbf{x}}_i,\hat{u}_i)]^T$ is zero, and hence, from (29),

34
$$p_i{}^0 - p_{i+1}^0 = 0 \qquad i = 0, 1, \ldots, k-1. \quad \square$$

35 **Remark.** It is customary to exhibit the relationship among the hamiltonian H, the system equations (2), and the adjoint equations (26). These are as follows:

36 $$\hat{\mathbf{x}}_{i+1} - \hat{\mathbf{x}}_i = \frac{\partial}{\partial \mathbf{p}} H(\hat{\mathbf{x}}_i,\hat{u}_i,\mathbf{p}_{i+1},i) \qquad i = 0, 1, \ldots, k-1,$$

and

37 $$\mathbf{p}_i - \mathbf{p}_{i+1} = \frac{\partial}{\partial \mathbf{x}} H(\hat{\mathbf{x}}_i,\hat{u}_i,\mathbf{p}_{i+1},i) \qquad i = 0, 1, \ldots, k-1. \quad \square$$

Observe that condition (31) *of the necessary-conditions theorem* (28) *does not express a true maximum principle.* At most, it may be interpreted to read: "If the gradient of the hamiltonian H with respect to u, evaluated on the optimal trajectory, is not zero and not orthogonal to all the admissible perturbations $\delta u \in RC(\hat{u}_i,U_i)$, then H has a local maximum with respect to u at $u = \hat{u}_i$." However, the fact that (28) is not a maximum principle does not necessarily decrease its utility as a necessary condition.

Let us now consider an example of how the conditions of theorem (28) can be used to reduce the optimization problem (1) to a two-point-boundary-value problem for a system of difference equations.

38 **A minimum-energy problem.** Consider the particular case of problem (1) when the augmented difference equation (2) has the form

39 $$\mathbf{x}_{i+1} - \mathbf{x}_i = A\mathbf{x}_i + \mathbf{g}(u_i) \qquad i = 0, 1, \ldots, k-1,$$

where A is an $(n+1) \times (n+1)$ constant matrix of the form

40 $$A = \left[\begin{array}{c|ccc} 0 & 0 & \cdots & 0 \\ \hline 0 & & & \\ \vdots & & B & \\ 0 & & & \end{array}\right].$$

The controls u_i are assumed to be real valued (that is, $m = 1$), and for $i = 0, 1, \ldots, k$, $U_i = \{u\colon |u| \leq 1\}$. The function $\mathbf{g}(\cdot)$ is defined to be

41 $$\mathbf{g}(u_i) = ((u_i)^2, u_i d^1, \ldots, u_i d^n).$$

That is, referring to Section 1.3, we observe that we have here a linear plant with a quadratic cost functional. The hamiltonian H for this problem has the form

42 $$H(\mathbf{x}_i, u_i, \mathbf{p}_{i+1}, i) = \langle \mathbf{p}_{i+1}, A\mathbf{x}_i + \mathbf{g}(u_i)\rangle \qquad i = 0, 1, \ldots, k-1,$$

and condition (31) becomes

43 $$\left(2\hat{u}_i p_{i+1}^0 + \sum_{j=1}^{n} p_{i+1}^j d^j\right) \delta u_i \leqq 0 \qquad \text{for all } \delta u_i \in \overline{RC}(\hat{u}_i, U_i).$$

Examining (43) above, we conclude that if $(2\hat{u}_i p_{i+1}^0 + \Sigma_{j=1}^n p_{i+1}^j d^j) > 0$, then $RC(\hat{u}_i, U_i)$ must be the set $\{\delta u_i\colon \delta u_i \leqq 0\}$, and hence $\hat{u}_i = +1$. Similarly, if this expression is negative, then $\hat{u}_i = -1$. Otherwise $2\hat{u}_i p_{i+1}^0 + \Sigma_{j=1}^n p_{i+1}^j d^j = 0$. We can now combine the above three statements to express the optimal control sequence in terms of the vectors $p_0, p_1, \ldots, p_k$ as follows:[1]

44 $$\hat{u}_i = \text{sat}\left(-\sum_{j=1}^{n} \frac{p_{i+1}^j d^j}{2p_{i+1}^0}\right) \qquad i = 0, 1, 2, \ldots, k-1,$$

where

45 $$\text{sat}\,(y) = \begin{cases} y & \text{if } |y| \leqq 1 \\ \dfrac{y}{|y|} & \text{if } |y| > 1. \end{cases}$$

As a result, the problem is reduced to an ordinary two-point-boundary-value problem: solve the system of equations

46 $$\hat{\mathbf{x}}_{i+1} - \hat{\mathbf{x}}_i = A\mathbf{x}_i + \mathbf{g}\left(\text{sat}\left(\sum_{j=1}^{n} \frac{p_{i+1}^j d^j}{2p_{i+1}^0}\right)\right)$$

47 $$\mathbf{p}_i - \mathbf{p}_{i+1} = A^T \mathbf{p}_{i+1}$$

with the boundary conditions

48 $$\hat{\mathbf{x}}_0 = (0, \hat{x}_0^1, \hat{x}_0^2, \ldots, \hat{x}_0^n) \qquad \hat{\mathbf{x}}_k \in \{\mathbf{x}\colon \mathbf{x} = (x^0, \hat{x}_k^1, \hat{x}_k^2, \ldots, \hat{x}_k^n)\},$$

where $\hat{x}_0^1, \hat{x}_0^2, \ldots, \hat{x}_0^n$ and $\hat{x}_k^1, \hat{x}_k^2, \ldots, \hat{x}_k^n$ are given. □

REFERENCES

1. M. D. Canon, C. D. Cullum, and E. Polak: Constrained Minimization Problems in Finite Dimensional Spaces, *SIAM J. Control*, **4**:528–547 (1966).

[1] We anticipate here some of the results which will be developed in Chapter 4, where it will be shown that for minimum-energy problems such as the one described, p_i^0 = constant < 0 (not zero) and condition (31) is not only necessary, but also sufficient.

2. L. W. Neustadt: An Abstract Variational Theory with Applications to a Broad Class of Optimization Problems, I. General Theory, II. Applications, *SIAM J. Control*, **4**:505–527 (1966), **5**:90–137 (1967).
3. L. M. Graves: "Theory of Functions of Real Variables," p. 149, McGraw-Hill Book Company, New York, 1946.
4. W. Hurewicz and H. Wallman: "Dimension Theory," pp. 40–41, Princeton University Press, Princeton, N.J., 1960.
5. H. W. Kuhn and A. W. Tucker: Nonlinear Programming, *Proc. Second Berkeley Symp. Math. Stat. Probability*, pp. 481–492, University of California Press, Berkeley, Calif., 1951.
6. E. J. Messerli and E. Polak: On Second Order Conditions of Optimality, *SIAM J. Control*, **7** (1969), in press.
7. L. S. Pontryagin, V. G. Boltyanskii, R. V. Gamkrelizde, and E. F. Mishchenko: "The Mathematical Theory of Optimal Processes," Interscience Publishers, Inc., New York, 1962.
8. B. W. Jordan and E. Polak: Theory of a Class of Discrete Optimal Control Systems, *J. Electron. Control*, **17**:697–713 (1964).
9. H. Halkin: A Maximum Principle of the Pontryagin Type for Systems Described by Nonlinear Difference Equations, *SIAM J. Control*, **4**:90–111 (1966).

3

Some necessary and some sufficient conditions for nonlinear programming problems

3.1 INTRODUCTION

The Fundamental Theorem (2.3.12) is remarkable in that virtually all the known necessary conditions of optimality for nonlinear programming and discrete optimal control problems can be deduced from it. However, the manner in which these necessary conditions are obtained is not always straightforward. This is because to obtain a meaningful condition we must first obtain a nontrivial conical approximation to the constraint set [see (2.3.1) and (2.3.3)]. This chapter is therefore devoted to the application of the Fundamental Theorem (2.3.12) to nonlinear programming problems and to establishing certain cases for which the resulting necessary conditions are also sufficient.

1 **The nonlinear programming problem.** Given a real-valued continuously differentiable function $f(\cdot)$ defined on E^n, a continuously differentiable function $r(\cdot)$ from E^n into E^m, and a continuously

differentiable function $q(\cdot)$ from E^n into E^k, find a vector $\hat{z} \in E^n$ satisfying

2 $$\hat{z} \in \Omega \triangleq \{z: q(z) \leqq 0\}$$
3 $$r(\hat{z}) = 0$$

such that

4 $$f(\hat{z}) \leqq f(z)$$

for all $z \in E^n$ satisfying (2) and (3). □

Thus the nonlinear programming problem is simply a form of the Basic Problem (1.4.1) in which the constraint set Ω is given the specific description $\Omega = \{z: q(z) \leqq 0\}$, as in (2). In the following sections we shall consider a number of versions of the nonlinear programming problem (1) which will be found to be of increasing complexity as far as application of the Fundamental Theorem (2.3.12) is concerned. We begin with the simplest case possible, $\Omega = E^n$, that is, $q(\cdot) \equiv 0$.

3.2 THEORY OF LAGRANGE MULTIPLIERS

The simplest case of the nonlinear programming problem (1.1) is the one in which $\Omega = E^n$, that is, where the inequality-constraint function $q(\cdot)$ is identically zero. Thus we are given the continuously differentiable functions $f(\cdot)$ and $r^1(\cdot), r^2(\cdot), \ldots, r^m(\cdot)$ [that is, $r(\cdot) = (r^1(\cdot), r^2(\cdot), \ldots, r^m(\cdot))$] from E^n into the reals, and we are required to find a $\hat{z} \in E^n$ satisfying $r^i(\hat{z}) = 0$ for $i = 1, 2, \ldots, m$ such that $f(\hat{z}) \leqq f(z)$ for all $z \in E^n$ also satisfying $r^i(z) = 0$ for $i = 1, 2, \ldots, m$.

Obviously, this is a special case of the Basic Problem (1.4.1), with the set $\Omega = E^n$. Now, E^n is a conical approximation to E^n at any point $\hat{z} \in E^n$, and hence we conclude from the Fundamental Theorem (2.3.12) that if $\hat{z}$ is an optimal solution to the Basic Problem and $\Omega = E^n$, then there exists a nonzero vector $\psi \in E^{m+1}$ such that

1 $$\left\langle \psi, \frac{\partial F(\hat{z})}{\partial z} \delta z \right\rangle \leqq 0 \qquad \text{for all } \delta z \in E^n,$$

where the function $F(\cdot)$ from E^n into E^{m+1} is as defined in (2.2.30): $F(z) = (f(z), r^1(z), r^2(z), \ldots, r^m(z))$; that is, $F^0(\cdot) = f(\cdot)$, $F^1(\cdot) = r^1(\cdot), \ldots, F^m(\cdot) = r^m$. Obviously, (1) may be rewritten as

2 $$\left\langle \left[\frac{\partial F(\hat{z})}{\partial z}\right]^T \psi, \delta z \right\rangle \leqq 0 \qquad \text{for all } \delta z \in E^n.$$

Since for any $\delta z \in E^n$, $-\delta z$ is also in E^n, we conclude from (2) that

3 $$\left\langle \left[\frac{\partial F(\hat{z})}{\partial z}\right]^T \psi, \delta z \right\rangle = 0 \qquad \text{for all } \delta z \in E^n,$$

and hence

4 $$\left[\frac{\partial F(\hat{z})}{\partial z}\right]^T \psi = 0.$$

Now, $\partial F(\hat{z})/\partial z$ is an $(m + 1) \times n$ matrix with rows, from top to bottom, $\nabla f(\hat{z})$, $\nabla r^1(\hat{z})$, . . . , $\nabla r^m(\hat{z})$, where $\nabla f(\hat{z}) = (\partial f(\hat{z})/\partial z^1$, . . . ,$\partial f(\hat{z})/\partial z^n)$ and $\nabla r^i(\hat{z}) = (\partial r^i(\hat{z})/\partial z^1$, . . . ,$\partial r^i(\hat{z})/\partial z^n)$ for $i =$ 1, 2, . . . , m. We may therefore expand (4) into the form

5 $$\psi^0 \nabla f(\hat{z}) + \sum_{i=1}^{m} \psi^i \nabla r^i(\hat{z}) = 0.$$

We have thus proved the following classical Lagrange multiplier rule.

6 **Theorem: Lagrange multiplier rule.** Let f and $r^1, r^2, \ldots, r^m$ be real-valued continuously differentiable functions on E^n. If $\hat{z} \in E^n$ minimizes $f(z)$ subject to the constraints $r^i(z) = 0$ for $i = 1, 2, \ldots, m$, then there exist scalar multipliers $\psi^0, \psi^1, \ldots, \psi^m$, not all zero, such that the real-valued function $L(\cdot)$ defined on E^n by

7 $$L(z) = \psi^0 f(z) + \sum_{i=1}^{m} \psi^i r^i(z)$$

has a stationary point at $z = \hat{z}$; that is, $\partial L(\hat{z})/\partial z = 0$. □

Clearly, this merely says that (5) is satisfied.

8 **Corollary.** If the functions r^i for $i = 1, 2, \ldots, m$ are affine, then the conditions of theorem (6) can be satisfied with $\psi^0 < 0$.

Proof. We shall show that the assumption of corollary (2.2.48) is satisfied, that is, that the cone $K(\hat{z})$ is closed. In the particular case where $\Omega = E^n$, $RC(\hat{z},\Omega) = E^n$, and hence

$$K(\hat{z}) = \left\{\frac{\partial F(\hat{z})}{\partial z} \delta z \colon \delta z \in E^n\right\}.$$

Obviously, $K(\hat{z})$ is closed. □

9 **Corollary.** If the vectors $\nabla r^i(\hat{z})$ for $i = 1, 2, \ldots, m$ are linearly independent, then any vector ψ satisfying the conditions of theorem (6) also satisfies $\psi^0 < 0$. □

It is usual to assume that every point of the set $\{z: r^i(z) = 0, i = 1, 2, \ldots, m\}$ is a *normal point* i.e., that the gradient vectors $\nabla r^i(z)$ for $i = 1, 2, \ldots, m$ are linearly independent for all z satisfying $r^i(z) = 0$ for $i = 1, 2, \ldots, m$. When the gradient vectors $\nabla r^i(z)$ for $i = 1, 2, \ldots, m$ are not linearly independent, it is always possible to find multipliers $\psi^1, \psi^2, \ldots, \psi^m$, not all zeros, such that $\Sigma_{i=1}^m \psi^i \nabla r^i(z) = 0$. Hence by setting $\psi^0 = 0$ we can make $\psi^0 \nabla f(z) + \Sigma_{i=1}^m \psi^i \nabla r^i(z) = 0$ whether z is an optimal solution or not. Obviously, in this case theorem (6) is trivial. However, when the vectors $\nabla r^i(\hat{z})$ for $i = 1, 2, \ldots, m$ are linearly independent, it is not possible to satisfy (5) with $\psi^0 = 0$.

When $\psi^0 \neq 0$, we can multiply the ψ^i in (7) by $1/\psi^0$ and let $\hat{\lambda}_i = \psi^i/\psi^0$ for $i = 1, 2, \ldots, m$. This results in the following somewhat better-known condition.

10 **Theorem.** Let f and $r^1, r^2, \ldots, r^m$ be real-valued continuously differentiable functions on E^n. If $\hat{z}$ minimizes $f(z)$ subject to $r^i(z) = 0$ for $i = 1, 2, \ldots, m$ and either the $r^i(\cdot)$ are affine or the gradient vectors $\nabla r^i(\hat{z})$ for $i = 1, 2, \ldots, m$ are linearly independent, then there exists a vector $\hat{\lambda} \in E^m$ such that the real-valued function $L(\cdot,\cdot)$ defined on $E^n \times E^m$ by

11 $$L(z,\lambda) = f(z) + \sum_{i=1}^{m} \lambda^i r^i(z)$$

has a stationary point at $(\hat{z},\hat{\lambda})$.

Proof. Referring to (5), we note that $\partial L(\hat{z},\hat{\lambda})/\partial z = 0$, while $\partial L(\hat{z},\hat{\lambda})/\partial \lambda = r(\hat{z}) = 0$, by assumption. □

The reader should be careful not to read more into theorem (10) than it actually states. In particular, it is not true that every $\hat{z}$ which maximizes or minimizes, locally or globally, the function $f(\cdot)$ subject to the constraints $r^i(z) = 0$ for $i = 1, 2, \ldots, m$ also maximizes or minimizes the lagrangian $L(\cdot,\hat{\lambda})$ subject to no constraints on z, as will be seen from Example (14). The relationship between the extrema of these two functions is given in the next theorem, which is added as a digression to correct an occasionally encountered misconception.

12 **Theorem.** Let f and $r^1, r^2, \ldots, r^m$ be functions mapping E^n into the reals, and let $\hat{\lambda}_1, \hat{\lambda}_2, \ldots, \hat{\lambda}_m$ be given real numbers. If $\hat{z} \in E^n$

satisfies $r^i(\hat{z}) = 0$ for $i = 1, 2, \ldots, m$, and if for all $z \in N(\hat{z},\epsilon)$, an ϵ-ball about $\hat{z}$,

13 $$f(\hat{z}) + \sum_{i=1}^{m} \hat{\lambda}^i r^i(\hat{z}) \leqq f(z) + \sum_{i=1}^{m} \hat{\lambda}^i r^i(z),$$

then for all $z \in N(\hat{z},\epsilon) \cap \{z: r^i(z) = 0, i = 1, 2, \ldots, m\}$

$$f(\hat{z}) \leqq f(z).$$

(To paraphrase this theorem, if $\hat{z}$ satisfies $r^i(\hat{z}) = 0$ and if it is a point of unconstrained local minimum for the lagrangian $L(\cdot,\hat{\lambda})$, then it is also a point of local minimum for the function $f(\cdot)$ subject to the constraints $r^i(z) = 0$ for $i = 1, 2, \ldots, m$. Clearly, we could replace the word *minimum* by *maximum* and the word *local* by *global* in the statement of the theorem. Example (14) will show that the converse of this theorem is not true.)

Proof. Obviously, if $\hat{z}$ satisfies (13) for all $z \in N(\hat{z},\epsilon)$, it also satisfies (13) on the smaller set $N(\hat{z},\epsilon) \cap \{z: r^i(z) = 0, i = 1, 2, \ldots, m\}$ which is contained in $N(\hat{z},\epsilon)$. But for all z satisfying $r^i(z) = 0$ for $i = 1, 2, \ldots, m$ the lagrangian $L(z,\hat{\lambda}) = f(z) + \Sigma_{i=1}^m \hat{\lambda}^i r^i(z)$ is identically equal to $f(z)$. □

We conclude from the above theorem that if $\hat{z}$ is a point of constrained minimum (maximum) for a continuously differentiable function $f(\cdot)$ subject to continuously differentiable constraints $r^i(z) = 0$ for $i = 1, 2, \ldots, m$, and if $\hat{\lambda}^1, \hat{\lambda}^2, \ldots, \hat{\lambda}^m$ are Lagrange multipliers satisfying the conditions of theorem (10), then $\hat{z}$ is either a point of minimum (maximum) or a stationary point for the lagrangian $L(\cdot,\hat{\lambda})$, but it is never a point of maximum (minimum).

14 **Example.** Suppose that $z \in E^2$ and we wish to maximize the function

15 $$f(z) = (z^1)^4 + (z^2)^4$$

subject to the constraint

16 $$r^1(z) = (z^1)^2 + (z^2 - 1)^2 - 1 = 0.$$

Examining Figure 1, we see that $\hat{z} = (0,2)$ is the point of constrained maximum. We now form the lagrangian $L(\cdot,\cdot)$ on $E^2 \times E^1$ defined by

17 $$L(z,\lambda) = (z^1)^4 + (z^2)^4 + \lambda[(z^1)^2 + (z^2 - 1)^2 - 1]$$

and compute its stationary points $\hat{z}$ and $\hat{\lambda}$ by solving the equations $\partial L(z,\lambda)/\partial z = 0$ and $\partial L(z,\lambda)/\partial\lambda = 0$. One of the pairs that this yields

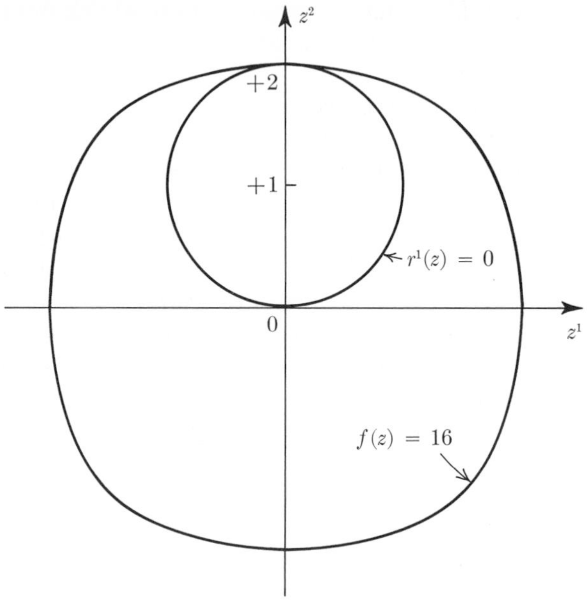

Figure 1

is ($\hat{z} = (0,2)$, $\hat{\lambda} = -16$). A simple calculation now shows that $\hat{z}$ is not a point of maximum for the function

18 $$L(z,-16) = (z^1)^4 + (z^2)^4 - 16[(z^1)^2 + (z^2 - 1)^2 - 1],$$

illustrating the fact that a point $\hat{z}$ which maximizes $f(z)$ subject to $r^i(z) = 0$ for $i = 1, 2, \ldots, m$ *does not necessarily* also maximize the lagrangian $L(z,\hat{\lambda})$, which is subject to no constraints. □

19 **Exercise.** Let f and $r^1, r^2, \ldots, r^m$ be twice-continuously differentiable functions defined on E^n, and let $\hat{z}$ and $\hat{\lambda}$ be such that $\partial L(\hat{z},\hat{\lambda})/\partial z = 0$ and $\partial L(\hat{z},\hat{\lambda})/\partial \lambda = 0$; that is, $\hat{z}$ and $\hat{\lambda}$ satisfy the necessary conditions of optimality in theorem (10). Show that if the $n \times n$ hessian matrix $\partial^2 L(\hat{z},\hat{\lambda})/\partial z^2$ of second-order partial derivatives is positive definite, then $\hat{z}$ is a local minimum of $f(\cdot)$ on the set $\{z\colon r^i(z) = 0,\ i = 1, 2, \ldots, m\}$. [*Hint:* Expand $L(\cdot,\hat{\lambda})$ about $\hat{z}$, using Taylor's theorem.] □

We now proceed to more complex optimization problems, those with inequality constraints.

3.3 THE KUHN-TUCKER THEORY

We shall examine in this section a particularly well-behaved class of nonlinear programming problems which were originally considered by Kuhn and Tucker [2]. Several extensions of their work can also be found in a monograph by Arrow, Hurwicz, and Uzawa [4].

This material is included partly for historical reasons and partly to exhibit the relation between some of the earlier work and the approach we are taking. Consequently, there is some duplication of results between this section and Sections 3.4 and 3.5. The reader will observe that with the Fundamental Theorem (2.3.12) established, it is often easier to obtain necessary conditions of optimality by proceeding as in Sections 3.5 and 3.6, rather than as in this section.

Kuhn and Tucker made the very interesting observation that in a number of cases the tangent cone [see (2.2.8)] to the set $\Omega' = \{z: r(z) = 0, q(z) \leqq 0\}$ can be given a very simple characterization. They formalized this observation into an assumption, which they called a *constraint qualification.* A paraphrase of their statement is as follows.

1 **Constraint qualification.** Let $r(\cdot)$ be a continuously differentiable function from E^n into E^m, let $q(\cdot)$ be a continuously differentiable function from E^n into E^k, and let $\Omega' = \{z: r(z) = 0, q(z) \leqq 0\}$. Let $\hat{z} \in \Omega'$, and let the index set $I(\hat{z}) = \{i: q^i(\hat{z}) = 0, i \in \{1,2, \ldots, k\}\}$.† We say that the set Ω' satisfies the (Kuhn–Tucker) constraint qualification at $\hat{z}$ if

2 $$TC(\hat{z},\Omega') = \left\{\delta z: \frac{\partial r(\hat{z})}{\partial z}\,\delta z = 0,\ \langle \nabla q^i(\hat{z}),\delta z\rangle \leqq 0 \text{ for all } i \in I(\hat{z})\right\},$$

where $TC(\hat{z},\Omega')$ is the tangent cone to Ω' at $\hat{z}$ [see (2.2.8)]. □

This assumption has subsequently been relaxed (see Arrow, Hurwicz, and Uzawa [3]) to the following form.

3 **Weakened constraint qualification.** We say that the set Ω', defined as in (1), satisfies the weakened constraint qualification at $\hat{z} \in \Omega'$ if

4 $$\overline{\text{co}}\ TC(\hat{z},\Omega') = \left\{\delta z: \frac{\partial r(\hat{z})}{\partial z}\,\delta z = 0,\ \langle \nabla q^i(\hat{z}),\delta z\rangle \leqq 0 \quad \text{for all } i \in I(\hat{z})\right\}. \quad \square$$

The effect of the constraint qualifications is twofold: first, they identify an important class of problems to which theorem (2.2.12) can be applied to yield nontrivial conditions of optimality; second, they result in a description of the tangent cone which enables us to

† The constraint functions $q^i(\cdot)$ satisfying $q^i(\hat{z}) = 0$ [that is, $i \in I(\hat{z})$] are usually called the *active constraints* at $\hat{z}$.

combine theorem (2.2.12) with Farkas' lemma (A.5.34) to obtain the following important result.[1]

5 **Theorem.** Let $\hat{z}$ be an optimal solution to the nonlinear programming problem (1.1). If the set $\Omega' = \{z: r(z) = 0, q(z) \leqq 0\}$ satisfies at $\hat{z}$ either the constraint qualification (1) or the weakened constraint qualification (3), then there exist scalar multipliers $\psi^1, \psi^2, \ldots, \psi^m$, undefined in sign, and nonpositive scalar multipliers $\mu^1 \leqq 0, \mu^2 \leqq 0, \ldots, \mu^k \leqq 0$ such that

6 $$-\nabla f(\hat{z}) + \sum_{i=1}^{m} \psi^i \nabla r^i(\hat{z}) + \sum_{i=1}^{k} \mu^i \nabla q^i(\hat{z}) = 0$$

and

7 $$\mu^i q^i(\hat{z}) = 0 \qquad i = 1, 2, \ldots, k.$$

Proof. First we observe that if the set Ω' satisfies the constraint qualification (1) at $\hat{z}$, then $\overline{\text{co}}\ TC(\hat{z},\Omega') = TC(\hat{z},\Omega')$, and therefore Ω' also satisfies (3). Thus we need prove the theorem only under the assumption that (3) is satisfied.

From Theorem (2.2.12), if $\hat{z}$ is an optimal solution, then

8 $$\langle -\nabla f(\hat{z}), \delta z\rangle \leqq 0 \qquad \text{for all } \delta z \in \overline{\text{co}}\ TC(\hat{z},\Omega').$$

We now write (4) as

9 $$\overline{\text{co}}\ TC(\hat{z},\Omega') = \left\{\delta z: \frac{\partial r(\hat{z})}{\partial z}\,\delta z \leqq 0,\ -\frac{\partial r(\hat{z})}{\partial z}\,\delta z \leqq 0, \langle \nabla q^i(\hat{z}), \delta z\rangle \leqq 0,\ i \in I(\hat{z})\right\},$$

where $I(\hat{z}) = \{i: q^i(\hat{z}) = 0,\ i \in \{1,2, \ldots ,k\}\}$, and use Farkas' lemma (A.5.34) to combine (8) and (9) to yield (6), with $\mu^i = 0$ for all i not in $I(\hat{z})$. Equation (7) then follows immediately, since for each $i \in \{1,2, \ldots ,k\}$ either μ^i or $q^i(\hat{z})$ is zero. From Farkas' lemma, $\mu^i \leqq 0$ for $i = 1, 2, \ldots, k$, but the sign of the ψ^i for $i = 1, 2, \ldots, m$ is indefinite, since each ψ^i can be seen to have arisen as the sum of a negative and a positive number. □

10 **Remark.** Probably the most important feature of theorem (5) is that it gives a condition for the multiplier associated with $\nabla f(\hat{z})$ in (6) to be -1. It is common experience that computational methods derived

[1] The following theorems remain true when the sequential tangent cone $TC_s(\hat{z},\Omega')$ [defined in (2.2.28)] is substituted for the tangent cone $TC(\hat{z},\Omega')$ in the constraint qualifications.

from necessary conditions become considerably simplified whenever the cost-gradient multiplier in (6) is -1. □

Generally speaking, it is not possible to establish by a direct approach whether a particular set Ω' does or does not satisfy condition (1) or (3). However, there are several sufficient conditions which can be checked numerically by pivotal methods and which ensure that a set Ω' satisfies (1) or (3). Let us examine some of them.

Our first observation is that $\overline{\text{co}}\ TC_s(\hat{z},\Omega')$ is always contained in the right-hand side of (4) and hence that we need only prove that the right-hand side of (4) is contained in $\overline{\text{co}}\ TC(\hat{z},\Omega')$ or in $TC(\hat{z},\Omega')$. We now prove this observation.

11 **Lemma.** Consider the constraint set $\Omega' = \{z: r(z) = 0,\ q(z) \leqq 0\}$, defined as in (1). Then

12 $$\overline{\text{co}}\ TC_s(\hat{z},\Omega') \subset \left\{ \delta z: \frac{\partial r(\hat{z})}{\partial z}\,\delta z = 0,\ \langle \nabla q^i(\hat{z}),\delta z\rangle \leqq 0 \quad \text{for all } i \in I(\hat{z}) \right\},$$

where the sequential tangent cone $TC_s(\hat{z},\Omega')$ is as defined in (2.2.28) and the active-constraint index set $I(\hat{z})$ is as defined in (1).

Proof. Let $\delta z \in TC_s(\hat{z},\Omega')$ be arbitrary. Then, by definition (2.2.28), there exists a sequence of vectors δz_i for $i = 1, 2, 3, \ldots$ such that $(\hat{z} + \delta z_i) \in \Omega'$, $\delta z_i \to 0$ as $i \to \infty$, and $\delta z_i/\|\delta z_i\| \to \alpha\,\delta z$ as $i \to \infty$ for some $\alpha > 0$. Hence

13 $$r(\hat{z} + \delta z_i) = 0 + \frac{\partial r(\hat{z})}{\partial z}\,\delta z_i + o(\delta z_i) = 0, \qquad i = 1, 2, 3, \ldots.$$

Dividing (13) by $\|\delta z_i\|$, we obtain

14 $$\frac{\partial r(\hat{z})}{\partial z}\,\frac{\delta z_i}{\|\delta z_i\|} + \frac{o(\delta z_i)}{\|\delta z_i\|} = 0.$$

But $\delta z_i \to 0$, and $\|o(\delta z)\|/\|\delta z\| \to 0$ as $\|\delta z\| \to 0$; hence, in the limit, (14) results in

$$\frac{\partial r(\hat{z})}{\partial z}\,\delta z = 0.$$

Now let $j \in I(\hat{z})$ be arbitrary; then $q^j(\hat{z}) = 0$ and

15 $$q^j(\hat{z} + \delta z_i) = 0 + \langle \nabla q^j(\hat{z}),\delta z_i\rangle + o(\delta z_i) \leqq 0.$$

Dividing (15) by $\|\delta z_i\|$ and letting $i \to \infty$, we obtain

$$\langle \nabla q^j(\hat{z}), \delta z \rangle \leqq 0 \qquad \text{for all } j \in I(\hat{z}),$$

since $o(\delta z)/\|\delta z\| \to 0$ as $\|\delta z\| \to 0$. This proves that

16 $$TC_s(\hat{z},\Omega') \subset \left\{ \delta z: \frac{\partial r(\hat{z})}{\partial z}\, \delta z = 0,\ \langle \nabla q^j(\hat{z}), \delta z \rangle \leqq 0 \text{ for all } j \in I(\hat{z}) \right\}.$$

The set $\{\delta z: [\partial r(\hat{z})/\partial z]\, \delta z = 0,\ \langle \nabla q^j(\hat{z}), \delta z \rangle \leqq 0 \text{ for all } j \in I(\hat{z})\}$ is convex and closed [the set $TC_s(\hat{z},\Omega')$ is closed, by (2.2.29)]; hence (12) follows. □

We now proceed with our theorems, with some of the proofs left as exercises.

17 **Theorem.** Consider the constraint set $\Omega' = \{z: r(z) = 0, q(z) \leqq 0\}$, let $\hat{z}$ be any point in Ω', and let the index set $I(\hat{z}) = \{i: q^i(\hat{z}) = 0, i \in \{1,2, \ldots, k\}\}$. If the vectors $\nabla r^i(\hat{z})$ for $i = 1, 2, \ldots, m$, together with the vectors $\nabla q^i(\hat{z})$ for $i \in I(\hat{z})$, are fewer than n in number and are linearly independent,[1] then the set Ω' satisfies the constraint qualification (1) at $\hat{z}$. □

18 **Remark.** This theorem is almost as long and difficult to prove as the Fundamental Theorem (2.3.12). Since the fact that $\psi^0 \neq 0$ in (6) follows trivially under the above assumptions from corollary (4.28) or theorem (5.11), the proof of theorem (17) is omitted here. The interested reader may wish to prove this theorem without resorting to the Fundamental Theorem. □

19 **Theorem.** Consider the constraint set $\Omega' = \{z: r(z) = 0, q(z) \leqq 0\}$, and let $\hat{z}$ be any point in Ω'. If the functions r and q are affine, then the set Ω' satisfies the constraint qualification (1) at $\hat{z}$.

Proof. Let $\delta\hat{z} \in E^n$ be any vector such that

20 $$\frac{\partial r(\hat{z})}{\partial z}\, \delta\hat{z} = 0$$
$$\langle \nabla q^i(\hat{z}), \delta\hat{z} \rangle \leqq 0 \qquad \text{for } i \in I(\hat{z}).$$

[1] This assumption guarantees that the set $\{z: r(z) = 0, q^i(z) = 0, i \in I(\hat{z})\}$ is a manifold whose tangent plane is the set $\{\delta z: [\partial r(\hat{z})/\partial z]\, \delta z = 0, \langle \nabla q^i(\hat{z}), \delta z \rangle = 0, i \in I(\hat{z})\}$. When the functions r^i and q^i are linear or affine, this assumption is no longer necessary, since the set $\{z: r(z) = 0, q^i(z) = 0, i \in I(\hat{z})\}$ is then always a linear manifold [see (19)]. For a discussion of manifolds and tangent subspaces see reference [7].

Since r and q are affine, it follows that for any $t \geqq 0$

$$r(\hat{z} + t\,\delta\hat{z}) = r(\hat{z}) + t\,\frac{\partial r(\hat{z})}{\partial z}\,\delta\hat{z} = 0$$

and there must exist a $t_1 > 0$ such that

$$q(\hat{z} + t\,\delta\hat{z}) = q(\hat{z}) + t\,\frac{\partial q(\hat{z})}{\partial z}\,\delta\hat{z} \leqq 0 \qquad 0 \leqq t \leqq t_1.$$

Hence $\{z\colon z = \hat{z} + t\,\delta\hat{z},\ 0 \leqq t \leqq t_1\}$ is the arc required by the definition of the constraint qualification. □

21 **Theorem.** Consider the constraint set $\Omega' = \{z\colon r(z) = 0,\ q(z) \leqq 0\}$. If there exists a vector $\delta\hat{z} \in E^n$ such that $[\partial r(\hat{z})/\partial z]\,\delta\hat{z} = 0$ and $\langle \nabla q^i(\hat{z}),\delta\hat{z}\rangle < 0$ for $i \in I(\hat{z}) = \{i\colon q^i(\hat{z}) = 0,\ i \in \{1,2, \ldots ,k\}\}$, and either the vectors $\nabla r^1(\hat{z}), \nabla r^2(\hat{z}), \ldots, \nabla r^m(\hat{z})$ are linearly independent or else the function $r(\cdot)$ is affine, then the set Ω' satisfies the constraint qualification (1) at $\hat{z}$ when it is stated in terms of the sequential tangent cone $TC_s(\hat{z},\Omega')$ to Ω' at $\hat{z}$. □

22 **Remark.** Again, the lengthy proof of theorem (21) is omitted, since under the above assumptions $\psi^0 \neq 0$ in (6) follows trivially from corollary (4.31). □

23 **Theorem.** Consider the constraint set $\Omega' = \{z\colon r(z) = 0,\ q(z) \leqq 0\}$. Suppose that the function r is affine and for $i = 1, 2, \ldots, k$ the components q^i, of q are convex. If there is a vector z^* in Ω' satisfying $q^i(z^*) < 0$ for $i = 1, 2, \ldots, k$, then Ω' satisfies the constraint qualification (1) at any point $\hat{z}$ in Ω' when it is stated in terms of the sequential cone tangent $TC_s(\hat{z},\Omega')$.

Proof. Let $\hat{z} \in \Omega'$ be arbitrary, and let $\delta z = z^* - \hat{z}$. Then, since r is affine, $[\partial r(\hat{z})/\partial z]\,\delta z = r(z^*) - r(\hat{z}) = 0$. If $I(\hat{z})$ is empty, then the conditions of theorem (21) are satisfied automatically, and theorem (23) follows directly. Therefore suppose that $I(\hat{z})$ is not empty. Then, since the functions q^i for $i = 1, 2, \ldots, k$ are convex, for $\delta z = z^* - \hat{z}$, and $i = 1, 2, \ldots, k$ we obtain [see (A.6.25)]

24 $$0 > q^i(\hat{z} + \lambda\,\delta z) \geqq q^i(\hat{z}) + \lambda\langle \nabla q^i(\hat{z}),\delta z\rangle,\ 0 < \lambda \leqq 1.$$

But for $i \in I(\hat{z})$, $q^i(\hat{z}) = 0$, and hence for all $i \in I(\hat{z})$

25 $$\langle \nabla q^i(\hat{z}),\delta z\rangle < 0.$$

Since this shows that the conditions of theorem (21) are satisfied, it follows that the set Ω' satisfies the constraint qualification (1). □

26 **Exercise.** Show that the following sets Ω' in E^2 (the plane) satisfy the constraint qualification (1) at all points in these sets:

27 $$\Omega' = \{z: -(z^1)^2 - (z^2)^2 + 1 \leqq 0,\ (z^1)^2 + 2(z^2)^2 - 2 \leqq 0\}.$$

28 $$\Omega' = \{z: z^1 - (z^2)^3 = 0,\ (z^1 - 1)^2 + (z^2)^2 - 2 \leqq 0,\ (z^1 + 1)^2 + (z^2)^2 - 2 \leqq 0\}.$$ □

29 **Exercise.** Show that the set

30 $$\Omega' = \{z: z^1 z^2 = 0\}$$

satisfies the weakened constraint qualification (3) but does not satisfy the constraint qualification (1) at $z = 0$. □

31 **Exercise.** Show that the set $\Omega_4 \subset E^2$ defined by

$$\Omega' = \{z: -(1 - z^1)^3 + z^2 \leqq 0\} \cap \{z: -(1 - z_1)^3 - z^2 \leqq 0\}$$

satisfies neither the constraint qualification (1) nor the weakened constraint qualification (3) at the point $\hat{z} = (1,0)$. Show, however, that there are nontrivial conical approximations of the first kind to Ω' at $\hat{z}$. □

We now turn to problems whose constraint sets do not necessarily satisfy the constraint qualification (1) or the weakened qualification (3).

3.4 GENERAL NONLINEAR PROGRAMMING PROBLEMS

In this section we relax the requirement that the weakened constraint qualification (3.3) be satisfied by the set $\Omega' = \{z: r(z) = 0, q(z) \leqq 0\}$ to the requirement that it be satisfied by the set $\Omega = \{z: q(z) \leqq 0\}$. Consequently, we shall consider a broader class of nonlinear programming problems than we did in the last section.

Since the problem no longer falls within the assumptions of theorem (2.2.12), our first task is to try to find a satisfactory convex approximation to the set $\Omega = \{z: q(z) \leqq 0\}$. In connection with this, as in the preceding section, given a particular point $z \in \Omega$, we shall often need to divide the components q^i for $i = 1, 2, \ldots, k$ of the inequality constraint function q into two sets: the *active* constraints satisfying $q^i(z) = 0$ and the *inactive* constraints satisfying $q^i(z) < 0$. Recall that in (3.1) we introduced the index set $I(\hat{z})$ for identifying the active constraints. Its definition is repeated here for convenience.

1 **Definition.** For any $\hat{z} \in \Omega = \{z\colon q^i(z) \leqq 0,\ i = 1, 2, \ldots, k\}$ the *index set* $I(\hat{z})$ is defined by

$$I(\hat{z}) = \{i\colon q^i(\hat{z}) = 0,\ i \in \{1,2, \ldots, k\}\}.$$

We shall denote by $\bar{I}(\hat{z})$ the complement of $I(\hat{z})$ in $\{1,2, \ldots, k\}$. □

We can now define a rather natural conical approximation to the set Ω.

2 **Definition.** Let $\Omega = \{z\colon q(z) \leqq 0\}$, where $q(\cdot)$ is a continuously differentiable function from E^n into E^k. For any $\hat{z} \in \Omega$ the *internal cone* to Ω at $\hat{z}$, denoted by $IC(\hat{z},\Omega)$, is defined by

3 $$IC(\hat{z},\Omega) = \{\delta z\colon \langle \nabla q^i(\hat{z}), \delta z\rangle < 0 \text{ for all } i \in I(\hat{z})\} \cup \{0\}.$$

4 **Theorem.** Let $\Omega = \{z\colon q(z) \leqq 0\}$, where $q(\cdot)$ is a continuously differentiable function from E^n into E^k. If the internal cone to Ω, $IC(\hat{z},\Omega)$, at a point $\hat{z} \in \Omega$ is not the origin, then:

a. The set Ω satisfies the constraint qualification (3.1) [with the sequential tangent cone $TC_s(\hat{z},\Omega)$ in (3.3)].

b. The internal cone $IC(\hat{z},\Omega)$ is a conical approximation of the first kind [see (2.3.1)].

c. The closure of the internal cone $IC(\hat{z},\Omega)$ is given by

5 $$\overline{IC}(\hat{z},\Omega) = \{\delta z\colon \langle \nabla q^i(\hat{z}), \delta z\rangle \leqq 0 \text{ for all } i \in I(\hat{z})\}.$$

Proof. Part (*a*) is trivial, since it follows directly from theorem (3.21).

To prove (*b*) we begin by showing that $IC(\hat{z},\Omega)$ is a convex cone. It is a cone, by inspection, so if we let δz_1 and δz_2 be any two vectors in $IC(\hat{z},\Omega)$, then

6 $$\langle \nabla q^i(\hat{z}),\ \delta z_1 + \delta z_2\rangle \leqq 0 \qquad \text{for all } i \in I(\hat{z}),$$

with equality holding if and only if $\delta z_1 = \delta z_2 = 0$. Hence $IC(\hat{z},\Omega)$ is a convex cone [see (A.4.6)], since $(\delta z_1 + \delta z_2) \in IC(\hat{z},\Omega)$.

Now let us exhibit an $\epsilon > 0$ satisfying the assumptions of definition (2.3.1). Let $\delta z_1, \delta z_2, \ldots, \delta z_p$ be any set of linearly independent (and hence nonzero) vectors in $IC(\hat{z},\Omega)$, and let λ be a positive number. Then any vector $z \in \text{co}\,\{\hat{z}, \hat{z} + \lambda\,\delta z_1, \hat{z} + \lambda\,\delta z_2, \ldots, \hat{z} + \lambda\,\delta z_p\}$ can be expressed in the form

7 $$z = \hat{z} + \lambda \sum_{j=1}^{p} \mu^j\,\delta z_j,$$

where $\mu^j \geqq 0$ and $\sum_{j=1}^{p} \mu^j \leqq 1$, and since the functions $q^i(\cdot)$ for $i = 1, 2, \ldots, k$ are continuously differentiable, we obtain for $i = 1, 2, \ldots, k$

8 $$q^i(z) = q^i\left(\hat{z} + \lambda \sum_{j=1}^{p} \mu^j\, \delta z_j\right) = q^i(\hat{z}) + \lambda \sum_{j=1}^{p} \mu^j \langle \nabla q^i(\hat{z}), \delta z_j\rangle + o^i\left(\lambda \sum_{j=1}^{p} \mu^j\, \delta z_j\right),$$

where $o^i(\lambda \Sigma_{j=1}^{p} \mu^j\, \delta z_j)/\lambda \to 0$ as $\lambda \to 0$ uniformly in $\delta z = \Sigma_{j=1}^{p} \mu^j\, \delta z_j$, with $\mu^j \geqq 0$ and $\Sigma_{j=1}^{p} \mu^j \leqq 1$ (that is, $\delta z \in \text{co}\,\{\delta z_1, \delta z_2, \ldots, \delta z_p\}$).

Now let

9 $$\beta = \max_{i,j} \langle \nabla q^i(\hat{z}), \delta z_j\rangle \qquad j \in \{1,2, \ldots ,p\},\ i \in I(\hat{z}).$$

Clearly, since $\delta z_j \neq 0$, by assumption, $\beta < 0$ for $i \in I(\hat{z})$. Hence for all $i \in I(\hat{z})$ (8) and (9) yield

10 $$q^i\left(\hat{z} + \lambda \sum_{j=1}^{p} \mu^j\, \delta z_j\right) \leqq \lambda\beta + o^i\left(\lambda \sum_{j=1}^{p} \mu^j\, \delta z_j\right).$$

Since $o^i(\lambda \Sigma_{j=1}^{p} \mu^j\, \delta z_j)/\lambda \to 0$ as $\lambda \to 0$ uniformly in $\delta z = \Sigma_{j=1}^{p} \mu^j\, \delta z_j \in \text{co}\,\{\delta z_1, \delta z_2, \ldots ,\delta z_p\}$, and $\beta < 0$, there exists an $\epsilon' > 0$ such that

11 $$q^i\left(\hat{z} + \lambda \sum_{j=1}^{p} \mu^j\, \delta z_j\right) \leqq \lambda\beta + o^i\left(\lambda \sum_{j=1}^{p} \mu^j\, \delta z_j\right) \leqq 0 \qquad \text{for all } \lambda \in [0,\epsilon'],\ i \in I(\hat{z}).$$

The functions $q^i(\cdot)$ are continuous and $q^i(\hat{z}) < 0$ for all $i \in \bar{I}(\hat{z})$, the complement of $I(\hat{z})$ in $\{1,2, \ldots ,k\}$. Consequently, since $\text{co}\,\{\delta z_1, \delta z_2, \ldots , \delta z_p\}$ is compact, there exists an $\epsilon'' > 0$ such that for all $\sum_{j=1}^{p} \mu^i\, \delta z_i \in \text{co}\,\{\delta z_1, \delta z_2, \ldots , \delta z_p\}$

12 $$q^i\left(\hat{z} + \lambda \sum_{j=1}^{p} \mu^j\, \delta z_j\right) \leqq 0 \qquad \text{for all } \lambda \in [0,\epsilon''],\ i \in \bar{I}(\hat{z}).$$

Let $\epsilon = \min\,\{\epsilon',\epsilon''\}$. Then, from (11) and (12), $\text{co}\,\{\hat{z}, \hat{z} + \epsilon\, \delta z_1, \hat{z} + \epsilon\, \delta z_2, \ldots , \hat{z} + \epsilon\, \delta z_r\}$ is in Ω, which proves that $IC(\hat{z},\Omega)$ is a conical approximation of the first kind.

We shall now prove part (c). Let

13 $$C = \{\delta z \colon \langle \nabla q^i(\hat{z}), \delta z\rangle \leqq 0 \text{ for all } i \in I(\hat{z})\}.$$

Clearly, C is closed and $C \supset IC(\hat{z},\Omega)$; hence $C \supset \overline{IC}(\hat{z},\Omega)$. Now let δz be any vector in C. Since $IC(\hat{z},\Omega) \neq \{0\}$, by assumption, there is a nonzero vector $\delta z^* \in IC(\hat{z},\Omega)$. Then for $j = 1, 2, 3, \ldots$ the vectors $\delta z_j = 1/j\, \delta z^* + \delta z$ are in $IC(\hat{z},\Omega)$, and $\delta z_j \to \delta z$ as $j \to \infty$. Hence $C \subset \overline{IC}(\hat{z},\Omega)$. □

14 **Exercise.** Suppose that the functions $q^i(\cdot)$ for $i = 1, 2, \ldots, l$, with $l \leqq k$, are affine, and let

15
$$IC'(\hat{z},\Omega) = \{\delta z: \langle \nabla q^i(\hat{z}),\delta z\rangle \leqq 0 \text{ for all } i \in I(\hat{z}) \cap \{1,2,\ldots,l\}\} \cap \{\delta z: \langle \nabla q^i(\hat{z}),\delta z\rangle < 0 \text{ for all } i \in I(\hat{z}) \cap \{l+1,\ldots,k\}\} \cup \{0\}.$$

Show that if $IC'(\hat{z},\Omega) \neq \{0\}$, then conditions (*a*), (*b*), and (*c*), of theorem (4) hold. Note that if $l = k$, that is, if all the functions $q^i(\cdot)$ are affine, then the cone defined in (15) is the radial cone. □

Obviously, given a specific constraint set $\Omega = \{z: q(z) \leqq 0\}$ and a point $\hat{z} \in \Omega$, $IC(\hat{z},\Omega)$ either contains some point other than the origin or it does not. We shall now concentrate on the more interesting case when the internal cone $IC(\hat{z},\Omega)$ is not the origin, and we shall consider the other possibility in the next section. Unfortunately, when $IC(\hat{z},\Omega) = \{0\}$, we can obtain only very weak necessary conditions of optimality.

For the remainder of this section we shall make the following assumption.

16 **Assumption.**[1] If $\hat{z} \in \Omega$ is an optimal solution to the nonlinear programming problem (1.1), then there exists at least one vector $v \in E^n$ such that

17
$$\langle \nabla q^i(\hat{z}),v\rangle < 0 \qquad \text{for all } i \in I(\hat{z});$$

that is, we shall assume that $IC(\hat{z},\Omega) \neq \{0\}$. □

It will be shown in corollary (5.10) that this condition is always satisfied if the vectors $\nabla q^i(\hat{z})$, with $i \in I(\hat{z})$, are linearly independent.

18 **Remark.** If the set $\Omega' = \{z: r(z) = 0, q(z) \leqq 0\}$ satisfies the assumptions of theorem (3.21), then the set $\Omega = \{z: q(z) \leqq 0\}$ obviously satisfies assumption (16). The converse, of course, is not true. This indicates the extent to which the assumptions in this section are weaker than those in the preceding section. □

When specialized to the nonlinear programming problem (1.1), the Fundamental Theorem (2.3.12) yields the following necessary

[1] When some of the functions q^i, with $i \in I(\hat{z})$, are affine, it suffices to require that there exist a vector $h \in E^n$ such that $\langle \nabla q^i(\hat{z}),h\rangle \leqq 0$ for these functions and that $\langle \nabla q^i(\hat{z}),h\rangle < 0$ for the remaining functions q^i, with $i \in I(\hat{z})$.

condition of optimality, provided, of course, that the internal cone $IC(\hat{z},\Omega)$ is not the origin [recall from theorem (4) that the cone $IC(\hat{z},\Omega)$ is a conical approximation of the first kind to Ω at $\hat{z} \in \Omega$].

19 **Theorem.** If $\hat{z}$ is an optimal solution to the nonlinear programming problem (1.1) and assumption (16) is satisfied, then there exists a nonzero vector $\psi = (\psi^0,\psi^1, \ldots ,\psi^m)$ in E^{m+1}, with $\psi^0 \leqq 0$, such that

20 $$\left\langle \psi, \frac{\partial F(\hat{z})}{\partial z} \delta z \right\rangle \leqq 0 \qquad \text{for all } \delta z \in \overline{IC}(\hat{z},\Omega),$$

where, by theorem (4), $\overline{IC}(\hat{z},\Omega) = \{\delta z: \langle \nabla q^i(\hat{z}),\delta z\rangle \leqq 0 \text{ for all } i \in I(\hat{z})\}$ and $F(z) = (f(z),r^1(z),r^2(z), \ldots , r^m(z))$. Alternatively, with (20) in expanded form, ψ satisfies

21 $$\left\langle \left(\psi^0 \nabla f(\hat{z}) + \sum_{i=1}^{m} \psi^i \nabla r^i(\hat{z})\right), \delta z\right\rangle \leqq 0 \qquad \text{for all } \delta z \in \overline{IC}(\hat{z},\Omega). \qquad \square$$

Using this theorem and Farkas' lemma (A.5.34), we obtain necessary conditions for optimality in the more familiar form of a multiplier rule, as shown below.

22 **Theorem.** If $\hat{z}$ is an optimal solution to the nonlinear programming problem (1.1) and assumption (16) is satisfied, then there exist a nonzero vector $\psi = (\psi^0,\psi^1, \ldots ,\psi^m)$ in E^{m+1}, with $\psi^0 \leqq 0$, and a vector $\mu = (\mu^1,\mu^2, \ldots ,\mu^k)$ in E^k, with $\mu^i \leqq 0$ for $i = 1, 2, \ldots , k$, such that

23 $$\psi^0 \nabla f(\hat{z}) + \sum_{i=1}^{m} \psi^i \nabla r^i(\hat{z}) + \sum_{i=1}^{k} \mu^i \nabla q^i(\hat{z}) = 0$$

and

24 $$\mu^i q^i(\hat{z}) = 0 \qquad i = 1, 2, \ldots , k.$$

Proof. From theorem (19), there exists a nonzero vector $\psi = (\psi^0,\psi^1, \ldots ,\psi^m)$ in E^{m+1}, with $\psi^0 \leqq 0$, such that

25 $$\left\langle \left(\psi^0 \nabla f(\hat{z}) \sum_{i=1}^{m} \psi^i \nabla r^i(\hat{z})\right), \delta z\right\rangle \leqq 0$$

for all δz such that $\langle \nabla q^i(\hat{z}),\delta z\rangle \leqq 0$, with $i \in I(\hat{z})$. It therefore follows from Farkas' lemma that there exist scalars $\mu^i \leqq 0$, with $i \in I(\hat{z})$, such that

26 $$\psi^0 \nabla f(\hat{z}) + \sum_{i=1}^{m} \psi^i \nabla r^i(\hat{z}) + \sum_{i \in I(\hat{z})} \nabla q^i(\hat{z}) = 0.$$

Let $\mu^i = 0$ for $i \in \bar{I}(\hat{z})$, the complement of $I(\hat{z})$ in $\{1,2, \ldots ,k\}$; then the vectors $\psi = (\psi^0,\psi^1, \ldots ,\psi^m)$ in E^{m+1} and $\mu = (\mu^1,\mu^2, \ldots ,\mu^k)$ in E^k satisfy (23) and (24). □

Most of the other well-known necessary conditions for nonlinear programming problems can be obtained from theorem (22) by means of additional assumptions on the functions r and q. For example, the following corollaries are immediate consequences.

27 **Corollary.** If assumption (16) is satisfied and the vectors $\nabla r^i(\hat{z})$ for $i = 1, 2, \ldots , m$ are linearly independent, then any vectors $\psi \in E^{m+1}$ and $\mu \in E^k$ which satisfy the conditions of theorem (22) are such that $(\psi^0,\mu) \neq 0$.

Proof. Let $\psi = (\psi^0,\psi^1, \ldots ,\psi^m)$ and $\mu = (\mu^1,\mu^2, \ldots ,\mu^k)$ be vectors satisfying the conditions of theorem (22). Then, by assumption, $\psi \neq 0$. Hence if $\psi^0 = 0$, then $\Sigma_{i=1}^m \psi^i \nabla r^i(\hat{z}) \neq 0$, since not all $\psi^i = 0$ and the vectors $\nabla r^i(\hat{z})$ for $i = 1, 2, \ldots , m$ are linearly independent. It therefore follows that if $\psi^0 = 0$, then $\mu \neq 0$. Now suppose that $\mu = 0$; clearly, we cannot have $\psi^0 = 0$ and $\psi \neq 0$ and still have equation (23) satisfied. We therefore conclude that $(\psi^0,\mu) \neq 0$. □

28 **Corollary.** If $\nabla r^i(\hat{z})$ for $i = 1, 2, \ldots , m$, together with $\nabla q^i(\hat{z})$ for $i \in I(\hat{z})$, are linearly independent vectors, then any vector $\psi \in E^{m+1}$ satisfying the conditions of theorem (22) also satisfies $\psi^0 < 0$ [cf (3.17)].

Proof. Let $\psi = (\psi^0,\psi^1, \ldots ,\psi^m)$ and $\mu = (\mu^1,\mu^2, \ldots ,\mu^k)$ be vectors satisfying the conditions of theorem (22). Since $\psi \neq 0$, not all $\psi^i = 0$, with $i = 1, 2, \ldots , m$. Consequently, since the vectors $\nabla r^i(\hat{z})$ and $\nabla q^i(\hat{z})$ appearing in (23) (with nonzero multipliers) are linearly independent, it follows that if $\psi^0 = 0$, then

29 $$\psi^0 \nabla f(\hat{z}) + \sum_{i=1}^{m} \psi^i \nabla r^i(\hat{z}) + \sum_{i=1}^{k} \mu^i \nabla q^i(\hat{z}) \neq 0,$$

which contradicts (23). Hence $\psi^0 \neq 0$, and therefore $\psi^0 < 0$. □

30 **Remark.** It is clear that when $\psi^0 = 0$ in (23), the necessary condition expressed by (23) does not involve the cost function $f(\cdot)$ and hence cannot carry too much information. Indeed, if we find that $\psi^0 = 0$ for *all* vectors ψ satisfying theorem (22), then we are faced with a degeneracy in the problem (see Section 2.3). □

This remark points out the importance of the preceding corollary, as well as that of the following ones.

31 **Corollary.** If there exists a nonzero vector $v \in IC(\hat{z},\Omega)$ such that $\langle \nabla r^i(\hat{z}),v \rangle = 0$ for $i = 1, 2, \ldots, m$, and the vectors $\nabla r^1(\hat{z})$, $\nabla r^2(\hat{z})$, $\ldots$, $\nabla r^m(\hat{z})$ are linearly independent, then any vector $\psi \in E^{m+1}$ satisfying the conditions of theorem (22) also satisfies $\psi^0 < 0$ [cf (3.26)].

Proof. Let $\psi \in E^{m+1}$ and $\mu \in E^k$ be any vectors satisfying (23) and (24), and let $0 \neq v \in IC(\hat{z},\Omega)$ be any vector satisfying $\langle \nabla r^i(\hat{z}),v \rangle = 0$ for $i = 1, 2, \ldots, m$. Then we get from (23) that

32 $$\psi^0 \langle \nabla f(\hat{z}),v \rangle + \sum_{i=1}^{m} \psi^i \langle \nabla r^i(\hat{z}),v \rangle + \sum_{i=1}^{k} \mu^i \langle \nabla q^i(\hat{z}),v \rangle = 0.$$

Eliminating in (32) the terms which are obviously zero, we get

$$\psi^0 \langle \nabla f(\hat{z}),v \rangle + \sum_{i=1}^{k} \mu^i \langle \nabla q^i(\hat{z}),v \rangle = 0.$$

It follows from corollary (27) that $(\psi^0,\mu) \neq 0$, since the vectors $\nabla r^i(\hat{z})$ for $i = 1, 2, \ldots, m$ are linearly independent. Therefore, if $\mu = 0$, then $\psi^0 < 0$. Alternatively, suppose that $\mu \neq 0$; then, since $0 \neq v \in IC(\hat{z},\Omega)$ and $\mu^i \leqq 0$, it is clear that $\Sigma_{i=1}^{k} \mu^i \langle \nabla q^i(\hat{z}),v \rangle > 0$. This implies that $\psi^0 < 0$, and thus the lemma is proved. □

33 **Corollary.** If the functions $r^i(\cdot)$ for $i = 1, 2, \ldots, m$ and $q^i(\cdot)$ for $i = 1, 2, \ldots, k$ are affine, then there exists a vector $\psi \in E^{m+1}$ satisfying the conditions of theorem (22) which also satisfies $\psi^0 < 0$ [cf (3.19)].

Proof. If the functions $q^i(\cdot)$ for $i = 1, 2, \ldots, k$ are affine, then, by exercise (14), we may omit assumption (16) in theorem (19), since in place of the internal cone we may use the radial cone

$$RC(\hat{z},\Omega) = \{\delta z \colon \langle \nabla q^i(\hat{z}),\delta z \rangle \leqq 0 \text{ for all } i \in I(\hat{z})]\}.$$

Since $RC(\hat{z},\Omega)$ is a closed convex polyhedron and $\partial F(\hat{z})/\partial z$ is a linear map, the set

$$K(\hat{z}) = \left\{ \frac{\partial F(\hat{z})}{\partial z} \delta z \colon \delta z \in RC(\hat{z},\Omega) \right\}$$

is closed (see, e.g., ref. [6]). Thus, by corollary (2.2.45), we may choose $\psi^0 < 0$. □

When the set $\Omega' = \{z: r(z) = 0,\ q(z) \leqq 0\}$ has even more specialized structure than is implied by assumption (16), it is sometimes possible to recast theorem (19) as a "maximum principle." The reader may explore this possibility in the exercises below.

34 **Definition.** We say that a set Ω is *star shaped* at $\hat{z} \in \Omega$ if for every $z \in \Omega$ $(\lambda z + (1 - \lambda)\hat{z}) \in \Omega$, with $0 \leqq \lambda \leqq 1$. □

35 **Exercise.** Let $\hat{z}$ be a solution of the nonlinear programming problem (1.1), and suppose that assumption (16) is satisfied. Show that when the see $\Omega = \{z: q(z) \leqq 0\}$ is *star shaped* at $\hat{z}$, then (21) is equivalent to the maximum principle

36 $$\left\langle \left(\psi^0 \nabla f(\hat{z}) + \sum_{i=1}^{m} \psi^i \nabla r^i(\hat{z})\right), \hat{z} \right\rangle \geqq \left\langle \left(\psi^0 \nabla f(\hat{z}) + \sum_{i=1}^{m} \psi^i \nabla r^i(\hat{z})\right), z \right\rangle \quad \text{for all } z \in \Omega. \quad \square$$

37 **Exercise.** Suppose that the set $\Omega' = \{z: r(z) = 0,\ q(z) \leqq 0\}$ is *star shaped* at $\hat{z}$, a solution of the nonlinear programming problem (1.1). Show that

38 $$\langle -\nabla f(\hat{z}),\hat{z}\rangle \geqq \langle -\nabla f(\hat{z}),z\rangle \qquad \text{for all } z \in \Omega'$$

independently of whether (16) is satisfied or not. [*Hint:* Use Theorem (2.2.12).] □

We now go on to nonlinear programming problems whose constraint sets are not assumed to satisfy a constraint qualification.

3.5 A FURTHER GENERALIZATION

In the preceding section we assumed that the internal cone $IC(\hat{z},\Omega)$ [see (4.3)] was not the origin, and we then established the multiplier rule, theorem (4.22). That is, we showed that if $\hat{z}$ is an optimal solution to the nonlinear programming problem (1.1), then there exist Lagrange multipliers satisfying (4.23) and (4.24). The multipliers associated with the equality constraints were of indefinite sign, while the multipliers associated with the inequalities were nonpositive. We shall now show that even when assumption (4.16) is not satisfied, we can still get a condition of the same form as theorem (4.24), but it now carries considerably less information.

The necessary condition we are about to discuss was first proved by Mangasarian and Fromovitz [5], using the implicit-function theorem and a lemma by Motzkin. We begin by showing that whenever assumption (4.16) is not satisfied, it is possible to sum the vectors $\nabla q^i(\hat{z})$, with $i \in I(\hat{z})$ [see (4.1)], to zero with nonpositive scalars, not all of which are zero. This is established in the following lemma.

1 **Lemma** Suppose that assumption (4.16) is not satisfied for the set $\Omega = \{z: q(z) \leqq 0\}$. Then there exists a nonzero vector $\mu \in E^k$, with $\mu^i \leqq 0$ for $i = 1, 2, \ldots, k$, such that

2 $$\sum_{i=1}^{k} \mu^i \nabla q^i(\hat{z}) = 0$$

and

3 $$\mu^i q^i(\hat{z}) = 0 \qquad i = 1, 2, \ldots, k.$$

Proof. Suppose that $I(\hat{z}) = \{i_1, i_2, \ldots, i_\alpha\}$ and consider the linear subspace of E^α,

4 $$L = \{v: v = (\langle \nabla q^{i_1}(\hat{z}), h\rangle, \ldots, \langle \nabla q^{i_\alpha}(\hat{z}), h\rangle),\ h \in E^n\}.$$

By hypothesis, L has no rays in common with the convex cone

5 $$C = \{v = (v^1, v^2, \ldots, v^\alpha): v^j < 0,\ j = 1, 2, \ldots, \alpha\}.$$

Hence L can be separated from $\bar{C}$; that is, there exists a nonzero vector $\beta \in E^\alpha$ such that

6 $$\langle \beta, v\rangle \geqq 0 \qquad \text{for all } v \in \bar{C}$$
7 $$\langle \beta, v\rangle \leqq 0 \qquad \text{for all } v \in L.$$

It is obvious from (6) that $\beta \leqq 0$. Since L is a linear subspace, $\langle \beta, v\rangle = 0$ for all $v \in L$, which implies that

8 $$\left\langle \sum_{j=1}^{\alpha} \beta^j \nabla q^{i_j}(\hat{z}), h \right\rangle = 0 \qquad \text{for all } h \in E^n,$$

and therefore

9 $$\sum_{j=1}^{\alpha} \beta^j \nabla q^{i_j}(\hat{z}) = 0.$$

If we now let $\mu^i = \beta^j$ when $i = i_j \in I(\hat{z})$ and $\mu^i = 0$ when $i \in \bar{I}(\hat{z})$, then $\mu = (\mu^1, \mu^2, \ldots, \mu^k)$ is the desired vector. □

10 **Corollary.** A sufficient condition for assumption (4.16) to be satisfied is that the vectors $\nabla q^i(\hat{z})$, with $i \in I(\hat{z})$, be linearly independent. □

Lemma (1) may now be combined with theorem (4.19) to give a necessary condition for optimality which does not require that

(4.16) be satisfied. Thus for the most general case of the nonlinear programming problem (1.1) we obtain the following necessary condition for optimality.

11 **Theorem.** If $\hat{z}$ is an optimal solution to the nonlinear programming problem (1.1). then there exists a vector $\psi = (\psi^0,\psi^1, \ldots ,\psi^m)$ in E^{m+1} and a vector $\mu = (\mu^1,\mu^2, \ldots ,\mu^k)$ in E^k, with $\psi^0 \leqq 0$ and $\mu^i \leqq 0$ for $i = 1, 2, \ldots , k$, and with ψ and μ not both zero, such that

12 $$\psi^0 \nabla f(\hat{z}) + \sum_{i=1}^{m} \psi^i \nabla r^i(\hat{z}) + \sum_{i=1}^{k} \mu^i \nabla q^i(\hat{z}) = 0$$

13 $$\mu^i q^i(\hat{z}) = 0 \qquad i = 1, 2, \ldots , k.$$

Proof. If (4.16) is satisfied, then theorem (11) follows directly from theorem (4.22) and is seen to be a slightly weaker statement of theorem (4.22). If (4.16) is not satisfied, let μ be the vector specified in lemma (1), and let $\psi = 0$. □

14 **Remark.** Theorem (11) is essentially trivial when assumption (4.16) is not satisfied, because, by lemma (1), when (4.16) is not satisfied, we can find a $\mu \neq 0$ satisfying (2) and (3) without depending in any way on the optimality of $\hat{z}$, and we can then satisfy (12) and (13) with this μ and $\psi = 0$. □

Under suitable assumptions equation (12) may be converted into a maximum principle, and it is left to the reader to develop this idea in the following exercises.

15 **Exercise.** Consider the nonlinear programming problem (1.1). Let $Q = \{q^{i_1},q^{i_2}, \ldots ,q^{i_j}\}$ be any subset of components of the inequality constraint function q with the property that the see $\Omega_1 = \{z\colon q^{i_\alpha}(z) \leqq 0, \alpha = 1, 2, \ldots , j\}$ has a nonempty interior cone $IC(\hat{z},\Omega_1)$ at $\hat{z}$, an optimal solution to problem (1.1). Renumber the functions $q^1, q^2, \ldots , q^k$ so that $q^i \notin Q$ for $i = 1, 2, \ldots , l$, with $l = k - j$, and $q^i \in Q$ for $i = l + 1, l + 2, \ldots , k$; that is, $\Omega_1 = \{z\colon q^i(z) \leqq 0, i = l + 1, l + 2, \ldots , k\}$. Show that if $\hat{z}$ is an optimal solution to (1.1), then there exist a vector $\psi = (\psi^0,\psi^1, \ldots ,\psi^m)$ in E^{m+1}, with $\psi^0 \leqq 0$, and a vector $\mu = (\mu^1,\mu^2, \ldots ,\mu^l)$ in E^l, with $\mu^i \leqq 0$ for $i = 1, 2, \ldots , l$, such that $(\psi,\mu) \neq 0$ and

16 $$\left\langle \left(\psi^0 \nabla f(\hat{z}) + \sum_{i=1}^{m} \psi^i \nabla r^i(\hat{z}) + \sum_{i=}^{l} \mu^i \nabla q^i(\hat{z})\right), \delta z\right\rangle \leqq 0 \qquad \text{for all } \delta z \in IC(\hat{z},\Omega_1)$$

17 $$\mu^i q^i(\hat{z}) = 0 \qquad i = 1, 2, \ldots, l.$$

Show that if, in addition, the set Ω_1 is star shaped at $\hat{z}$, [that is, for all $z \in \Omega_1$, $(\lambda z + (1-\lambda)\hat{z}) \in \Omega_1$, with $0 \leqq \lambda \leqq 1$], then (16) becomes

18 $$\left\langle \psi^0 \nabla f(\hat{z}) + \sum_{i=1}^{m} \psi^i \nabla r^i(\hat{z}) + \sum_{i=1}^{l} \mu^i \nabla q^i(\hat{z}), z - \hat{z} \right\rangle \leqq 0 \qquad \text{for all } z \in \Omega_1,$$

which again is a condition in the form of a maximum principle. □

19 **Remark.** Finally, note that if we let $r \equiv 0$ in problem (1.1), then theorem (11) becomes the well-known *Fritz John necessary condition for optimality* [1]. □

We have thus seen that most of the known necessary conditions for nonlinear programming problems can be obtained simply by applying the Fundamental Theorem (2.3.12) and Farkas' lemma (A.5.34).

3.6 A SUFFICIENT CONDITION

Whenever a continuously differentiable real-valued function is convex or concave, we find that it assumes its unique extreme value, if it has one, at every point at which it is stationary. We are therefore led to believe that the necessary conditions expressed by theorem (3.5) may become sufficient whenever all the functions entering the description of the nonlinear programming problem (1.1) are convex or concave.

1 **Theorem.** Consider the nonlinear programming problem (1.1) [minimize $f(z)$ subject to $r(z) = 0$ and $q(z) \leqq 0$], and suppose that $f: E^n \to E^1$ is convex, that $r: E^n \to E^m$ is affine, and that $q^i: E^n \to E^1$ for $i = 1, 2, \ldots, k$ (the components of the function $q: E^n \to E^k$) are convex. If $\hat{z} \in E^n$ is a feasible solution to (1.1) [that is, $r(\hat{z}) = 0$ and $q(\hat{z}) \leqq 0$], and if there exist vectors $\lambda = (\lambda^1, \lambda^2, \ldots, \lambda^m)$ in E^m and $\mu = (\mu^1, \mu^2, \ldots, \mu^k)$ in E^k, with $\mu^i \leqq 0$ for $i = 1, 2, \ldots, k$, such that

2 $$-\nabla f(\hat{z}) + \sum_{i=1}^{m} \lambda^i \nabla r^i(\hat{z}) + \sum_{i=1}^{k} \mu^i \nabla q^i(\hat{z}) = 0$$

and

3 $$\mu^i q^i(\hat{z}) = 0 \qquad i = 1, 2, \ldots, k,$$

then $\hat{z}$ is an optimal solution.

Proof. Suppose $\hat{z}$ is a feasible solution for which there exist $\lambda \in E^m$ and $\mu \in E^k$ satisfying (2) and (3). Consider the function $L: E^n \to E^1$, defined by

4 $$L(z) = -f(z) + \sum_{i=1}^{m} \lambda^i r^i(z) + \sum_{i=1}^{k} \mu^i q^i(z).$$

By assumption, the functions $f(\cdot)$ and $q^i(\cdot)$ for $i = 1, 2, \ldots, k$ are convex and the functions $r^i(\cdot)$ for $i = 1, 2, \ldots, m$ are affine. Furthermore, by assumption, $\mu^i \leqq 0$ for $i = 1, 2, \ldots, k$. Consequently, the function $L(\cdot)$ is concave, and therefore [see theorem (A.6.37)] it assumes its maximum value at its stationary point $\hat{z}$; that is, for all $z \in E^n$

5 $$-f(\hat{z}) + \sum_{i=1}^{m} \lambda^i r^i(\hat{z}) + \sum_{i=1}^{k} \mu^i q^i(\hat{z}) \geqq -f(z) + \sum_{i=1}^{m} \lambda^i r^i(z) + \sum_{i=1}^{k} \mu^i q^i(z).$$

Since (5) is true for all $z \in E^n$, it must be true for all z satisfying $r(z) = 0$ and $q(z) \leqq 0$. Since, by (3), $\mu^i q^i(\hat{z}) = 0$ for $i = 1, 2, \ldots, k$, it follows that for all z satisfying $r(z) = 0$ and $q(z) \leqq 0$

6 $$-f(\hat{z}) \geqq -f(z) + \sum_{i=1}^{k} \mu^i q^i(z).$$

But $q^i(z) \leqq 0$ and $\mu^i \leqq 0$ for $i = 1, 2, \ldots, k$, and hence

7 $$-f(\hat{z}) \geqq -f(z) \qquad \text{for all } z \in \{z: r(z) = 0,\ q(z) \leqq 0\},$$

which proves that $\hat{z}$ is an optimal solution to the nonlinear programming problem (1.1). □

8 **Corollary.** Suppose that the functions f, r, and q are as in theorem (1). If $\hat{z}$ is a feasible solution and the internal cone $IC(\hat{z},\Omega)$, with $\Omega = \{z: q(z) \leqq 0\}$, is not the origin [see (4.3)], and there exists a vector $\lambda = (\lambda^1,\lambda^2, \ldots, \lambda^m)$ in E^m such that

9 $$\left\langle\left(-\nabla f(\hat{z}) + \sum_{i=1}^{m} \lambda^i \nabla r^i(\hat{z})\right), \delta z\right\rangle \leqq 0 \qquad \text{for all } \delta z \in \overline{IC}(\hat{z}\ \Omega)$$

then $\hat{z}$ is an optimal solution to the nonlinear programming problem (1.1).

Proof. By assumption, (9) is satisfied for all δz such that

10 $$\langle \nabla q^i(\hat{z}), \delta z \rangle \leqq 0 \qquad i \in I(\hat{z})$$

[see (4.3) and (4.5)]. Hence, by Farkas' lemma (A.5.34), there exists a vector $\mu = (\mu^1, \mu^2, \ldots, \mu^k)$ in E^k, with $\mu^i \leqq 0$ for $i = 1, 2, \ldots, k$, such that

11 $$-\nabla f(\hat{z}) + \sum_{i=1}^{m} \lambda^i \nabla r^i(\hat{z}) + \sum_{i=1}^{k} \mu^i \nabla q^i(\hat{z}) = 0$$

and

12 $$\mu^i q^i(\hat{z}) = 0 \qquad i = 1, 2, \ldots, k.$$

Hence (9) implies (2) and (3). □

13 **Exercise.** Give an independent proof for corollary (8). □
It is possible to relax somewhat the assumptions made in theorem (1). The reader might explore this possibility by proving theorem (20).

An Extension to Quasi-convex and pseudoconvex Functions

In the case the reader is not familiar with quasi-convex and pseudoconvex functions, let us begin with their definitions. Incidentally, the concepts of quasi- and pseudo-convexity suffer considerably from the fact that in general it is extremely difficult to establish whether a given function is quasi-convex or pseudoconvex.

14 **Definition.** A function $g(\cdot)$ mapping E^n into the reals is said to be *quasi-convex* if the set

15 $$S_\alpha = \{z \colon g(z) \leqq \alpha\}$$

is convex for all real α. □

16 **Definition.** A continuously differentiable function $g(\cdot)$ mapping E^n into the reals is said to be *pseudoconvex* if

17 $$g(z_1) \geqq g(z_2)$$

for every pair (z_1, z_2) satisfying

18 $$\langle \nabla g(z_2), z_1 - z_2 \rangle \geqq 0. \quad \square$$

19 **Exercise.** Prove that if $\hat{z}$ is a feasible solution for the nonlinear programming problem (1.1), $f(\cdot)$ is pseudoconvex and $\nabla f(\hat{z}) = 0$, then $\hat{z}$ is optimal. □

20 **Exercise.** Prove the following theorem.

21 **Theorem.** Consider the nonlinear programming problem (1.1). Suppose $\hat{z}$ is a feasible solution, $\nabla f(\hat{z}) \neq 0$, $f(\cdot)$ is quasi-convex, $r(\cdot)$ is

affine, the set $\Omega = \{z: q(z) \leqq 0\}$ is star shaped at $\hat{z}$, and that there exist multipliers $\psi^1, \psi^2, \ldots, \psi^m$, and $\mu^1, \mu^2, \ldots, \mu^k$ with $\mu^i \leqq 0$ $i = 1, 2, \ldots, k$, such that

22
$$-\nabla f(\hat{z}) + \sum_{i=1}^{m} \psi^i \nabla r^i(\hat{z}) + \sum_{i=1}^{k} \mu^i \nabla q^i(\hat{z}) = 0$$
$$\mu^i q^i(\hat{z}) = 0 \qquad i = 1, 2, \ldots, k$$

Then $\hat{z}$ is an optimal solution.
Hint: The proof should be constructed in two steps. First, show that $r(\cdot)$ affine and Ω star-shaped at $\hat{z}$, in conjunction with (23), gives the condition

23
$$\langle \nabla f(\hat{z}), z - \hat{z} \rangle \geqq 0$$

for any feasible z. Next show that for any $f(\cdot)$, quasi-convex and differentiable,

24
$$\langle \nabla f(\hat{z}), z - \hat{z} \rangle \leqq 0 \qquad \text{for all } z \in \{z: f(z) \leqq f(\hat{z})\},$$

and that, as a result, if $\nabla f(\hat{z}) \neq 0$,

25
$$f(z) > f(\hat{z}) \qquad \text{for all } z \in \{z: \langle \nabla f(\hat{z}), z - \hat{z} \rangle > 0\}.$$

Finally, for any z feasible, use the sequence $z_i = z + \frac{1}{i} \nabla f(\hat{z})$, $i = 1, 2, \ldots$, together with (24) and (26) to show that $f(z) \geqq f(\hat{z})$. □

This concludes our discussion of nonlinear programming problems, and we now proceed to optimal control problems, which, by their very nature, have considerably more structure, and hence gives rise to more complex conditions of optimality.

REFERENCES

1. F. John: Extremum Problems with Inequalities as Side Conditions, in K. O. Friedrichs, O. W. Neugebauer, and J. J. Stoker (eds.), "Studies and Essays: Courant Anniversary Volume," pp. 187–204, Interscience Publishers, Inc., New York, 1948.
2. H. W. Kuhn and A. W. Tucker: Nonlinear Programming, *Proc. Second Berkeley Symp. Math. Stat. Probability*, pp. 481–492, University of California Press, Berkeley, Calif., 1951.
3. K. J. Arrow, L. Hurwicz, and H. Uzawa, Constraint Qualifications in Maximization Problems, *Naval Res. Logistics Quart.*, **8**:175–191 (1961).
4. K. J. Arrow, L. Hurwicz, and H. Uzawa (eds.): "Studies in Linear and Nonlinear Programming, "Stanford Mathematical Studies in the Social Sciences, II, Stanford University Press, Stanford, Calif., 1958.

5. O. L. Mangasarian and S. Fromovitz: The Fritz John Necessary Optimality Conditions in the Presence of Equality and Inequality Constraints, *Shell Development Company Paper* P1433, 1965.
6. A. J. Goldman: Resolution and Separation Theorems for Polyhedral Convex Sets, *Ann. Math. Studies* 38, pp. 41–51, Princeton University Press, Princeton, N.J., 1956.
7. W. F. Fleming: "Functions of Several Variables," McGraw-Hill Book Company, New York, 1965.

4

Discrete optimal control problems

4.1 THE GENERAL CASE

Discrete optimal control problems were first defined in Section 1.2, and in Section 1.5 it was shown that fixed-time discrete optimal problems can be transcribed into the form of the Basic Problem (1.4.1), for which necessary conditions are given by the Fundamental Theorem (2.3.12). Consequently, theorem (2.3.12) also gives necessary conditions for the optimality of a solution to any fixed-time discrete optimal control problem whose defining quantities satisfy the assumptions of this theorem. However, as in the case of nonlinear programming problems, the considerable structure of optimal control problems may lead to substantially more detailed necessary conditions than either the original statement of the Fundamental Theorem (2.3.12) or theorem (3.4.22).

To illustrate this fact, let us examine a very general optimal control problem whose formulation is governed by the following two considerations. First, we want to obtain necessary conditions in separated form, that is conditions stated in terms of the time index i (with $i = 0, 1, \ldots, k - 1$), the optimal state $\hat{x}_i$, and the optimal control $\hat{u}_i$, at time i only. This precludes trajectory constraints of the form $h(\mathfrak{X},\mathfrak{U}) \in D$ [see (1.2.4)] which cannot be separated into the form $x_i \in X_i$ for $i = 0, 1, \ldots, k$ and $u_i \in U_i$ for $i = 0, 1, \ldots, k-1$. Second, we wish to obtain easily specifiable transversality conditions, and therefore we can allow only differentiable equality and inequality constraints on the state vectors. These restrictions lead to the following particular case of the discrete optimal control problem (1.2.8).

1 **Optimal control problem.** Consider a dynamical system described by the difference equation

2 $$x_{i+1} - x_i = f_i(x_i,u_i) \qquad \text{for } i = 0, 1, \ldots, k-1,$$

where $x_i \in E^n$ is the state of the system at time i, $u_i \in E^m$ is the input to the system at time i, and $f_i(\cdot,\cdot)$ is a function mapping $E^n \times E^m$ into E^n. Find a control sequence $\hat{\mathfrak{U}} = (\hat{u}_0,\hat{u}_1, \ldots ,\hat{u}_{k-1})$ and a corresponding trajectory $\hat{\mathfrak{X}} = (\hat{x}_0,\hat{x}_1, \ldots ,\hat{x}_k)$, determined by (2), which minimize the sum

$$\sum_{i=0}^{k-1} f_i^0(x_i,u_i),$$

where the $f_i^0(\cdot,\cdot)$ map $E^n \times E^m$ into the reals.

This minimization is subject to the following constraints, which we write as the intersection of inequality and equality constraints whenever appropriate. The *control constraints* are

3 $$u_i \in U_i \subset E^m \qquad i = 0, 1, \ldots, k-1.$$

the *initial boundary constraints* are

4 $$x_0 \in X_0 = X_0' \cap X_0'' \qquad X_0' = \{x\colon q_0(x) \leqq 0\}, X_0'' = \{x\colon g_0(x) = 0\},$$

where $q_0(\cdot)$ maps E^n into E^{m_0} and $g_0(\cdot)$ maps E^n into E^{l_0}. The *terminal boundary constraints* are

5 $$x_k \in X_k = X_k' \cap X_k'' \qquad X_k' = \{x\colon q_k(x) \leqq 0\}, X_k'' = \{x\colon g_k(x) = 0\},$$

where $q_k(\cdot)$ maps E^n into E^{m_k} and $g_k(\cdot)$ maps E^n into E^{l_k}. The *state-space constraints* are

6 $$x_i \in X_i = X_i' \cap E^n = \{x\colon q_i(x) \leqq 0\} \qquad i = 1, 2, \ldots, k-1,$$

where $q_i(\cdot)$ maps E^n into E^{m_i}.

(Note that this formulation allows the initial and final sets, X_0 and X_k, to be manifolds, manifolds with boundaries, or "solid figures," i.e., sets with nonempty interiors. The state-space-constraint sets X_i, with $i = 1, 2, \ldots, k-1$, usually have nonempty interiors.)

To complete the formulation of the problem we now introduce some assumptions on the various sets and functions above:

7 For $i = 0, 1. \ldots, k-1$ the functions $f_1: E^n \times E^m \to E^n$ and $f_i^0: E^n \times E^m \to E^1$ are continuously differentiable.

8 For every $u \in U_i$ and $i \in \{0,1, \ldots, k-1\}$ there exists a conical approximation $C(u,U_i)$ [see (2.3.1) and (2.3.3)] for the set U_i at u.

9 The functions $g_0: E^n \to E^{l_0}$ and $g_k: E^n \to E^{l_k}$ are continuously differentiable, and *unless they are identically zero*, they have jacobian matrices $\partial g_0(x)/\partial x$ and $\partial g_k(x)/\partial x$ which are of maximum rank[1] for all x in X_0 and X_k, respectively.

10 For all $x_i \in X_i'$ and $i = 0, 1, \ldots, k$ the gradients of the active inequality constraints (that is, $\nabla q_i^j(x_i)$, with $j \in \{j: q_i^j(x_i) = 0, j \in \{1,2, \ldots, l^i\}\}$) are linearly independent vectors.[2] □

As we saw in Sec. 1.5, this problem may be recast in the form of the Basic Problem (1.4.1) [minimize $f(z)$ subject to $r(z) = 0$ and $z \in \Omega$] by making the following identifications. Let $z = (x_0,x_1, \ldots, x_k,u_0,u_1, \ldots, u_{k-1}) \in E^{(k+1)n+km}$ and let f, r, and Ω be defined by

11 $$f(z) = \sum_{i=0}^{k-1} f_i^0(x_i,u_i)$$

12 $$r(z) = \begin{bmatrix} x_1 - x_0 - f_0(x_0,u_0) \\ \cdots\cdots\cdots\cdots \\ x_k - x_{k-1} - f_{k-1}(x_{k-1},u_{k-1}) \\ g_0(x_0) \\ g_k(x_k) \end{bmatrix}$$

13 $$\Omega = X_1' \times X_1' \times X_2' \times \cdots \times X_{k-1}' \times X_k' \times U_0 \times U_1 \times \cdots \times U_{k-1}.$$

Clearly, f and r have the required differentiability properties. Now, suppose that $\hat{z} \in \Omega$ is an optimal solution to the optimal control

[1] When this assumption is not satisfied it is possible for all the costates p_0, p_1, $\ldots$, p_k and the scalar p^0 appearing in theorem (17) to be zero, in which case this theorem becomes trivial.

[2] This assumption guarantees the existence of conical approximations of the first kind for the sets X_i' for $i = 0, 1, \ldots, k$ [see corollary (3.5.10)].

problem under consideration. Then the cone

14 $$C(\hat{z},\Omega) = IC(\hat{x}_0,X'_0) \times IC(\hat{x}_1,X'_1) \times \cdots \times IC(\hat{x}_{k-1},X'_{k-1}) \times IC(\hat{x}_k,X'_k) \times C(\hat{u}_0,U_0) \times \cdots \times C(\hat{u}_{k-1},U_{k-1}),$$

which is the cartesian product of internal cones, first defined in (3.4.2), and of conical approximations, which exist by assumption (8), is obviously a conical approximation for the set Ω at $\hat{z}$. This follows from the fact that assumption (10) and corollary (3.5.10) guarantee that the cones $IC(\hat{x}_i,X'_i)$, with $i = 0, 1, \ldots, k$, are nonempty, while theorem (3.4.4) ensures that they are conical approximations of the first kind. We may therefore apply the Fundamental Theorem (2.3.12) to the optimal control problem under consideration and conclude that if $\hat{z}$ is an optimal solution, then there exists a nonzero vector $\psi = (p^0,\pi)$, with $p^0 \leqq 0$ and $\pi = (-p_1,-p_2, \ldots, -p_k,\mu_0,\mu_k)$, where $p_i \in E^n$, $\mu_0 \in E^{l_0}$, and $\mu_k \in E^{l_k}$, such that, with $F = (f,r)$,

15 $$\left\langle \psi, \frac{\partial F(\hat{z})}{\partial z}\,\delta z \right\rangle = p^0\langle \nabla f(\hat{z}),\delta z\rangle + \left\langle \pi, \frac{\partial r(\hat{z})}{\partial z}\,\delta z \right\rangle \leqq 0 \qquad \text{for all } \delta z \in \bar{C}(\hat{z},\Omega).$$

Substituting for f and r in (15) from (11) and (12) and expanding, we get

16 $$p^0\left(\sum_{i=0}^{k-1}\left\langle \frac{\partial f_i{}^0(\hat{x}_i,\hat{u}_i)}{\partial x}, \delta x_i\right\rangle + \sum_{i=0}^{k-1}\left\langle \frac{\partial f_i{}^0(\hat{x}_i,\hat{u}_i)}{\partial u}, \delta u_i\right\rangle\right) + \sum_{i=0}^{k-1}\left\langle -p_{i+1}, \left[\delta x_{i+1} - \delta x_i - \frac{\partial f_i(\hat{x}_i,\hat{u}_i)}{\partial x}\,\delta x_i - \frac{\partial f_i(\hat{x}_i,\hat{u}_i)}{\partial u}\,\delta u_i\right]\right\rangle + \left\langle \mu_0, \frac{\partial g_0(\hat{x}_0)}{\partial x}\,\delta x_0\right\rangle + \left\langle \mu_k, \frac{\partial g_k(\hat{x}_k)}{\partial x}\,\delta x_k\right\rangle \leqq 0$$
$$\text{for every } \delta z = (\delta x_0, \ldots, \delta x_k, \delta u_0, \ldots, \delta u_{k-1}) \in \bar{C}(\hat{z},\Omega).$$

This condition can be refined by considering special cases for the vector $\delta z \in \bar{C}(\hat{z},\Omega)$. The result is the theorem below, which converts condition (16) into a classical form involving conditions on a hamiltonian at each sampling instant $i = 0, 1, \ldots, k-1$, with the hamiltonian defined by means of *costate vectors* which satisfy an adjoint equation depending on the state-space constraints and transversality conditions.

17 **Theorem.** If $\hat{z} = (\hat{x}_0,\hat{x}_1, \ldots, \hat{x}_k,\hat{u}_0,\hat{u}_1, \ldots, \hat{u}_{k-1})$ is an optimal solution to optimal control problem (1), then there exist *costate vectors* p_0 $p_1, \ldots, p_k$ in E^n, multiplier vectors $\lambda_0, \lambda_1, \ldots, \lambda_k$,

with $\lambda_i \in E^{m_i}$ satisfying $\lambda_i \leqq 0$, multiplier vectors $\mu_0 \in E^{l_0}$ and $\mu_k \in E^{l_k}$, and a scalar $p^0 \leqq 0$ with the following properties:

18 Not all the quantities $p^0, p_0, p_1, \ldots, p_k, \mu_0, \mu_k$ are zero.

19 The costate vectors p_i satisfy the "forced" adjoint equation

$$p_i - p_{i+1} = \left[\frac{\partial f_i(\hat{x}_i,\hat{u}_i)}{\partial x}\right]^T p_{i+1} + p^0 \left[\frac{\partial f_i{}^0(\hat{x}_i,\hat{u}_i)}{\partial x}\right]^T + \left[\frac{\partial q_i(\hat{x}_i)}{\partial x}\right]^T \lambda_i \qquad i = 0, 1, \ldots, k-1.$$

20 At the initial set X_0, the transversality condition

$$p_0 = \left[\frac{\partial g_0(\hat{x}_0)}{\partial x}\right]^T \mu_0$$

is satisfied.

21 At the terminal set X_k, the transversality condition

$$p_k = \left[\frac{\partial g_k(\hat{x}_k)}{\partial x}\right]^T \mu_k + \left[\frac{\partial q_k(\hat{x}_k)}{\partial x}\right]^T \lambda_k$$

is satisfied.

22 For $j = 1, 2, \ldots, m_i$ and $i = 0, 1, \ldots, k$,

$$\lambda_i{}^j q_i{}^j(\hat{x}_i) = 0$$

[equivalently, $\langle \lambda_i, q_i(\hat{x}_i)\rangle = 0$ for $i = 0, 1, \ldots, k$].

23 For $i = 0, 1, \ldots, k-1$ the hamiltonian $H\colon E^n \times E^m \times E^n \times E^1 \times \{0, 1, \ldots, k-1\} \to E^1$, defined by

$$H(x,u,p,p^0,i) = p^0 f_i{}^0(x,u) + \langle p, f_i(x,u)\rangle$$

satisfies the condition

24 $$\left\langle \frac{\partial H(\hat{x}_i,\hat{u}_i,p_{i+1},p^0,i)}{\partial u}, \delta u_i \right\rangle \leqq 0 \qquad \text{for all } \delta u_i \in \bar{C}(\hat{u}_i,U_i),$$

which becomes, in expanded form,

25 $$p^0 \left\langle \frac{\partial f_i{}^0(\hat{x}_i,\hat{u}_i)}{\partial u}, \delta u_i \right\rangle + \left\langle p_{i+1}, \frac{\partial f_i(\hat{x}_i,\hat{u}_i)}{\partial u} \delta u_i \right\rangle \leqq 0 \qquad \text{for all } \delta u_i \in \bar{C}(\hat{u}_i,U_i).$$

Proof. Condition (18) was established prior to the statement of the theorem. We therefore proceed with the remaining conditions.

First let us prove (25). Let

$$\delta z = (0,0, \ldots ,0,0,\delta u_i,0,0, \ldots ,0) \qquad \delta u_i \in \bar{C}(\hat{u}_i,U_i).$$

Then, from (16), we immediately get (25). Now let $\delta z = (0,0, \ldots , \delta x_k,0,0, \ldots ,0)$, with $\delta x_k \in IC(\hat{x}_k,X'_k)$. Then (16) yields

26 $$\langle -p_k,\delta x_k\rangle + \left\langle \mu_k, \frac{\partial g_k(\hat{x}_k)}{\partial x}\,\delta x_k \right\rangle \leqq 0 \qquad \text{for all } \delta x_k \in \overline{IC}(\hat{x}_k,X'_k).$$

But if $\delta x_k \in \overline{IC}(\hat{x}_k,X'_k)$, then $\langle[\partial q_k{}^j(\hat{x}_k)/\partial x],\ \delta x_k\rangle \leqq 0$ for all $j \in \{j\colon q_k{}^j(\hat{x}) = 0$ and $j \in \{1,2, \ldots ,m_k\}\}$. Applying Farkas' lemma (A.5.34), we find that there exists a vector $\lambda_k \in E^{m_k}$, with $\lambda_k \leqq 0$, such that

27 $$-p_k + \left[\frac{\partial g_k(\hat{x}_k)}{\partial x}\right]^T \mu_k + \left[\frac{\partial q_k(\hat{x}_k)}{\partial x}\right]^T \lambda_k = 0$$

and $\lambda_k{}^j q_k{}^j(\hat{x}_k) = 0$ for $j = 1, 2, \ldots , m_k$; that is, conditions (21) and (22) are satisfied for $j = k$. Similarly, for $i = 0, 1, \ldots , k - 1$, letting $\delta z = (0,0, \ldots ,\delta x_i,0, \ldots ,0,0, \ldots ,0)$, with $\delta x_i \in \overline{IC}(\hat{x}_i,X'_i)$, and again applying Farkas' lemma, we get (19) and (22). Condition (20) is now seen to be simply the result of an arbitrary but consistent definition. □

This theorem is still too general for most applications, and we shall therefore specialize it further by considering special cases in the following corollaries.

28 **Corollary.** If the functions $q_i \equiv 0$ for $i = 1, 2, \ldots , k - 1$ and $\hat{z} = (\hat{x}_0,\hat{x}_1, \ldots ,\hat{x}_k,\hat{u}_0,\hat{u}_1, \ldots ,\hat{u}_{k-1})$ is an optimal solution to problem (1), then there exist costate vectors $p_0, p_1, \ldots , p_k$ in E^n, multiplier vectors $\lambda_0 \leqq 0$ in E^{m_0} and $\lambda_k \leqq 0$ in E^{m_k} and $\mu_0 \in E^{l_0}$ and $\mu_k \in E^{l_k}$, and a scalar $p^0 \leqq 0$ with the following properties:

29 Not all quantities $p^0, p_0, p_1, \ldots , p_k$, and μ_0 and μ_k are zero.

30 $$p_i - p_{i+1} = \left[\frac{\partial f_i(\hat{x}_i,\hat{u}_i)}{\partial x}\right]^T p_{i+1} + p^0 \left[\frac{\partial f_i(\hat{x}_i,\hat{u}_i)}{\partial x}\right]^T \quad \text{for } i = 0, 1, \ldots , k - 1;$$

31 $$p_0 = -\left[\frac{\partial g_0(\hat{x}_0)}{\partial x}\right]^T \mu_0;$$

32 $$p_k = \left[\frac{\partial g_k(\hat{x}_k)}{\partial x}\right]^T \mu_k + \left[\frac{\partial q_k(\hat{x}_k)}{\partial x}\right]^T \lambda_k;$$

33 $\lambda_i{}^j q_i{}^j(\hat{x}_i) = 0$ for $j = 1, 2, \ldots , m_i$ and $i = 0, k$.

34 $$p^0 \left\langle \frac{\partial f_i^0(\hat{x}_i,\hat{u}_i)}{\partial u}, \delta u_i \right\rangle + \left\langle p_{i+1}, \frac{\partial f_i(\hat{x}_i,\hat{u}_i)}{\partial u} \delta u_i \right\rangle \leqq 0 \text{ for all } \delta u_i \in$$

$\bar{C}(\hat{u}_i,U_i)$ and $i = 0, 1, \ldots, k-1$. □

35 **Corollary.** If X_0 and X_k are singletons (points in the state space), then (31) and (32) carry no information, and corollary (28) becomes identical with theorem (2.4.28).

Proof. Let $X_0 = \{\hat{x}_0\}$ and $X_k = \{\hat{x}_k\}$. Then we have $g_0(x) = x - \hat{x}_0$, $q_0 \equiv 0$, $g_k(x) = x - \hat{x}_k$, and $q_k \equiv 0$. Hence $\partial g_0(\hat{x}_0)/\partial x = \partial g_k(\hat{x}_k)/\partial x = I$, the identity matrix, and (31) and (32) reduce to $p_0 = -\mu_0$ and $p_k = \mu_k$, which is hardly enlightening. □

36 **Corollary.** If $X_k = E^n$, or if $g_k(x) \equiv 0$ and $q_k(\hat{x}_k) < 0$, then corollary (28) holds, with $p^0 = -1$ and $p_k = 0$.

Proof. Suppose that $X_k = E^n$. This implies that both g_k and q_k are identically zero, that $g_k(x)$ does not appear in (12) (making $\mu_k = 0$), and that $IC(\hat{x}_k,X_k') = X_k' = E^n$. Hence, from (32), $p_k = 0$. Now suppose that $q_k(\hat{x}_k) < 0$ and $g_k \equiv 0$. Then again $\mu_k = 0$, from (33) $\lambda_k = 0$, and from (32) $p_k = 0$. Now suppose that $p^0 = 0$; then from (30) $p_0 = p_1 = p_2 = \cdots = p_{k-1} = p_k = 0$, and from (31) $\mu_0 = 0$. But this contradicts the fact that the vector $\psi = (p^0,-p_1,-p_2, \ldots,-p_k,\mu_0,\mu_k)$ is not zero in (15). □

Theorem (17) and its corollaries show how the Fundamental Theorem (2.3.12) can be interpreted to obtain necessary conditions for optimal control problems with various types of constraint. A specific characteristic of these theorems is the condition on the hamiltonian given by (25). At first glance, one might conclude that (25) is some sort of a maximum condition on the hamiltonian. That this is not necessarily so is demonstrated by the following example.

37 **Example.** Consider the system described by the scalar difference equation

38 $$x_{i+1} - x_i = u_i \qquad i = 0, 1,$$

and suppose that we wish to minimize the cost function

39 $$f(\mathfrak{X},\mathfrak{U}) = \sum_{i=0}^{1} \{x_i^2 - \tfrac{1}{2}(-2)^i[(u_i+2)^2 - 1]\}$$

subject to the constraints that $x_0 = 1$ and $-3 \leqq u_i \leqq 1$ for $i = 0, 1$. This problem is simple enough to solve explicitly. From (38), $x_1 = (1 + u_0)$, and hence, with $x_0 = 1$, the cost function becomes

39 $$f(\mathfrak{X},\mathfrak{U}) = \tfrac{1}{2}u_0^2 + (u_1+2)^2 - \tfrac{1}{2}.$$

Obviously, (39) is minimized by setting $\hat{u}_0 = 0$ and $\hat{u}_1 = -2$, both of these values satisfying the constraint $-3 \leqq u_i \leqq +1$ for $i = 0, 1$. The corresponding trajectory is seen to be $\hat{x}_0 = 1$, $\hat{x}_1 = 1$, $\hat{x}_2 = -1$.

Now let us go back to corollary (28). Since $g_2 \equiv 0$ and $q_2 \equiv 0$, we find that $p_2 = 0$. Equation (30) becomes

40 $$p_i - p_{i+1} = p^0 \cdot 2\hat{x}_i \qquad i = 0, 1.$$

Since $X_2 = E^1$ (the real line), we may set $p^0 = -1$, by corollary (36). Therefore, from (40), $p_1 = -2$. We can now evaluate the hamiltonian $H(\hat{x}_i,u_i,p_{i+1},p^0,i)$, defined in condition (23), for $i = 0, 1$. Thus

41 $$H(\hat{x}_0,u_0,p_1,0) = -\{1 - \tfrac{1}{2}[(u_0 + 2)^2 - 1]\} - 2u_0 = \tfrac{1}{2}u_0^2 + \tfrac{1}{2}$$

and

42 $$H(\hat{x}_1,u_1,p_2,1) = -(u_1 + 2)^2.$$

It is clear by inspection that $H(\hat{x}_0,u_0,p_1,0)$ is minimized by $u_0 = 0$ and $H(\hat{x}_1,u_1,p_2,1)$ is maximized by $u_1 = -2$. Thus the optimal control sequence $(\hat{u}_0,\hat{u}_1)$ does not necessarily maximize the hamiltonian H. □

In the next section we shall consider a class of problems for which we do indeed obtain a maximum condition for the hamiltonian H.

Conditions for $p^0 < 0$

As we have already pointed out, it may be quite important to know whether or not $p^0 = 0$ in theorem (17). The following set of exercises is designed to shed some light on this matter.

43 **Exercise.** Suppose that for optimal control problem (1) we have $X_0 = \{x: g_0(x) = 0\}$, $x_k = \{x: g_k(x) = 0\}$, and $X_i = E^n$ for $i = 1, 2, \ldots, k-1$, and the sets U_i are convex for $i = 0, 1, \ldots, k-1$. Furthermore, suppose that $\hat{x}_0, \hat{x}_1, \ldots, \hat{x}_k, \hat{u}_0, \hat{u}_1, \ldots, \hat{u}_{k-1}$ is an optimal solution to this problem, and that the matrices A_i and B_i for $i = 0, 1, \ldots, k-1$ and $\tilde{Q}_c$ are defined by

44 $$A_i = I + \frac{\partial f_i}{\partial x}(\hat{x}_i,\hat{u}_i) \qquad i = 0, 1, \ldots, k-1$$

45 $$B_i = \frac{\partial f_i}{\partial u}(\hat{x}_i,\hat{u}_i) \qquad i = 0, 1, \ldots, k-1$$

46 $$\tilde{Q}_c = [B_{k-1} \mid A_{k-1}B_{k-2} \mid \cdots \mid A_{k-1}A_{k-2} \cdots A_1B_0].$$

Assume (*a*) that the linear system

47 $$\delta x_{i+1} = A_i \delta x_i + B_i\, \delta u_i \qquad i = 0, 1, \ldots, k-1,$$

with boundary conditions $[\partial g_0(\hat{x}_0)/\partial x]\, \delta x_0 = 0$ and $[\partial g_k(\hat{x}_k)/\partial x]\, \delta x_k = 0$, has a solution $\delta x_0^*, \ldots, \delta x_k^*, \delta u_0^*, \ldots, \delta u_{k-1}^*$, with δu_i^* in the interior of $RC(\hat{u}_i, U_i)$, for $i = 0, 1, \ldots, k-1$, (*b*) that $\partial g_0(\hat{x}_0)/\partial x$ and $\partial g_k(\hat{x}_k)/\partial x$ have maximum rank, and (*c*) that the controllability matrix $\tilde{Q}_c$ has rank n. Show that if costate vectors $p_0, p_1, \ldots, p_k$, multiplier vectors μ_0 and μ_k, and a scalar $p^0 \leqq 0$ satisfy the conditions of theorem (17), with $C(\hat{u}_0, U_i) = RC(\hat{u}_i, U_i)$ for $i = 1, 0, \ldots, k-1$, then $p^0 < 0$. [*Hint:* Show that, under the above assumptions, with the optimal control problem transcribed into Basic Problem form, $\partial r(\hat{z})/\partial z$ has maximum rank and there is a vector δz^* in the interior of $C(\hat{z},\Omega)$ such that $[\partial r(\hat{z})/\partial z]\, \delta z = 0$. Then use (2.3.50).] □

48 **Exercise.** Consider the two-point-boundary-value optimal control problem, $X_0 = \{\hat{x}_0\}$, $X_k = \{\hat{x}_k\}$, and $X_i = E^n$ for $i = 1, 2, \ldots, k-1$. Suppose that the functions $f_i(\cdot,\cdot)$ are linear for $i = 0, 1, \ldots, k-1$ [that is, $f_i(x,u) = A_i x + B_i u$] and that the sets U_i are convex for $i = 0, 1, \ldots, k-1$. Show that there are a set of costates $p_0, p_1, \ldots, p_k$ and a scalar $p^0 < 0$ satisfying the conditions of theorem (17), whenever there exists a control sequence $u_0, u_1, \ldots, u_{k-1}$, with u_i in the relative interior of U_i, such that the corresponding trajectory $\hat{x}_0, x_1, \ldots, x_k$ satisfies the boundary conditions; that is, $x_0 = \hat{x}_0$ and $x_k = \hat{x}_k$. [*Hint:* Show that, under the above assumptions, with the optimal control problem transcribed into Basic Problem form, there exists a δz^* in the relative interior of $C(\hat{z},\Omega)$ such that $[\partial r(\hat{z})/\partial z]\, \delta z^* = 0$. Show that this fact, with the convexity of U_i for $i = 0, 1, \ldots, k-1$ and the linearity of $r(\cdot)$, can be used to verify that

$$TC_s(\hat{z},\Omega') = TC_s(\hat{z},\Omega) \cap \left\{\delta z\colon \frac{\partial r(\hat{z})}{\partial z}\, \delta z = 0\right\};$$

that is, use the results of exercise (2.3.47).] □

49 **Remark.** Note that if *all the constraint functions* appearing in the statement of the optimal control problem are linear, or affine, then, by corollary (3.4.33), the conditions of theorem (17) can be satisfied with $p^0\ (= \psi^0) \neq 0$. □

This concludes our discussion of the general discrete optimal control problem. In the next section we shall consider a special class of optimal control problems for which the hamiltonian H does in fact assume a global maximum with respect to the controls, along an optimal trajectory.

4.2 A MAXIMUM PRINCIPLE

Convexity is the magic word in optimization theory. In the presence of convexity, local extrema become global extrema, sufficient conditions of optimality can be obtained, and conditions for the existence and uniqueness of an optimal solution come within our reach. Actually, as was shown by Holtzman [3] in his extension of Halkin's maximum principle [2] for discrete optimal control problems, we can often relax the requirement that a set be convex to the requirement that it be directionally convex.

1 **Definition.** Let e be any vector in E^s. A set $S \subset E^s$ is said to be *e-directionally convex* if for every vector z' in the convex hull of S there exists a vector z in S such that

2 $$z = z' + \beta e \qquad \beta \geqq 0. \quad \square$$

A couple of examples of directionally convex sets are shown in Figure 1. We now establish the most relevant property of directionally convex sets as far as the following discussion is concerned.

3 **Theorem.** Let $e_1, e_2, \ldots, e_s$ be any basis for E^s. If the set $S \subset E^s$ is e_1-directionally convex, then its projection S_L onto the subspace L spanned by the vectors $e_2, e_3, \ldots, e_s$ is convex.[1]

Proof. Let z_1 and z_2 be any two vectors in S. We can decompose them uniquely as follows: $z_1 = z_1' + z_1''$ and $z_2 = z_2' + z_2''$, where $z_1' = \beta^1 e_1$, $z_2' = \beta^2 e_1$, and z_1'' and z_2'' are vectors in S_L. Let λ be any scalar satisfying $0 \leqq \lambda \leqq 1$; then, since S is e_1-directionally convex, we have, by (2), that

4 $$\{[\lambda z_1'' + (1 - \lambda)z_2''] + [\lambda\beta^1 + (1 - \lambda)\beta^2]e_1\} + \beta e_1 \in S \qquad \text{for some } \beta \geqq 0.$$

Hence, by inspection, $[\lambda z_1'' + (1 - \lambda)z_2''] \in S_L$ for $0 \leqq \lambda \leqq 1$, and therefore S_L is convex. $\square$

Before we can return to our discussion of optimal control problems, we need to extend the Fundamental Theorem (2.3.12) to

[1] Given a basis $e_1, e_2, \ldots, e_s$ for the space E^s and the subspace L spanned by $e_2, e_3, \ldots, e_s$, we say that S_L is the *projection* of S onto L if $S_L \subset L$ and if every vector $z \in S$ can be uniquely represented as $z = z' + z''$, with $z' = \beta e_1$ and $z'' \in S_L$.

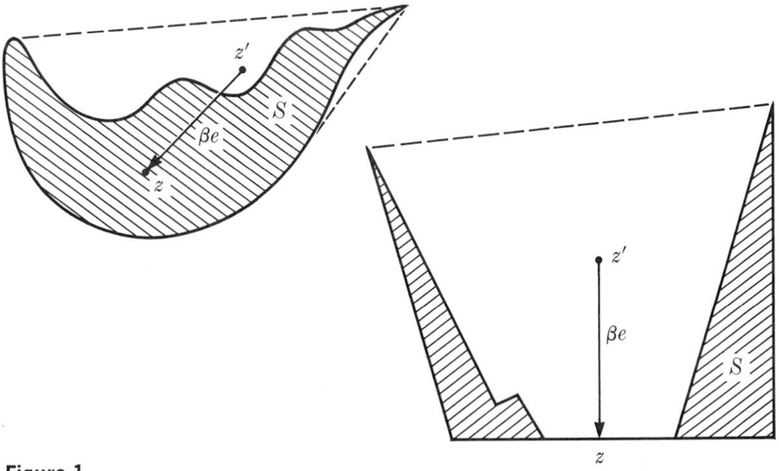

Figure 1

a more general form. First, after examining theorem (2.3.12) and its proof, we find that it can be restated in the following alternative form:

5 **Theorem.** Suppose that $\hat{z}$ is a feasible solution to the Basic Problem (1.4.1), that is, $\hat{z} \in \Omega$ and $r(\hat{z}) = 0$, and that $C(\hat{z},\Omega)$ is a conical approximation to Ω at $\hat{z}$ [see (2.3.3)]. If the ray $R = \{y: y = (-1,0, \ldots ,0),\ \beta \geqq 0\}$ is an interior ray of the cone $[\partial F(\hat{z})/\partial z]C(\hat{z},\Omega)$, where $F = (f,r)$, then there exists a $z^* \in \Omega$ such that $r(z^*) = r(\hat{z}) = 0$ and $f(z^*) < f(\hat{z})$. □

Note that this version of theorem (2.3.12) does not require that $\hat{z}$ be optimal. It is merely a theorem which establishes a property of continuously differentiable functions. We can now prove an extension of the Fundamental Theorem (2.3.12).

6 **Theorem.** Let $\Omega' \subset E^n$ be any set with the property that for every $z' \in \Omega'$ there exists a $z \in \Omega$ satisfying $r(z) = r(z')$ and $f(z) \leqq f(z')$. If $\hat{z}$ is an optimal solution to the Basic Problem (1.4.1), if $\hat{z} \in \Omega'$, and if $C(\hat{z},\Omega')$ is a conical approximation to the set Ω' at $\hat{z}$, then there exists a nonzero vector $\psi = (\psi^0,\psi^1, \ldots ,\psi^m) \in E^{m+1}$, with $\psi^0 \leqq 0$, such that for all $\delta z \in C(\hat{z},\Omega')$

7 $$\left\langle \psi, \frac{\partial F(\hat{z})}{\partial z}\,\delta z \right\rangle \leqq 0.$$

Proof. Suppose that the ray $R = \{y: y = \beta(-1,0,0, \ldots ,0),\ \beta > 0\}$ is an interior ray of the cone $[\partial F(\hat{z})/\partial z]C(\hat{z},\Omega')$. Then it follows from theorem (5) that there exists a $z' \in \Omega'$ such that $r(z') = 0$ and $f(z') < f(\hat{z})$. But, by assumption, this implies that there exists a $z^* \in \Omega$ such that $r(z^*) = 0$ and $f(z^*) \leqq f(z') \leqq f(z)$, which contradicts the optimality of $\hat{z}$. Hence the ray R and the convex cone $[\partial F(\hat{z})/\partial z]C(\hat{z},\Omega')$ must be separated. The existence of a vector ψ satisfying (7) then follows from the definition of separation. □

8 **Directionally convex optimal control problem.** Given a dynamical system described by the difference equation

9 $$x_{i+1} - x_i = f_i(x_i,u_i) \qquad i = 0, 1, \ldots, k-1,$$

where $x_i \in E^n$ is the system state at time i, $u_i \in E^m$ is the system input at time i, and $f_i(\cdot,\cdot)$ is a function mapping $E^n \times E^m$ into E^n, find a control sequence $\hat{\mathfrak{u}} = (\hat{u}_0,\hat{u}_1, \ldots ,\hat{u}_{k-1})$ and a corresponding trajectory $\hat{\mathfrak{x}} = (\hat{x}_0,\hat{x}_1, \ldots ,\hat{x}_k)$, determined by (9), which minimize the sum

$$\sum_{i=0}^{k-1} f_i^0(x_i,u_i),$$

where the $f_i^0(\cdot,\cdot)$ map $E^n \times E^m$ into the reals, subject to constraints (1.3) to (1.6).

However, we now introduce a set of assumptions which are somewhat different from the ones made in Section 1.

10 For $i = 0, 1, \ldots, k-1$ and every $u \in U_i$ the functions $f_i(\cdot,u)$ are continuously differentiable on E^n. [Note that we no longer require the functions $f_i(\cdot,\cdot)$ to be differentiable in u; in fact, we do not even require the $f_i(\cdot,\cdot)$ to be continuous in u.]

11 Let $b_0 \in E^{n+1}$ be the vector $(-1,0,0, \ldots ,0)$, and for $i = 0, 1, \ldots, k-1$ let $\mathbf{f}_i(\cdot,\cdot)$ be the function from $E^n \times E^m$ into E^{n+1}, defined by $\mathbf{f}_i(x,u) = (f_i^0(x,u),f_i(x,u))$. For $i = 0, 1, \ldots, k-1$ and every $x \in E^n$ the sets $\mathbf{f}_i(x,U_i)$ are b_0-directionally convex; that is, for every $\mathbf{f}_i(x,u')$ and $\mathbf{f}_i(x,u'')$ in $\mathbf{f}_i(x,U_i)$ (that is, $u', u'' \in U_i$) and $0 \leqq \lambda \leqq 1$ there exists a $u(\lambda) \in U_i$ such that $f_i(x,u(\lambda)) = \lambda f_i(x,u') + (1-\lambda)f_i(x,u'')$ and $f_i^0(x,u(\lambda)) \leqq \lambda f_i^0(x,u') + (1-\lambda)f_i^0(x,u'')$.

12 The functions $g_0: E^n \to E^{l_0}$ and $g_k: E^n \to E^{l_k}$ are continuously differentiable and have jacobian matrices $\partial g_0(x)/\partial x$ and $\partial g_k(x)/\partial x$ which are of maximum rank for all x in X_0 and X_k, respectively.

13 For all $x \in X_i'$ and $i = 0, 1, \ldots, k$ the gradients of the active inequality constraints, $\nabla q_i^j(x)$, with $j \in \{j: q_i^j(x) = 0\}$, are linearly independent vectors. □

To transcribe this optimal control problem into the form of the Basic Problem (1.4.1), we make the following substitutions, which are somewhat different from the ones we used in the preceding section.[1]

For $i = 0, 1, \ldots, k-1$ let $\mathbf{v}_i = (v_i^0, v_i) \in E^{n+1}$, where $v_i = (v_i^1, v_i^2, \ldots, v_i^n) \in E^n$. Equation (9) is now seen to be equivalent to

14 $$x_{i+1} - x_i = v_i \qquad i = 0, 1, \ldots, k-1,$$

with $v_i \in f_i(x_i, U_i)$ for $i = 0, 1, \ldots, k-1$. Finally, let $z = (x_0, x_1, \ldots, x_k, \mathbf{v}_0, \mathbf{v}_1, \ldots, \mathbf{v}_{k-1}) \in E^{n(k+1)+k(n+1)}$. We can now define the functions f and r and the constraint set Ω as follows:

15 $$f(z) = \sum_{i=0}^{k-1} v_i^0$$

16 $$r(z) = \begin{bmatrix} x_1 - x_0 - v_0 \\ x_2 - x_1 - v_1 \\ \cdot \\ \cdot \\ \cdot \\ x_k - x_{k-1} - v_{k-1} \\ g_0(x_0) \\ g_k(x_k) \end{bmatrix}$$

17 $$\Omega = \{z = (x_0, x_1, \ldots, x_k, x_{k-1}, \mathbf{v}_0, \mathbf{v}_1, \ldots, \mathbf{v}_{k-1}) \colon x_i \in X_i',\ i = 0, 1, \ldots, k,\ \mathbf{v}_i \in \mathbf{f}_i(x_i, U_i),\ i = 0, 1, \ldots, k-1\}.$$

Thus in Ω the $\mathbf{v}_i$ are constrained not only by the sets U_i, but also by the values of the $x_i \in X_i'$. Note, in addition, that for $z \in \Omega$, $v_i^0 = f_i^0(x_i, u_i)$ for some $x_i \in X_i'$ and $u_i \in U_i$. Hence, from (15),

18 $$f(z) = \sum_{i=0}^{k-1} v_i^0 = \sum_{i=0}^{k-1} f_i^0(x_i, u_i) \qquad z \in \Omega,$$

and (18) becomes identical in form with the sum in problem (8). This completes our transcription of the optimal control problem into the form of the Basic Problem (1.4.1).

Unfortunately, we do not know how to construct a conical approximation for the set Ω. Let us therefore introduce a more

[1] The first reason for using a different substitution in this section is that, by definition, in (1.4.1) $r(z)$ must be continuously differentiable. Hence the terms $f_i(x_i, u_i)$ which may not be differentiable in u_i cannot appear in the definition of $r(z)$. The second reason is that substitution (16) is particularly suitable for exploiting the convexity of the sets U_i.

tractable set, Ω', which we can use in conjunction with theorem (6). Let Ω' be the set defined by

19 $$\Omega' = \{z = (x_0,x_1, \ldots ,x_k,\mathbf{v}_0,\mathbf{v}_1, \ldots ,\mathbf{v}_{k-1}): x_i \in X'_i, \; i = 0, 1, \ldots , k, \; \mathbf{v}_i \in \text{co } \mathbf{f}_i(x_i,U_i), \; i = 0, 1, \ldots , k-1\}.$$

Now let $z^* = (x_0^*,x_1^*, \ldots ,x_k^*,\mathbf{v}_0^*,\mathbf{v}_1^*, \ldots ,\mathbf{v}_{k-1}^*)$ be any point in Ω'. Then, since the sets $\mathbf{f}_i(x_i^*,U_i)$ are b_0-directionally convex, there exist points $\tilde{\mathbf{v}}_i \in \mathbf{f}_i(x_i^*,U_i)$, with $i = 0, 1, \ldots , k-1$, such that $\tilde{v}_i = v_i^*$ and $v_i^0 \leqq v_i^{*0}$. Hence for $\tilde{z} = (x_0^*,x_1^*, \ldots ,x_k^*,\tilde{\mathbf{v}}_0,\tilde{\mathbf{v}}_1, \ldots ,\tilde{\mathbf{v}}_{k-1})$ we have $r(\tilde{z}) = r(z^*)$ and $f(\tilde{z}) \leqq f(z^*)$, where r and f are as defined by (16) and (15), respectively. We thus see that the set Ω' satisfies the hypotheses of theorem (6) with respect to the set Ω, defined in (17), and the functions f and r defined in (15) and (16), respectively.

Now suppose that $\hat{z} = (\hat{x}_0,\hat{x}_1, \ldots ,\hat{x}_k,\hat{\mathbf{v}}_0,\hat{\mathbf{v}}_1, \ldots ,\hat{\mathbf{v}}_{k-1})$ is an optimal solution to problem (8); that is, $(\hat{x}_0,\hat{x}_1, \ldots ,\hat{x}_k)$ is an optimal trajectory and $\hat{\mathbf{v}}_i = \mathbf{f}_i(\hat{x}_i,\hat{u}_i)$ for $i = 0, 1, \ldots , k-1$, where $(\hat{u}_0,\hat{u}_1, \ldots ,\hat{u}_{k-1})$ is an optimal control sequence. We shall now show that the set

20 $$C(\hat{z},\Omega') = \{\delta z = (\delta x_0,\delta x_1, \ldots ,\delta x_k,\delta\mathbf{v}_0,\delta\mathbf{v}_1, \ldots ,\delta\mathbf{v}_{k-1}): \; \delta x_i \in IC(\hat{x}_i,X'_i), \; (\delta\mathbf{v}_i - [\partial\mathbf{f}_i(\hat{x}_i,\hat{u}_i)/\partial x]\, \delta x_i) \in RC(\hat{\mathbf{v}}_i, \text{co } \mathbf{f}_i(\hat{x}_i,U_i))\}$$

is a conical approximation to the set Ω' at $\hat{z}$.

First we must prove that $C(\hat{z},\Omega')$ is a convex cone. Let δz be any nonzero vector in $C(\hat{z},\Omega')$, and let $\lambda \geqq 0$ be an arbitrary scalar. Then

21 $$\lambda\, \delta x_i \in IC(\hat{x}_i,X'_i)$$

and

$$\left[\lambda\, \delta\mathbf{v}_i - \frac{\partial\mathbf{f}_i(\hat{x}_i,\hat{u}_i)}{\partial x}\lambda\, \delta x_i\right] \in RC(\hat{\mathbf{v}}_i, \text{co } \mathbf{f}_i(\hat{x}_i,U_i)).$$

Hence $C(\hat{z},\Omega')$ is a cone. Now let $\delta z'$ and $\delta z''$ be any two points in $C(\hat{z},\Omega')$. It is simple to show that $\lambda\, \delta z' + (1 - \lambda)\, \delta z''$ is also a vector in $C(\hat{z},\Omega')$ for $0 \leqq \lambda \leqq 1$. Hence $C(\hat{z},\Omega')$ is convex.

Finally [see (2.3.3)], for every finite collection $\{\delta z_1,\delta z_2, \ldots , \delta z_p\}$ of linearly independent vectors in $C(\hat{z},\Omega')$ we must exhibit the existence of an $\epsilon > 0$ and a continuous map ζ from co $\{\hat{z}, \hat{z} + \epsilon\, \delta\hat{z}_1, \ldots , \hat{z} + \epsilon\, \delta z_p\}$ into Ω' such that $\zeta(\hat{z} + \delta z) = \hat{z} + \delta z + o(\delta z)$ where $\|o(\delta z)\|/\|\delta z\| \to 0$ as $\|\delta z\| \to 0$. Let $\delta z_1, \delta z_2, \ldots , \delta z_p$ be any finite collection of linearly independent vectors in $C(\hat{z},\Omega')$, with $\delta z_j = (\delta x_{0j},\delta x_{1j}, \ldots ,\delta x_{kj},\delta\mathbf{v}_{0j},\delta\mathbf{v}_{1j}, \ldots ,\delta\mathbf{v}_{k-1j})$. Hence, by definition (20),

22 $$\delta x_{ij} \in IC(\hat{x}_i, X_i') \qquad i = 0, 1, \ldots, k, j = 1, 2, \ldots, p$$

and

23 $$\delta \mathbf{v}_{ij} = \frac{\partial \mathbf{f}_i(\hat{x}_i, \hat{u}_i)}{\partial x} \delta x_{ij} + (\mathbf{v}_{ij} - \hat{\mathbf{v}}_i) \qquad i = 0, 1, \ldots, k-1, \quad j = 1, 2, \ldots, p,$$

where $(\mathbf{v}_{ij} - \hat{\mathbf{v}}_i) \in RC(\hat{\mathbf{v}}_i, \text{co } \mathbf{f}_i(\hat{x}_i, U_i))$.

Since both internal cones and radial cones are conical approximations of the first kind [see (2.3.1)], there must exist an $\epsilon > 0$ such that for any scalars $\mu^1, \mu^2, \ldots, \mu^p$ which satisfy $\mu^j \geqq 0$ for $j = 1, 2, \ldots, p$, and $\Sigma_{j=1}^p \mu^j \leqq 1$, $(\hat{x}_i + \epsilon \Sigma_{j=1}^p \mu^j \delta x_{ij}) \in X_i'$ for $i = 0, 1, \ldots, k$ and $[\hat{\mathbf{v}}_i + \epsilon \Sigma_{j=1}^p \mu^j (\mathbf{v}_{ij} - \hat{\mathbf{v}}_i)] \in \text{co } \mathbf{f}_i(\hat{x}_i, U_i)$ for $i = 0, 1, \ldots, k$. We claim that the above-indicated $\epsilon > 0$ will serve our purpose and that we can therefore proceed to construct the map ζ (we shall justify this claim in the process of construction). We construct the map ζ in two steps. First, we obtain a representation for vectors $z = \hat{z} + \delta z$ in co $\{\hat{z}, \hat{z} + \epsilon\, \delta z_1, \ldots, \hat{z} + \epsilon\, \delta z_p\}$ in terms of vectors in X_i' and in $\mathbf{f}_i(\hat{x}_i, U_i)$. Then, since we know that the map ζ must have an expansion of the form $\zeta(\hat{z} + \delta z) = \hat{z} + \delta z + o(\delta z)$, we define ζ in such a way that its linear part has the representation obtained in the first step and, furthermore, $\zeta(\hat{z} + \delta z)$ is in Ω'. This last step is arrived at essentially by inspection.

Thus we let $C = \text{co } \{\hat{z}, \hat{z} + \epsilon\, \delta z_1, \hat{z} + \epsilon\, \delta z_2, \ldots, \hat{z} + \epsilon\, \delta z_p\}$. Then for any $z \in C$ we have

24 $$\delta z = z - \hat{z} = \epsilon \sum_{j=1}^{p} \mu^j(z)\, \delta z_j \qquad \mu^j(z) \geqq 0, \sum_{j=1}^{p} \mu^j(z) \leqq 1.$$

Furthermore, since the vectors δz_j are linearly independent, for any $z \in C$ the scalars $\mu^j(z)$ for $j = 1, 2, \ldots, p$ are uniquely determined by (24).

Now, since $[\hat{\mathbf{v}}_i + \epsilon(\mathbf{v}_{ij} - \hat{\mathbf{v}}_i)] \in \text{co } \mathbf{f}_i(\hat{x}_i, U_i)$ for $i = 0, 1, \ldots, k-1$ and $j = 1, 2, \ldots, p$, there exist controls $u_{ij}{}^\alpha \in U_{ij}$ with $\alpha = 1, 2, \ldots, s_i$, such that

25 $$\hat{\mathbf{v}}_i + \epsilon(\mathbf{v}_{ij} - \hat{\mathbf{v}}_i) = \sum_{\alpha=1}^{s_i} \lambda_i{}^\alpha \mathbf{f}_i(\hat{x}_i, u_{ij}{}^\alpha) \qquad i = 0, 1, \ldots, k-1,$$

$$j = 1, 2, \ldots, p, \text{ where } \lambda_i{}^\alpha \geqq 0 \text{ and } \sum_{\alpha=1}^{s_i} \lambda_i{}^\alpha = 1.$$

Consequently, for any $\delta z = (\delta x_0, \delta x_1, \ldots, \delta x_k, \delta \mathbf{v}_0, \delta \mathbf{v}_1, \ldots, \delta \mathbf{v}_{k-1}) = z - \hat{z}$, where $z \in C$, we have, from (24) and (25),

26 $$\delta x_i = \epsilon \sum_{j=1}^{p} \mu^j(z)\, \delta x_{ij} \qquad i = 0, 1, \ldots, k-1$$

and

27 $$\delta \mathbf{v}_i = \frac{\partial \mathbf{f}_i(\hat{x}_i,\hat{u}_i)}{\partial x}\,\delta x_i + \epsilon \sum_{j=1}^{p} \mu^j(z)(\mathbf{v}_{ij} - \hat{\mathbf{v}}_i)$$
$$= \frac{\partial \mathbf{f}_i(\hat{x}_i,\hat{u}_i)}{\partial x}\,\delta x_i + \sum_{j=1}^{p} \mu^j(z)\left[\sum_{\alpha=1}^{s_i} \lambda_i{}^\alpha \mathbf{f}_i(\hat{x}_i,u_{ij}{}^\alpha) - \hat{\mathbf{v}}_i\right]$$
$$i = 0, 1, \ldots, k-1.$$

Expressions (26) and (27) give the desired representations for vectors in C in terms of vectors in X_i and in $\mathbf{f}_i(\hat{x}_i,U_i)$.

We now define the map ζ from the set C into Ω' as follows. Let $z = (x_0,x_1, \ldots ,x_k,\mathbf{v}_0,\mathbf{v}_1, \ldots ,\mathbf{v}_{k-1}) \in C$ be arbitrary, and let $\delta z = z - \hat{z}$; then

28 $$\zeta(z) = (y_0,y_1, \ldots ,y_k,\mathbf{w}_0,\mathbf{w}_1, \ldots ,\mathbf{w}_{k-1}),$$

where

29 $$y_i(z) = x_i \qquad i = 0, 1, \ldots, k$$

and

30 $$\mathbf{w}_i(z) = \mathbf{f}_i(x_i,\hat{u}_i) + \sum_{j=1}^{p} \mu^j(z)\left[\sum_{\alpha=1}^{s_i} \lambda_i{}^\alpha \mathbf{f}_i(x_i,u_{ij}{}^\alpha) - \mathbf{f}_i(x_i,\hat{u}_i)\right],$$

with the $\mu^j(z)$ determined uniquely by (24). First we observe that, by construction, for every $z = (x_0,x_1, \ldots ,x_k,\mathbf{v}_0,\mathbf{v}_1, \ldots ,\mathbf{v}_{k-1}) \in C$ we have $x_i \in X'_i$, with $i = 0, 1, \ldots, k$. Hence y_i is also in X'_i. Since the controls $u_{ij}{}^\alpha$ are in U_i and the scalars $\mu^j(z)$ satisfy $\mu^j(z) \geqq 0$ and $\Sigma_{j=1}^{p} \mu^j(z) \leqq 1$, it is clear that the $\mathbf{w}_i$, as determined by (30), are in co $\mathbf{f}_i(x_i,U_i)$.

Thus the map ζ does indeed map C into Ω'. We must still show that it can be written in the form $\zeta(\hat{z} + \delta z) = \hat{z} + \delta z + o(\delta z)$. We therefore expand (30) about $\hat{z}$ and get, with $z = \hat{z} + \delta z$,

31 $$\mathbf{w}_i(\hat{z} + \delta z) = \mathbf{f}_i(\hat{x}_i,\hat{u}_i) + \frac{\partial \mathbf{f}_i(\hat{x}_i,\hat{u}_i)}{\partial x}\,\delta x_i + \sum_{j=1}^{p} \mu^j(z)$$
$$\left[\sum_{\alpha=1}^{s_i} \lambda_i{}^\alpha \mathbf{f}_i(x_i,u_{ij}{}^\alpha) - \mathbf{f}_i(x_i,\hat{u}_i)\right] + o(\delta z)$$
$$i = 0, 1, \ldots, k-1,\dagger$$

† Let $\mu(z) = (\mu^1(z),\mu^2(z), \ldots ,\mu^p(z))$; then we conclude from (24) that there exists a matrix Y with p rows such that $\mu(z) = Y(z - \hat{z})$. Let $Z_i(z)$ be a matrix with p columns whose jth column is $\Sigma_{\alpha=1}^{s_i} \lambda_i{}^\alpha \mathbf{f}_i(x_i,u_{ij}{}^\alpha) - \mathbf{f}_i(x_i,\hat{u}_i)$; then, from (30), $\mathbf{w}_i(\hat{z} + \delta z) = \mathbf{f}_i(\hat{x}_i + \delta x_i, \hat{u}_i) + z_i(\hat{z} + \delta z)Y\,\delta z$. Now, $\mathbf{f}_i(\hat{x}_i + \delta x_i, \hat{u}_i) = \mathbf{f}_i(\hat{x}_i,\hat{u}_i) + [\partial \mathbf{f}_i(\hat{x}_i,\hat{u}_i)/\partial x]\,\delta x_i + o(\delta x_i)$ and $Z_i(\hat{z} + \delta z)Y\,\delta z = Z_i(\hat{z})Y\,\delta z + o(\delta z)$, and hence (31) follows.

where $\|o(\delta z)\|/\|\delta z\| \to 0$ as $\|\delta z\| \to 0$. Comparing (31) with (27) and taking into account (29), we see that for any $z = \hat{z} + \delta z \in C$, $\zeta(\hat{z} + \delta z) = \hat{z} + \delta z + o(\delta z)$, where $o(\delta z)$ is obviously continuous and satisfies $\|o(\delta z)\|/\|\delta z\| \to 0$ as $\|\delta z\| \to 0$. Hence $C(\hat{z},\Omega')$ is indeed a conical approximation to the set Ω' at $\hat{z}$.

Now that we have established that the set Ω' defined by (19) satisfies the conditions of theorem (6) with respect to the set Ω defined by (17) and the functions $f(\cdot)$ and $r(\cdot)$ defined by (15) and (16), respectively, and that the set $C(\hat{z},\Omega')$ defined by (20) is a conical approximation to the set Ω' at $\hat{z}$, we conclude from theorem (6) that there exists a nonzero vector $\psi = (p^0,\pi)$, with $p^0 \leqq 0$ and $\pi = (-p_1,-p_2, \ldots ,-p_k,\mu_0,\mu_k)$, where $p_i \in E^n$, $\mu_0 \in E^{l_0}$, and $\mu_k \in E^{l_k}$, such that

32 $$p^0\langle\nabla f(\hat{z}),\delta z\rangle + \left\langle \pi, \frac{\partial r(\hat{z})}{\partial z}\,\delta z \right\rangle \leqq 0 \qquad \text{for all } \delta z \in C(\hat{z},\Omega').$$

Substituting for f and r from (15) and (16), respectively, into (32), for all $\delta z \in C(\hat{z},\Omega')$ we get

33 $$p^0 \sum_{i=0}^{k-1} \delta v_i^0 + \sum_{i=0}^{k-1} \langle -p_{i+1},(\delta x_{i+1} - \delta x_i - \delta v_i)\rangle + \left\langle \mu_0, \frac{\partial g_0(x_0)}{\partial x}\,\delta x_0 \right\rangle + \left\langle \mu_k, \frac{\partial g_k(x_k)}{\partial x}\,\delta x_k \right\rangle \leqq 0.$$

As in the preceding section, we now convert the result expressed by (33) into a classical form for necessary conditions, involving a costate, a hamiltonian, and transversality conditions.

34 **Theorem: the maximum principle.** If $(\hat{u}_0,\hat{u}_1, \ldots ,\hat{u}_{k-1})$ is an optimal control sequence and $(\hat{x}_0,\hat{x}_1, \ldots ,\hat{x}_k)$ is an optimal trajectory for control problem (8), then there exist costate vectors $p_0, p_1, \ldots , p_k$ in E^n, multiplier vectors $\lambda_0, \lambda_1, \ldots , \lambda_k$, with $\lambda_i \in E^{m_i}$ satisfying $\lambda_i \leqq 0$, $\mu_0 \in E^{l_0}$, and $\mu_k \in E^{l_k}$, and a scalar $p^0 \leqq 0$ such that:

35 Not all the quantities $p^0, p_0, p_1, \ldots , p_k$, and μ_0,μ_k are zero.

36 The costate vectors p_i satisfy the "forced" adjoint equation

$$p_i - p_{i+1} = \left[\frac{\partial f_i(\hat{x}_i,\hat{u}_i)}{\partial x}\right]^T p_{i+1} + p^0 \left[\frac{\partial f_i^0(\hat{x}_i,\hat{u}_i)}{\partial x}\right]^T + \left[\frac{\partial q_i(\hat{x}_i)}{\partial x}\right]^T \lambda_i \qquad i = 0, 1, \ldots , k - 1.$$

37 At the initial set X_0 the transversality condition

$$p_0 = -\left[\frac{\partial g_0(\hat{x}_0)}{\partial x}\right]^T \mu_0$$

is satisfied.

38 At the terminal set X_k the transversality condition

$$p_k = \left[\frac{\partial g_k(\hat{x}_k)}{\partial x}\right]^T \mu_k + \left[\frac{\partial q_k(\hat{x}_k)}{\partial x}\right]^T \lambda_k$$

is satisfied.

39 $$\langle \lambda_i, q_i(\hat{x}_i)\rangle = 0 \qquad i = 0, 1, \ldots, k.$$

40 For $i = 0, 1, \ldots, k-1$ the hamiltonian $H: E^n \times E^m \times E^n \times E^1 \times \{0, 1, \ldots, k-1\} \to E^1$, defined by

$$H(x,u,p,p^0,i) = p^0 f_i^0(x,u) + \langle p, f_i(x,u)\rangle,$$

satisfies the maximum condition

41 $$H(\hat{x}_i,\hat{u}_i,p_{i+1},p^0,i) \geqq H(\hat{x}_i,u_i,p_{i+1},p^0,i) \qquad \text{for all } u_i \in U_i.$$

This last condition is known as a *maximum principle.*

Proof. Condition (35) was established prior to the statement of the theorem. Now let us turn to (41). Suppose $\delta z = (0,0, \ldots ,0,\delta \mathbf{v}_i,0, \ldots ,0)$ is in $C(z,\Omega')$. Then, from (33), we have

42 $$p^0\, \delta v_i^0 + \langle p_{i+1}, \delta v_i\rangle \leqq 0 \text{ for all } \delta \mathbf{v}_i \in RC(\hat{\mathbf{v}}_i, \text{co } \mathbf{f}_i(\hat{x}_i,U_i)).$$

But $\mathbf{f}_i\,(\hat{x}_i,U_i) \subset \text{co } \mathbf{f}_i\,(\hat{x}_i,U_i) \subset RC(\hat{\mathbf{v}}_i, \text{co } \mathbf{f}_i(\hat{x}_i,U_i))$ and therefore we obtain from (42) that

43 $$p^0[f_i^0(\hat{x}_i,\hat{u}_i) - f_i^0(\hat{x}_i,u_i)] + \langle p_{i+1},[f_i(\hat{x}_i,\hat{u}_i) - f_i(x_i,u_i)]\rangle \geqq 0,$$

which is readily recognized as an expansion of (41). We now observe that the closure of set $RC(\hat{\mathbf{v}}_i, \text{co } \mathbf{f}_i(\hat{x}_i,U_i)) + \{\hat{\mathbf{v}}_i\}$ contains the set $\text{co } \mathbf{f}_i(\hat{x}_i,U_i)$, since the latter is convex, and hence (43) is true for all $u_i \in U_i$, which proves (41).

Now let $\delta z = (0,0, \ldots ,0,\delta x_k,0,0, \ldots ,0)$, with $\delta x_k \in \overline{IC}(x_k,X_k')$. Then (33) yields

44 $$\left\langle -p_k + \left[\frac{\partial g_k(\hat{x}_k)}{\partial x}\right]^T \mu_k,\, \delta x_k \right\rangle \leqq 0 \qquad \text{for all } \delta x_k \in \overline{IC}(\hat{x}_k,X_k'),$$

that is, for all δx_k satisfying $[\partial q_k^j(\hat{x}_k)/\partial x]\, \delta x_k \leqq 0$, with $q_k^j(\hat{x}_k) = 0$ and $j \in \{1,2, \ldots ,m_k\}$. Applying Farkas' lemma (A.5.34), we find that there exists a vector $\lambda_k \leqq 0$ in E^{m_k} such that[1]

45 $$-p_k + \left[\frac{\partial g_k(\hat{x}_k)}{\partial x}\right]^T \mu_k = -\left[\frac{\partial q_k(\hat{x}_k)}{\partial x}\right]^T \lambda_k$$

and $\langle \lambda_k, g_k(\hat{x}_k)\rangle = 0$, that is, such that (38) and (39) are satisfied. Similarly, let $\delta z = (0,0, \ldots, \delta x_i, 0, \ldots, 0, \delta \mathbf{v}_i, 0, \ldots, 0)$ in $C(z,\Omega')$, $i \neq 0$, $i \neq k$, with $\delta \mathbf{v}_i = [\partial \mathbf{f}_k(\hat{x}_i,\hat{u}_i)/\partial x]\, \delta x_i$. Then, from (33), we get

46 $$p^0 \left\langle \frac{\partial f_i^0(\hat{x}_i,\hat{u}_i)}{\partial x}, \delta x_i \right\rangle + \left\langle p_{i+1}, \frac{\partial f_i(\hat{x}_i,\hat{u}_i)}{\partial x} \delta x_i \right\rangle + \langle p_{i+1}, \delta x_i\rangle$$
$$- \langle p_i, \delta x_i\rangle \leqq 0 \qquad \text{for all } \delta x_i \in \overline{IC}(\hat{x}_i, X_i'),$$

that is, for all δx_i satisfying $[\partial q_i^j(\hat{x}_i)/\partial x_i]\, \delta x_i \leqq 0$, when $q_i^j(\hat{x}_i) = 0$, with $j \in \{1,2, \ldots, m_i\}$. Again applying Farkas' lemma, we get (36) and (39). Finally, condition (37) is seen to be merely an arbitrary but consistent definition. □

It is clear at this stage that we can proceed to specialize theorem (34) even further, exactly as we have done in the previous section. However, this is left as an exercise for the reader.

47 **Exercise.** Show that for the problem considered in example (2.4.38) the maximum principle (34) gives the same control law as theorem (2.4.28). □

At first glance, the maximum principle (34) appears to be a considerably stronger result than theorem (1.17). In practice, however, it is difficult to find a problem for which it is more useful than theorem (1.17). However, as will be seen from the following example, the maximum principle (34) may be somewhat easier to apply (provided its assumptions are satisfied, of course).

48 **Example: a minimum-fuel problem.** Given the system

49 $$x_{i+1} - x_i = Ax_i + bu_i \qquad i = 0, 1, \ldots, k-1,$$

where A is an $n \times n$ matrix and b is an $n \times 1$ matrix (that is, $x_i \in E^n$ for $i = 0, 1, \ldots, k$ and $u_i \in E^1$ for $i = 0, 1, \ldots, k-1$), minimize

50 $$\sum_{i=0}^{k-} |u_i|$$

[1] We can now see the effect of assumption (12), that $\nabla g_k^j(x)$ for $j = 1, 2, \ldots, l_k$ are linearly independent. When they are dependent, we may choose $\mu_k \neq 0$ such that $[\partial g_k(x_k)/\partial x]^T \mu_k = 0$ and let $p_0 = p_1 = \cdots = p_k = 0$, $p^0 = 0$, and $\mu_0 = 0$, satisfying the theorem trivially.

subject to the constraint on the input

51 $$|u_i| \leqq 1 \qquad i = 0, 1, \ldots, k-1$$

and to the boundary constraints

52 $$x_0 = \hat{x}_0 \qquad \text{and} \qquad x_k = \hat{x}_k,$$

where $\hat{x}_0$ and $\hat{x}_k$ are given vectors in E^n and x_k is the solution of system (49) at time k corresponding to the initial conditions $x_0 = \hat{x}_0$ and the input sequence $u_0, u_1, \ldots, u_{k-1}$.

First approach. Since $|u_i|$ is not a continuously differentiable function, we cannot apply theorem (1.17) to this problem directly. Hence let us make the following substitution:

53 $$u_i = v_i - w_i \qquad i = 0, 1, \ldots, k-1$$
54 $$|u_i| = v_i + w_i \qquad i = 0, 1, \ldots, k-1$$
55 $$0 \leqq v_i \leqq 1, \qquad 0 \leqq w_i \leqq 1 \qquad i = 0, 1, \ldots, k-1.$$

Note that (54) is valid only if either v_i or w_i is zero for each i. We shall show that this is indeed the case if $\hat{v}_i$ and $\hat{w}_i$, with $i = 0, 1, \ldots, k-1$, are an optimal control sequence for the problem:

56 $$\text{Minimize} \sum_{i=0}^{k-1} (v_i + w_i) \text{ subject to (55), subject to}$$

57 $$x_{i+1} - x_i = Ax_i + b(v_i - w_i),$$

and subject to (52).

Obviously, we can now apply theorem (1.17) to obtain, for $i = 0, 1, \ldots, k-1$,

58 $$p^0(\delta v_i + \delta w_i) + \langle p_{i+1}, b\rangle(\delta v_i - \delta w_i) \leqq 0$$

for all $\delta v_i \in RC(\hat{v}_i, \Omega)$ and $\delta w_i \in RC(\hat{w}_i, \Omega)$, where $\Omega = \{\alpha : 0 \leqq \alpha \leqq 1\}$, p_i is the costate vector defined as in theorem (1.17), and $\hat{v}_i$ and $\hat{w}_i$ for $i = 0, 1, \ldots, k-1$ are optimal control sequences.

By remark (1.49), $p^0 = -1$ in (58), and hence (58) becomes

59 $$(-1 + \langle p_{i+1}, b\rangle)\, \delta v_i - (1 + \langle p_{i+1}, b\rangle)\, \delta w_i \leqq 0.$$

Suppose that $\langle p_{i+1}, b\rangle > 1$. Then for $\delta w_i = 0$ (59) can be satisfied for all $\delta v_i \in RC(\hat{v}_i, \Omega)$ only if

60 $$\delta v_i \leqq 0 \qquad \text{for all } \delta v_i \in RC(\hat{v}_i, \Omega),$$

that is, only if

61 $$\hat{v}_i = +1.$$

Similarly, if we set $\delta v_i = 0$, we find that (58) can be satisfied for all $\delta w_i \in RC(\hat{w}_i,\Omega)$ only if

$$\delta w_i \geqq 0 \qquad \text{for all } \delta w_i \in RC(\hat{w}_i,\Omega);$$

that is, we must have

62 $$\hat{w}_i = 0.$$

Thus when $\langle p_{i+1},b\rangle > 1$, we must have $\hat{v}_i = +1$ and $\hat{w}_i = 0$. Similarly, when $\langle p_{i+1},b\rangle < -1$ we find that

63 $$\hat{v}_i = 0 \qquad \text{and} \qquad \hat{w}_i = +1.$$

Now suppose that $|\langle p_{i+1},b\rangle| < 1$. Then, putting, $\delta v_i = 0$ and $\delta w_i = 0$, consecutively, we find that all must have

64 $$\hat{v}_i = \hat{w}_i = 0.$$

Finally, suppose that $|\langle p_{i+1},b\rangle| = 1$. If $\langle p_{i+1},b\rangle = 1$, then for (59) to hold we must have

65 $$\hat{w}_i = 0$$

(since δw_i must be positive), but $\hat{v}_i$ is not determinable from (59). However, if $\langle p_{i+1},b\rangle = -1$, then, from (59),

66 $$\hat{v}_i = 0$$

(since δv_i must be positive), but $\hat{w}_i$ is not determinable from (59).

The indeterminacy caused by $|\langle p_{i+1},b\rangle| = 1$ must be resolved by recourse to boundary conditions. Thus (62) to (66) indicate the extent to which theorem (1.17) determines the optimal control sequence $\hat{u}_i = \hat{v}_i - \hat{w}_i$ for $i = 0, 1, \ldots, k-1$. Note that either $\hat{v}_i = 0$ or $\hat{w}_i = 0$ in (62) to (66), and hence our substitutions (53) and (54) are valid.

Second approach. Applying the maximum principle (34) to our minimum-fuel problem (48), we find that if $\hat{u}_i$ for $i = 0, 1, \ldots, k-1$ is an optimal control sequence, then it must maximize the hamiltonian

67 $$p^0|u_i| + \langle p_{i+1},Ax_i\rangle + \langle p_{i+1},b\rangle u_i$$

over $u_i \in [-1,+1]$, where, as before, we can show that $p^0 = -1$. Hence with $p^0 = -1$ we get

68 $$\hat{u}_i = \begin{cases} +1 & \text{if } \langle p_{i+1},b\rangle > 1 \\ -1 & \text{if } \langle p_{i+1},b\rangle < -1 \\ 0 & \text{if } |\langle p_{i+1},b\rangle| < 1, \end{cases}$$

and again we find that (67) does not define $\hat{u}_i$ when $|\langle p_{i+1},b\rangle| = 1$.

Both approaches yield exactly the same amount of information in this case, but the second approach is obviously more efficient. □

69 **Exercise.** Suppose that the cost functions $f_i^0(\cdot,\cdot)$ are of the form

70 $$f_i^0(x,u) = f_i^{0\prime}(x) + f_i^{0\prime\prime}(u) \qquad i = 0, 1, \ldots, k-1,$$

where $f_i^{0\prime}$ and $f_i^{0\prime\prime}$ are convex functions, but not necessarily differentiable. Furthermore, suppose that the functions $f_i(\cdot,\cdot)$ are of the form

71 $$f_i(x,u) = A_ix + B_iu \qquad i = 0, 1, \ldots, k-1,$$

where A_i is an $n \times n$ matrix and B_i is an $n \times m$ matrix. Assuming that the sets X_i for $i = 0, 1, \ldots, k$ and U_i for $i = 0, 1, \ldots, k-1$ are convex, use result (2.3.59) to obtain a version of the maximum principle (34) directly for this case. □

72 **Exercise.** In addition to the assumptions made in exercise (69), suppose that the sets $X_i = E^n$ for $i = 1, \ldots, k-1$, that $X_0 = \{\hat{x}_0\}$, that $X_k = \{\hat{x}_k\}$, and that there exists a control sequence $\mathcal{U} = (u_0,u_1, \ldots, u_{k-1})$, with u_i in the relative interior of U_i, such that the resulting trajectory $\mathfrak{X} = (x_0,x_1, \ldots, x_k)$ satisfies $x_0 = \hat{x}_0$ and $\hat{x}_k = \hat{x}_k$. Show that there exist costate vectors $p_0, p_1, \ldots, p_k$ and a scalar $p^0 < 0$ satisfying the conditions of theorem (34). [*Hint:* Proceed as in exercise (1.48), but now with respect to the function $\mathbf{r}(\cdot)$ and the set Ω^* defined in exercise (2.3.55).] □

This concludes our discussion of necessary conditions of optimality for optimal control problems. The reader interested in sufficient conditions will find that he can easily adapt to optimal control problems all the sufficient conditions developed for nonlinear programming problems with convex functions in Section 3.6. The remainder of this book is devoted to computational methods.

REFERENCES

1. M. D. Canon, C. D. Cullum, and E. Polak: Constrained Minimization Problems in Finite Dimensional Spaces, *SIAM J. Control*, **4**:528–547 (1966).
2. H. Halkin: A Maximum Principle of the Pontryagin Type for Systems Described by Nonlinear Difference Equations, *SIAM J. Control*, **4**:90–111 (1966).
3. J. M. Holtzman: On the Maximum Principle for Nonlinear Discrete-time Systems, *IEEE Trans. Automatic Control*, **4**:528–547 (1966).

4. J. B. Rosen: Optimal Control and Convex Programming, *IBM Symp. Control Theory Applications*, pp. 223–237, Yorktown Heights, N.Y., October, 1964.
5. A. I. Propoi: The Maximum Principle for Discrete Control Systems, *Avtomatica i Telemechanica*, **7**:1177–1187 (1965).
6. B. W. Jordan and E. Polak: Theory of a Class of Discrete Optimal Control Systems, *J. Electron. Control*, **17**:697–713 (1964).

5

Optimal control and linear programming

5.1 INTRODUCTION

Beginning with this chapter, we shall examine in detail certain classes of discrete optimal control problems, together with methods for their solution. These problems are characterized by *convex* cost functions, *linear* dynamics, *linear* equality constraints and *convex* inequality constraints. The reason for this restriction is that, by and large, these are the only problems for which satisfactory methods of solution exist. We shall group problems into classes according to the properties of the corresponding Basic Problem (see Sections 1.4 and 1.5).

In this chapter we shall treat a class of discrete optimal control problems for which the corresponding Basic Problem is a linear programming problem of the following form.

1 **The linear programming problem.** Minimize $\langle d,z \rangle$ subject to $Rz = c$, $Pz \leqq \nu$, and $\alpha \leqq z \leqq \beta$, where z, d, α, and β are in E^n, R is an $m \times n$ matrix, P is an $l \times n$ matrix, and $c \in E^m$ and $\nu \in E^l$ (we shall always assume that $\alpha^i < \beta^i$ for $i = 1, 2, \ldots, n$ and that it

is possible to have $\alpha^i = -\infty$ and $\beta^j = \infty$ for any i and j in $\{1,2, \ldots ,n\}$). □

5.2 LINEAR CONTROL PROBLEMS

The first class of problems we shall consider consists of problems in which the dynamics, the cost, and the constraints are all linear or affine.

1 **The linear control problem.** Consider a dynamical system described by the linear difference equation

2 $$x_{i+1} - x_i = Ax_i + Bu_i \qquad i = 0, 1, \ldots , k-1,$$

where $x_i \in E^n$ is the system state at time i, $u_i \in E^m$ is the system input at time i, A is an $n \times n$ matrix, and B is an $n \times m$ matrix. Find a control sequence $\hat{\mathfrak{u}} = (\hat{u}_0,\hat{u}_1, \ldots ,\hat{u}_{k-1})$ and a corresponding trajectory $\hat{\mathfrak{x}} = (\hat{x}_0,\hat{x}_1, \ldots ,\hat{x}_k)$, determined by (2), which minimize the linear cost function

3 $$\sum_{i=0}^{k} \langle d_i',x_i\rangle + \sum_{i=0}^{k-1} \langle d_i'',u_i\rangle,$$

where $d_i' \in E^n$ for $i = 0, 1, \ldots , k$ and $d_i'' \in E^m$ for $i = 0, 1, \ldots , k-1$. The minimization is subject to the constraints

4 $$u_i \in U_i = \{u: F_iu \leqq w_i\} \qquad i = 0, 1, \ldots , k-1$$
5 $$x_i \in X_i' = \{x: H_ix \leqq v_i\} \qquad i = 0, 1, \ldots , k,$$

and in addition, x_0 and x_k are required to satisfy

6 $$G_0x_0 = c_0 \qquad G_kx_k = c_k,$$

where the F_i and w_i for $i = 0, 1, \ldots , k-1$, the H_i and v_i for $i = 0, 1, \ldots , k$, and G_0, G_k, c_0, and c_k are appropriate-dimensional matrices and vectors [of course, some of the matrices in (4) to (6) may be zero]. □

Obviously, problem (1) is a special case of the general optimal control problem (4.1.1). Note, however, that assumptions (4.1.8) to (4.1.10) are not needed for the linear case.

The most straightforward way to reduce the linear control problem (1) to the form of the linear programming problem (1.1) is to follow the method of Section 1.5 for obtaining an equivalent Basic

Problem. Thus, letting $z = (x_0,x_1, \ldots ,x_k,u_0,u_1, \ldots ,u_{k-1})$, we obtain from (1) and (7) that

7 $$r(z) = \begin{bmatrix} x_1 - x_0 - Ax_0 - Bu_0 \\ \cdot \\ \cdot \\ \cdot \\ x_k - x_{k-1} - Ax_{k-1} - Bu_{k-1} \\ G_0x_0 - c_0 \\ G_kx_k - c_k \end{bmatrix} = Rz - c = 0$$

and from (4) and (5) that

8 $$z \in \Omega = \{z: Pz \leqq \nu, \alpha \leqq z \leqq \beta\},$$

where in (7) R is a matrix with $(k + 1)n + km$ columns and at least kn rows and in (8) P is a matrix defined by (4) and (5). The vectors α and β in (8) may or may not be finite.[1] Now, setting

9 $$f(z) = \langle d,z \rangle,$$

with

10 $$d = (d_0',d_1', \ldots ,d_k',d_0'',d_1'', \ldots ,d_{k-1}''),$$

and collecting expressions (3), (7), and (8), we see immediately that we have just rewritten problem (1) in the form of the linear programming problem (1.1).

Although the above method for transcribing problem (1) into the form of a linear programming problem is very direct, it results in a matrix R which usually has a very large number of rows. This makes problem (1) extremely difficult to solve by means of the simplex algorithm unless special codes are used which take advantage of the large number of zeros in R (usually such codes incorporate decomposition methods and are quite sophisticated).

It is possible to transcribe problem (1) into a linear programming problem with a matrix R which has considerably fewer rows than (9). However, this alternate transcription is obtained only at the expense of additional calculation. Thus, solving (2) for x_i, with $i = 1, 2, \ldots , k$, we obtain

11 $$x_i = (I - A)^i x_0 + \sum_{j=0}^{i-1} (I - A)^{i-j-1}Bu_j.$$

[1] In converting the control problem to Basic Problem form it is advantageous not to include constraints for the form $u^i \leqq \delta^i$ into the matrix P, but to collect them all together into the form $\alpha \leqq z \leqq \beta$.

12 **Exercise.** Use (11), together with (3) to (6), to transcribe the linear control problem (1) into the form of problem (1.1), with $z = (x_0, u_0, u_1, \ldots, u_{k-1})$. (*Hint:* See Section 2.4 for guidance.) □

In two-point-boundary-value problems, as well as in other problems with few constraints, the transcription indicated in (12) offers great advantages. However, as the complexity of the constraints increases, this transcription may prove to be less attractive (e.g., see Section 4).

5.3 CONTROL PROBLEMS WITH LINEAR DYNAMICS, LINEAR CONSTRAINTS, AND PIECEWISE-LINEAR COST

The linear control problems by no means exhaust the family of control problems which can be reduced to linear programming problems. In fact, there are a number of important control problems with dynamics (2.2) and constraints (2.4) to (2.6), but with nonlinear cost functions, which also reduce to linear-programming-problem form. We shall consider only two such cases.

We begin by considering a class of optimal control problems with dynamics as in (2.2) and constraints as in (2.4) to (2.6), but with a piecewise-linear cost function, which can be transcribed by either of the techniques used in Section 2, into the form

1 $$\text{Minimize } f(z) = \sum_{i=1}^{\mu} |\langle d_i, z\rangle + \eta^i| \text{ subject to } Rz = c,\ Pz \leqq \nu,$$

and $\alpha \leqq z \leqq \beta$.

When the first method discussed in Section 2 is used to transcribe the optimal control problem into the form (1), the quantities z, α, β, R and c in (1) are related to the control problem in exactly the same manner as in (2.7) and (2.8). The vectors $d_i \in E^{(k+1)n+km}$, the scalars η^i, and the integer μ are derived from the cost function originally given for the optimal control problem (2.1). Consider now the following situations where a piecewise-linear cost will arise.

2 **Example.** In a number of attitude-control systems for space vehicles the control force is obtained by ejecting fuel under pressure. Frequently, the magnitude of the force is proportional to the rate at which fuel is ejected. Under appropriate assumptions about the mode of operation of the system, the control system can be modeled as having dynamics of the form (2.2) and constraints of the form (2.4), (2.5), while the total amount of fuel expended is found to be proportional to the quantity

3 $$\sum_{i=0}^{k-1} \sum_{j=1}^{m} |u_{ij}|.$$

Thus an attempt to minimize the fuel expended in a certain maneuver leads to a cost of the form appearing in problem (1).

4 **Example.** In a number of practical control situations, we may be required to get the state of a dynamical system, such as (2.2), to agree "as closely as possible" with some desired value at a prespecified time k. If the criterion "as closely as possible" is a subjective one, it might be acceptable to take as the definition of magnitude the L_1 norm of the error $x_k - \xi_k$,

5 $$\sum_{i=1}^{n} |x_k^i - \xi_k^i|.$$

where ξ_k is the desired value of x_k, the state at time k. A comparison of the simplex algorithm to be presented in this chapter with the quadratic programming algorithm discussed in Chapter 6 indicates clearly that there are computational advantages in using (5) instead of the more usual euclidean norm.

The reduction of problem (1) to the form of the linear programming problem (1.1) is accomplished by showing that the optimal solutions of (1) can be obtained by solving the following problem.

6 Minimize $\sum_{i=1}^{\mu} (v^i + y^i)$ subject to $Rz = c$, $v^i - y^i = \langle d_i, z\rangle + \eta^i$ for $i = 1, 2, \ldots, \mu$, $Pz \leqq \nu$, $\alpha \leqq z \leqq \beta$, and $v^i \geqq 0$ and $y^i \geqq 0$ for $i = 1, 2, \ldots, \mu$.

It should be clear that this is indeed a linear programming problem, readily identified with form (1.1).

7 **Theorem.** The vector $\hat{z}$ is an optimal solution to problem (1) if and only if $\hat{z}$, together with the vectors $\hat{v}$ and $\hat{y}$, defined by

8 $$\hat{v}^i = \begin{cases} \langle d_i, \hat{z}\rangle + \eta^i & \text{if } \langle d_i, \hat{z}\rangle + \eta^i > 0 \\ 0 & \text{if } \langle d_i, \hat{z}\rangle + \eta^i \leqq 0 \end{cases}$$

and

9 $$\hat{y}^i = \begin{cases} 0 & \text{if } \langle d_i, \hat{z}\rangle + \eta^i \geqq 0 \\ -(\langle d_i, \hat{z}\rangle + \eta^i) & \text{if } \langle d_i, \hat{z}\rangle + \eta^i < 0, \end{cases}$$

$i = 1, 2, \ldots, \mu$, constitute an optimal solution to problem (6).

Proof. Let z be any vector satisfying the constraints of problem (1), that is, $Rz = c$, $Pz \leqq \nu$, and $\alpha \leqq z \leqq \beta$. If, for $i = 1, 2, \ldots, \mu$, we define v^i and y^i as in (8) and (9) above, with z taking the place of $\hat{z}$, then z, together with the v^i and y^i for $i = 1, 2, \ldots, \mu$, satisfies the constraints of problem (6). In addition, the cost function of (6) evaluated for this case becomes

10 $$\sum_{i=1}^{\mu} (v^i + y^i) = \sum_{i=1}^{\mu} |\langle d_i, z\rangle + \eta^i|,$$

which is the same as the cost in (1).

Next we show that if $\hat{z}$, together with $\hat{v}^i$ and $\hat{y}^i$ for $i = 1, 2, \ldots, \mu$, is an optimal solution to problem (6), then these quantities must be related by (8) and (9). To show this it is sufficient to show that $\hat{v}^i$ and $\hat{y}^i$ cannot simultaneously be strictly positive for any $i \in \{1,2, \ldots ,\mu\}$. Then (8) and (9) follow from the constraint that

11 $$\hat{v}^i - \hat{y}^i = \langle d_i, \hat{z}\rangle + \eta^i.$$

Thus suppose that for some i, $\hat{v}^i > 0$ and $\hat{y}^i > 0$. Let us first suppose that $\hat{v}^i \geqq \hat{y}^i$ and define the new variables $\dot{v}^i$ and $\dot{y}^i$ by

12 $$\dot{v}^i = \hat{v}^i - \hat{y}^i \geqq 0 \qquad \text{and} \qquad \dot{y}^i = \hat{y}^i - \hat{y}^i = 0.$$

Then

13 $$\dot{v}^i - \dot{y}^i = \hat{v}^i - \hat{y}^i = \langle d_i, \hat{z}\rangle + \eta^i,$$

and hence if we replace $\hat{v}^i$ and $\hat{y}^i$ by $\dot{v}^i$ and $\dot{y}^i$, respectively, in the optimal solution, we shall still satisfy the constraints. However,

14 $$\dot{v}^i + \dot{y}^i = \hat{v}^i - \hat{y}^i < \hat{v}^i + \hat{y}^i,$$

since $\hat{y}^i > 0$. This contradicts the optimality of $\hat{v}^i$ and $\hat{y}^i$. The case where $\hat{y}^i \geqq \hat{v}^i$ can be disposed of similarly.

It follows immediately from (8), (9), and the above that the optimal cost in (6) is given by

15 $$\sum_{i=1}^{\mu} (\hat{v}^i + \hat{y}^i) = \sum_{i=1}^{\mu} |\langle d_i, \hat{z}\rangle + \eta^i|.$$

The rest of the proof is obvious and we therefore omit it. □

Note that this reduction of problem (1) to a linear programming problem of form (1.1) is obtained only at the expense of increasing the dimensions of the problem. Specifically, we have added as many equality constraints as there are terms in the summation of the cost function, and twice this number of additional variables. This price is more than offset, however, by the fact that the problem can now be solved by means of the very efficient simplex algorithm.

Let us conclude our discussion of optimal control problems which are reducible to form (1.1) with the following, possibly less obvious, case. Consider an optimal control problem with dynamics as in (2.2) and constraints as in (2.4) to (2.6), which can be reduced, by the previously indicated techniques, to the form:

16 Minimize $f(z) = \max_{i \in \{1,2,\ldots,\mu\}} |\langle d_i,z \rangle + \eta^i|$ subject to $Rz = c$, $Pz \leqq \nu$, and $\alpha \leqq z \leqq \beta$.

The criterion in (16) is yet another form of a piecewise-linear function.

17 **Example.** Consider again the problem in example 4, where it was desired to minimize the distance between the actual terminal state x_k and some desired terminal state ξ_k. Instead of the L_1 norm (5), we could choose the L_∞ norm

18 $$\max_{i=1,\ldots,n} |x_k{}^i - \xi_k{}^i|$$

to indicate the deviation from the desired value. □

19 **Example.** Consider a control problem where it is desired to approximate a given trajectory $(\xi_0,\xi_1, \ldots ,\xi_k)$ as closely as possible. We could choose as the distance measure between the actual trajectory $(x_0,x_1, \ldots ,x_k)$ and the desired trajectory the norm

20 $$\max_{\substack{j=0,\ldots,k \\ i=1,\ldots,n}} |x_j{}^i - \xi_j{}^i|.$$

The resulting optimal trajectory is the so-called *Tchebyshev approximation* to $(\xi_0,\xi_1, \ldots ,\xi_k)$. □

Now consider the linear programming problem:

21 Minimize y subject to $Rz = c$, $Pz \leqq \nu$, $y + \langle d_i,z \rangle + \eta^i \geqq 0$ and $y - (\langle d_i,z \rangle + \eta^i) \geqq 0$ for $i = 1, 2, \ldots, \mu$, $\alpha \leqq z \leqq \beta$, and $y \geqq 0$, where R, c, d_i, η^i, α, β, and μ are as defined in (16).

We now relate the solutions of problems (16) and (21).

22 **Theorem.** The vector $\hat{z}$ is an optimal solution to problem (16) if and only if $\hat{z}$, together with

23 $$\hat{y} \triangleq \max_{i=1,\ldots,\mu} |\langle d_i,\hat{z} \rangle + \eta^i|,$$

is an optimal solution to problem (21).

Proof. Clearly, any vector z which is feasible for (16), taken together with a y defined as in (23), is feasible for (21), and vice versa. Suppose that $\hat{z}$ and $\hat{y}$ are an optimal solution for (21), and suppose that

$\hat{z}$ is not an optimal solution to (16). Let z be any optimal solution to (16). Then z, together with the corresponding y defined by (23), is feasible for (21), and it is necessarily true that $y < \hat{y}$, because (23) corresponds to the cost function in (16). This contradicts the optimality of $\hat{z}$ and $\hat{y}$ for (21).

The converse is proved in a similar manner. □

Note that we have considerably increased the dimensions of the problem in going from (16) to (21), which has 2μ inequalities more than (16). Since each of these inequalities must be converted to an equality eventually, we shall have to add still more variables. However, as before, we are now in a position to apply the powerful algorithms of linear programming to this problem.

24 **Exercise.** Perform the reduction to a linear programming problem for the case when $f(z) \triangleq \max_{i=1,\ldots,\mu} (\langle d_i,z\rangle + \eta_i)$ and the constraints are as in (16). □

5.4 THE CANONICAL LINEAR PROGRAMMING PROBLEM

The usual way to deal with a linear programming problem of form (1.1) is to transcribe it into the following form, which is then solved by the simplex algorithm.

1 **The canonical linear programming problem (CLP).** Given an $m \times n$ $(m \leqq n)$ full-rank matrix R and vectors $c \in E^m$ and $d \in E^n$, find a vector $\hat{z} \in E^n$ which minimizes $\langle z,d\rangle$ subject to the constraints

2 $$Rz = c$$
3 $$z \geqq 0. \quad \square$$

Obviously, this problem is a special case of problem (1.1). We shall now see that we can construct from (1.1) an equivalent problem of form (1) (but the resultant matrix R may not have full rank).

4 **Theorem.** Consider the linear programming problem (1.1):

5 Minimize $\langle d,z\rangle$ subject to $Rz = c$, $Pz \leqq \nu$, and $\alpha \leqq z \leqq \beta$. Let $\tilde{\alpha}$ and $\tilde{\beta}$ be vectors in E^n, defined for $i = 1, 2, \ldots, n$ by

6 $$\tilde{\alpha}^i = \begin{cases} \alpha^i & \text{if } -\infty < \alpha^i \\ 0 & \text{if } -\infty = \alpha^i \end{cases}$$

7 $$\tilde{\beta}^i = \begin{cases} \beta^i & \text{if } \beta^i < \infty \\ 0 & \beta^i = \infty. \end{cases}$$

Now consider the derived canonical linear programming problem:

8 Minimize $\langle d,w \rangle$ subject to $Rw = c - R\tilde{\alpha}$, $Pw + y = \nu - P\tilde{\alpha}$, $v + w = \tilde{\beta} - \tilde{\alpha}$, and $v \geqq 0$, $w \geqq 0$, and $y \geqq 0$.

Then $\hat{z}$ is an optimal solution for (5) if and only if $\hat{w} \triangleq \hat{z} - \tilde{\alpha}$, $\hat{v} \triangleq \tilde{\beta} - \hat{z}$, and $\hat{y} \triangleq \nu - P\hat{z}$ constitute an optimal solution for (8).

Proof. Suppose that $\hat{z}$ is an optimal solution to (5), but $\hat{w}$, $\hat{v}$, and $\hat{y}$, defined as above, are not an optimal solution to (8). Then there exists a feasible solution w^*, v^*, and y^* to (8) such that

9 $$\langle d,w^* \rangle + \langle d,\tilde{\alpha} \rangle < \langle d,\hat{w} \rangle + \langle d,\tilde{\alpha} \rangle.$$

Let $z^* = w^* + \tilde{\alpha}$. Then from the relations in (8), $Rz^* = c$, $Pz^* \leqq \nu$, and $\alpha \leqq z^* \leqq \beta$; that is, z^* is feasible. Furthermore, by (9),

10 $$\langle d,z^* \rangle < \langle d,\hat{z} \rangle,$$

which contradicts the optimality of $\hat{z}$.

The converse is established in a similar manner. □

Now let $x = (v,w,y) \in E^{(2n+l)}$, $\tilde{c} = c - R\tilde{\alpha}$, $\tilde{\nu} = \nu - P\tilde{\alpha}$, $\delta = \tilde{\beta} - \tilde{\alpha}$, and

11 $$\tilde{d} = (0,d,0) \in E^{2n+l}.$$

Then (8) becomes:

12 Minimize $\langle \tilde{d},x \rangle$ subject to $x \geqq 0$ and

$$\tilde{R}x = \begin{bmatrix} I & I & 0 \\ R & 0 & 0 \\ P & 0 & I \end{bmatrix} \begin{bmatrix} v \\ w \\ y \end{bmatrix} = \begin{bmatrix} \delta \\ \tilde{c} \\ \tilde{\nu} \end{bmatrix}.$$

The matrix $\tilde{R}$ is $(n + m + l) \times (2n + l)$ dimensional and will obviously have full rank if and only if the matrix R has full rank. Thus the full-rank property is preserved in the transcription; however, the number of equations and variables has increased considerably. Consequently, we shall examine, in Section 9, an algorithm which requires more logic operations than the simplex algorithm but which solves linear programming problems of the form: Minimize $\langle d,z \rangle$ subject to $Rz = c$ and $\alpha \leqq z \leqq \beta$ when both α and β are finite vectors. This form frequently arises in optimal control problems such as the minimum-fuel problem (4.2.48).

5.5 CHARACTERIZATION OF AN OPTIMAL SOLUTION TO THE CANONICAL LINEAR PROGRAMMING PROBLEM

We begin by obtaining necessary and sufficient conditions of optimality for the canonical linear programming problem (4.1). Note that we may appeal to theorems (3.3.5) and (3.6.1), because the cost function $\langle d,z\rangle$ is convex and the constraints $Rz = c$ and $z \geqq 0$ are affine. In the context of CLP (4.1), theorems (3.3.5) and (3.6.1) combine to yield the following result.

1 **Theorem.** A feasible solution $z \in E^n$ to CLP (4.1) is an optimal solution if and only if there exists a vector $\psi = (\psi^1,\psi^2, \ldots ,\psi^m) \in E^m$ such that for $i = 1, 2, \ldots , n$

2
$$\begin{aligned} \langle r_i,\psi\rangle - d^i &= 0 \qquad \text{if } z^i > 0 \\ \langle r_i,\psi\rangle - d^i &\leqq 0 \qquad \text{if } z^i = 0, \end{aligned}$$

where r_i is the ith column of R and d^i is the ith component of d.

Proof. Applying theorems (3.3.5) and (3.6.1), we conclude that a feasible solution z to CLP (4.1) is optimal if and only if there exist vectors $\psi \in E^m$ and $\mu \in E^n$ such that for $i = 1, 2, \ldots , n$

3
$$-d^i + \langle r_i,\psi\rangle + \mu^i = 0 \qquad \mu^i \geqq 0 \qquad \mu^i z^i = 0.$$

Obviously, (3) implies (2), and, by inspection, (2) implies the existence of a vector $\mu \in E^n$ satisfying (3). □

From a geometric point of view, it is clear that the constraint set $\Omega' = \{z \in E^n: Rz = c, z \geqq 0\}$ is a convex polyhedron and that the equation $\langle d,z\rangle$ = constraint specifies a hyperplane. Consequently, assuming that Ω' is not empty, to solve CLP (4.1) we must shift this hyperplane, parallel to itself, as far as possible in the direction of the vector $-d$, while still maintaining contact with the set Ω'. Since the boundaries of Ω' are portions of linear manifolds (planes), it is clear that the optimal cost plane ($\langle d,z\rangle = \langle d,\hat{z}\rangle$, with $\hat{z}$ an optimal solution) may contact the set Ω' along an entire face or edge; i.e., there may be many solutions. It is also clear that when Ω' is unbounded the optimal cost $\langle d,z\rangle$ might possibly be $-\infty$, in which case we shall say that CLP (4.1) has no solution. The simplex algorithm which will be presented later has a feature to establish whether the set Ω' is empty and whether $\langle d,z\rangle$ is unbounded on Ω'. Consequently, there is no need for a separate test to establish the existence of optimal solutions.

It is clear from the above that if the canonical linear programming problem (4.1) has an optimal solution, then either this solution is an extreme point (see Appendix A) of the convex polyhedron Ω' or else there exists another optimal solution which is an extreme point of Ω'. We shall now obtain a characterization of extreme points of Ω' and establish formally the existence of extreme point optimal solutions.

4 **Definition.** Let z be a feasible solution to CLP (4.1); that is, $z \in \Omega' = \{z: Rz = c, z \geqq 0\}$. Then the index sets $I(z)$ and $\bar{I}(z)$ are defined by

$$I(z) = \{i \in \{1,2, \ldots ,n\}: z^i = 0\}$$
$$\bar{I}(z) = \{i \in \{1,2, \ldots ,n\}: z^i > 0\};$$

that is, $I(z)$ is the *active-constraints index set* [cf. (3.4.1)]. □

5 **Exercise.** Show that a vector $\hat{z} \in \Omega' = \{z: Rz = c, z \geqq 0\}$ is an extreme point of Ω' if and only if the set of vectors $\{r_i: i \in \bar{I}(z)\}$ are linearly independent, where r_i is the ith column of the matrix R. [*Hint:* Use the fact that for any $\hat{z} \in \Omega'$, $\hat{z} = \sum_{i \in \bar{I}(\hat{z})} \hat{z}^i e_i$, where for $i = 1, 2, \ldots, n$ the $e_i = (0,0,0,1,0, \ldots ,0)$ are the usual unit basis vectors for E^n, and hence $R\hat{z} = \sum_{i=1}^{n} \hat{z}^i r_i = \sum_{i \in \bar{I}(\hat{z})} \hat{z}^i r_i$.] □

The existence of an extreme-point optimal solution for the canonical linear programming problem (4.1) is now concluded from the following result.

6 **Theorem.** If there exists an optimal solution to CLP (4.1), then there exists an optimal solution $\hat{z}$ such that the vectors in the set $\{r_i: i \in \bar{I}(\hat{z})\}$ are linearly independent.

Proof. Let z_0 be any optimal solution to CLP (4.1), and suppose that the vectors in the set $\{r_i: i \in \bar{I}(z_0)\}$ are linearly dependent. Then there exist scalars γ^i, with $i \in \bar{I}(z_0)$ and not all zero, such that

7 $$\sum_{i \in \bar{I}(z_0)} \gamma^i r_i = 0.$$

For any real number θ let $z(\theta) \in E^n$ be a vector whose components are

8 $$z^i(\theta) = \begin{cases} z_0{}^i = 0 & \text{if } i \in I(z_0) \\ z_0{}^i + \theta\gamma^i & \text{if } i \in \bar{I}(z_0). \end{cases}$$

It follows immediately that for any θ

9 $$\begin{aligned} Rz(\theta) &= \sum_{i=1}^{n} z^i(\theta) r_i \\ &= \sum_{i \in \bar{I}(z_0)} z_0{}^i r_i + \theta \sum_{i \in \bar{I}(z_0)} \gamma^i r_i = c. \end{aligned}$$

Thus $z(\theta)$ satisfies the equality constraints of CLP (4.1) for any value of θ. Since $z(\theta)$ differs from z_0 only in those components of z_0 which originally satisfied $z_0{}^i > 0$, it is clear that $z(\theta)$ will satisfy

$z(\theta) \geqq 0$ for all values of θ which are sufficiently small. Hence $z(\theta) \in \Omega'$ for all θ sufficiently small. By direct calculation,

10 $$\begin{aligned}\langle d, z(\theta)\rangle &= \sum_{i=1}^{n} d^i z^i(\theta) \\ &= \sum_{i \in \bar{I}(z_0)} d^i z_0^{\,i} + \theta \sum_{i \in \bar{I}(z_0)} \gamma^i d_i = \langle d, z_0\rangle + \theta \sum_{i \in \bar{I}(z_0)} \gamma^i d_i.\end{aligned}$$

It now follows that $\sum_{i \in \bar{I}(z_0)} \gamma^i d^i = 0$, for otherwise we could choose a $\theta \neq 0$ such that $z(\theta)$ is feasible and $\langle d, z(\theta)\rangle < \langle d, z_0\rangle$, which contradicts the optimality of z_0.

Now, there must be at least one $\gamma^i \neq 0$ in (7), and we may therefore assume that there is at least one $\gamma^i < 0$ for $i \in \bar{I}(z_0)$. Hence we may define

11 $$\theta_1 = \max \{\theta > 0 \colon z^i(\theta) = z_0^{\,i} + \theta\gamma^i \geqq 0,\ i \in \bar{I}(z_0)\}.$$

Clearly, by (9) to (11), $z(\theta_1)$ is also an optimal solution to CLP (4.1). Furthermore, since there is at least one $\gamma^i < 0$ for $i \in \bar{I}(z_0)$, we must have, for $z_1 \triangleq z(\theta_1)$,

12 $$\bar{I}(z_1) \subset \bar{I}(z_0),$$

and the inclusion is proper, by (11). Hence the cardinality of $\bar{I}(z_1)$ is at least one less than the cardinality of $\bar{I}(z_0)$.

If z_1 does not satisfy the property that the vectors in the set $\{r_i \colon i \in \bar{I}(z_1)\}$ are linearly independent, we may repeat the above process to obtain an optimal vector z_2, with the cardinality of $\bar{I}(z_2)$ again strictly smaller than the cardinality of $\bar{I}(z_1)$. Clearly, this process must terminate in a finite number of steps. □

Since the polyhedron Ω' must have a finite number of vertices, it is clear that an optimal solution (if it exists) can be found simply by enumeration, i.e., in a finite number of steps. The simplex algorithm we are about to examine is a systematic and very efficient procedure for finding an optimal extreme point.

5.6 SOME PRELIMINARY REMARKS ON THE SIMPLEX ALGORITHM

In Section 5 we observed that an optimal solution to the canonical linear programming problem (4.1) must be a point of the convex polyhedron $\Omega' = \{z \colon Rz = c,\ z \geqq 0\}$ which is located as far as possible in the direction of the vector $-d$. In exercise (5.5) and theorem (5.6) we established that if CLP (4.1) has a solution, then it has a solution which is also an extreme point of the convex set Ω'. The simplex algorithm proceeds in the following way.

First we find an extreme point z_0 of Ω'. Then we calculate the direction cosines of all the edges of Ω' leading away from this point, in order to determine the edges of Ω' which make an acute angle with $-d$. By following such an edge from the extreme point z_0, either (*a*) we reach an adjacent extreme point z_1 of Ω', with $\langle d,z_1\rangle < \langle d,z_0\rangle$, or (*b*) along this edge $\langle d,z\rangle \to -\infty$. If (*b*) occurs, CLP (4.1) does not have an optimal solution (since we do not accept $-\infty$ as an optimal value). If (*a*) occurs, the above process is repeated until no edge emanating from the current extreme point makes an acute angle with $-d$, and CLP (4.1) is solved.

Conceptually, we see that this algorithm is rather elementary. The question, of course, is whether the calculations can be carried out in an efficient manner. We shall see that they can be.

The algorithm divides naturally into two subprocedures, each of which we shall consider separately in the following sections.[1] The first subprocedure solves the problem of finding an initial extreme point z_0 of Ω', which is required to initiate the simplex algorithm. The second subprocedure is used for finding extreme points z_i, adjacent[2] to a given extreme point z_0, with the property that $\langle d,z_i\rangle < \langle d,z_0\rangle$.

Before proceeding any further, let us introduce some new notation and terminology.

1 **Definition.** A vector $z \in E^n$ is said to be a *basic solution* to CLP (4.1) if z is a feasible solution and the vectors in the set $\{r_i : i \in \bar{I}(z)\}$ are linearly independent [see (5.4)]. □

2 **Definition.** A vector $z \in E^n$ is said to be a *nondegenerate basic solution* to CLP (4.1) if z is a basic solution and the vectors in the set $\{r_i : i \in \bar{I}(z)\}$ form a basis for E^m. □

3 **Remark.** It is clear from exercise (5.5) that a basic solution to CLP (4.1) is an extreme point of Ω', and hence we shall use the term *extreme point* and *basic solution* interchangeably. However, in many texts on linear programming the term *basic solution* is given preference. □

4 **Remark.** A basic solution z can have at most m positive components z^i, whereas a nondegenerate basic solution z has exactly m positive components z^i. □

[1] The division of the algorithm into subprocedures is convenient in exposition. For computational purposes the two subprocedures can be merged [2].

[2] Two extreme points of a closed convex polyhedron are called *adjacent* if the line connecting them is an edge of the polyhedron.

Given a feasible solution z to CLP (4.1), we can always determine whether z is a basic solution (an extreme point of Ω') by checking the linear independence of the vectors $\{r_i: i \in \bar{I}(z)\}$. When z is a nondegenerate basic solution to CLP (4.1), these vectors form a basis for E^m, the significance of which will become apparent later. Let us note, however, that it is always possible to associate a set of m linearly independent columns of R with a basic solution z in the following way.

5 **Definition.** Let z be a basic solution to CLP (4.1). We shall mean by a *basis-indicator set* of z any index set $\bar{J}(z) \subset \{1,2, \ldots ,n\}$ with the following properties:

6 $\bar{I}(z) \subset \bar{J}(z)$.

7 The vectors $\{r_i: i \in \bar{J}(z)\}$ are a basis for E^m. □

(If z is a nondegenerate basic solution, then, of course, $\bar{J}(z) = \bar{I}(z)$.)

8 **Lemma.** Suppose z is a basic solution to CLP (4.1). Then there exists a basis-indicator set $\bar{J}(z) \subset \{1,2, \ldots ,n\}$ satisfying (6) and (7).

Proof. The vectors in the set $\{r_i: i \in \bar{I}(z)\}$ are linearly independent, since z is a basic solution. If the cardinality of $\bar{I}(z)$ is m, we are done. Since, by assumption, the rank of the matrix R is m (that is, there is at least one set of m linearly independent columns of R), we can always find a sufficient number of additional columns of R, say, $\{r_i: i \in K(z)\}$, with $K(z) \cap \bar{I}(z) = \phi$, such that the vectors in the set $\{r_i: i \in [\bar{I}(z) \cup K(z)] \triangleq \bar{J}(z)\}$ form a basis E^m. □

This concludes our preliminary remarks, and we are now ready to examine the problem of initializing the simplex algorithm.

5.7 PROCEDURE FOR DETERMINING AN INITIAL EXTREME POINT OF Ω'

As indicated in the preceding section, to apply the simplex algorithm to the canonical linear programming problem (4.1), we must first obtain an initial basic solution to constraints (4.2), (4.3), that is, a vector z_0 satisfying

1 $$Rz = c$$

2 $$z \geqq 0,$$

with the property that the columns r_i, with $i \in \bar{I}(z)$, of the matrix R are linearly independent. To compute such a z_0 we proceed as follows.

Step 1. Multiply every strictly negative component of c, together with the corresponding row of R in (1), by -1. At the end of this step we have a new system of equations of form (1), with the new $c \geqq 0$. We therefore proceed on the assumption that $c \geqq 0$ in (1).

Step 2. Use the simplex algorithm to solve the linear programming problem:

3 $$\text{Minimize } \sum_{i=1}^{m} \xi^i \text{ subject to the constraints}$$

4 $$Rz + \xi = c \qquad z \geqq 0 \qquad \xi \geqq 0.$$

Note that the $m \times (n + m)$ matrix

5 $$[R \vdots I]$$

has rank m, since the identity matrix I has rank m. Furthermore, note that $\tilde{z} = 0$ and $\tilde{\xi} = c$ constitute a basic solution to (4) which can be used as a starting point for the simplex algorithm in solving problem (3).

Note that $\sum_{i=1}^{m} \xi^i \geqq 0$ for all (z,ξ) satisfying (4). Hence if there is a $z \geqq 0$ such that $Rz = c$, and (z_0,ξ_0) is any optimal solution to problem (3), then $\xi_0 = 0$, and z_0 is a feasible solution to constraints (1) and (2). Furthermore, if (z_0,ξ_0) is obtained by means of the simplex algorithm, the columns of the matrix $[R \vdots I]$ associated with the strictly positive elements of (z_0,ξ_0) will be linearly independent; that is, z_0 will be a basic solution to (1) and (2). □

5.8 GENERATING IMPROVED ADJACENT EXTREME POINTS

Let z_0 be a basic solution to the canonical linear programming problem (4.1), and let $\bar{J}(z_0)$ be a basis-indicator set, defined as in (6.5); that is, $z_0{}^i \geqq 0$ for $i \in \bar{J}(z)$ and the set of vectors $\{r_i \colon i \in \bar{J}(z_0)\}$ form a basis for E^m. Then we may write

1 $$z_0 = \sum_{i \in \bar{J}(z_0)} z_0^i e_i,$$

where for $i = 1, 2, \ldots, n$, $e_i = (0,0, \ldots ,0,1,0, \ldots ,0) \in E^n$ are the usual unit basis vectors whose ith component is 1 and whose other components are zero.

Let $j \in J(z_0)$, the complement of $\bar{J}(z_0)$ in $\{1,2, \ldots ,n\}$. Then there exist scalars $\alpha_j{}^i$ for $i \in \bar{J}(z_0)$ such that

2 $$r_j = \sum_{i \in \bar{J}(z_0)} \alpha_j{}^i r_i.$$

Since z_0 is a basic solution to CLP (4.1), we have from (1) that

3 $$Rz_0 = \sum_{i \in \bar{J}'(z_0)} z_0^i r_i = c.$$

Hence if (2) is multiplied by any scalar $\theta \geqq 0$ and added to (3), we get, on rearranging terms,

4 $$\sum_{i \in \bar{J}(z)} (z_0^i - \theta \alpha_j^i) r_i + \theta r_j = c.$$

Suppose that $\alpha_j^i > 0$ for at least one $i \in \bar{J}(z_0)$.† Then let

5 $$\theta_0 = \min \left\{ \frac{z_0^i}{\alpha_j^i} : i \in \bar{J}(z_0),\ \alpha_j^i > 0 \right\} = \frac{z^k}{\alpha_j^k},$$

with the minimum taking place for $i = k$ (if ties occur, choose the smallest index k). It is easy to see that

6 $$z_0^k - \theta_0 \alpha_j^k = 0$$

and

7 $$z_0^i - \theta_0 \alpha_j^i \geqq 0 \qquad \text{for all } i \in \bar{J}(z_0).$$

Now let

8 $$z_1 = \sum_{i \in \bar{J}(z_0)} (z_0^i - \theta_0 \alpha_j^i) e_i + \theta_0 e_j.$$

From (6) and (7) we see that $z_1 \geqq 0$, and from (4) we see that $Rz_1 = c$; hence z_1 is a feasible solution to CLP (4.1).

We shall now show that z_1 is a basic solution, i.e., that the columns r_i of R, corresponding to the strictly positive components z_1^i, are linearly independent. To this end we define the index set $\bar{J}(z_1)$ by

9 $$\bar{J}(z_1) = \bar{J}(z_0) - \{k\} + \{j\},$$

where k is an index for which the minimum in (5) occurred and $j \in J(z_0)$ is as in (2) and (8). We shall show that $\bar{J}(z_1)$ conforms to definition (6.5), that is, that the vectors r_i for $i \in \bar{J}(z_1)$ form a basis for E^m. Note that if $i \in \bar{J}(z_1)$, then $z_1^i \geqq 0$, and if $i \in J(z_1)$, the complement of $\bar{J}(z_1)$ in $\{1,2, \ldots ,n\}$, then $z_1^i = 0$.

Suppose that the set of vectors $\{r_i\colon i \in \bar{J}(z_1)\}$ are linearly dependent. Then there exist scalars β^i for $i \in \bar{J}(z_1)$, not all zero, such that

$$\sum_{i \in \bar{J}(z_1)} \beta^i r_i = 0.$$

† When $\alpha_j^i \leqq 0$ for all the $i \in \bar{J}(z_0)$ and $j \in J(z_0)$ there are no extreme points adjacent to z_0 [see exercise (12)].

We claim that $\beta^j \neq 0$, for otherwise, by (9), we would have

10 $$\sum_{\substack{i \in \bar{J}(z_0) \\ i \neq k}} \beta^i r_i = 0,$$

which is impossible because the vectors $\{r_i: i \in \bar{J}(z_0)\}$ are linearly independent (and hence any subset of these vectors is linearly independent). We may therefore write

11 $$r_j = \sum_{\substack{i \in \bar{J}(z_0) \\ i \neq k}} \frac{\beta^i}{\beta^j} r_i.$$

Comparing (2) and (11) and again using the fact that the vectors in the set $\{r_i: i \in J(z_0)\}$ are linearly independent, we conclude that $\alpha_j^k = 0$ in (2). But this is a contradiction, since, by assumption, $\alpha_j^k > 0$. We must therefore conclude that the vectors in the set $\{r_i: i \in \bar{J}(z_1)\}$ are linearly independent, and hence that z_1 is a basic solution to CLP (4.1).

12 **Exercise.** Show that the extreme points z_0 and z_1 discussed above are adjacent extreme points. Also show that if all the α_j^i for $i \in \bar{J}(z_0)$ are negative or zero in (2) for all $j \in J(z_0)$, then z_0 is the only extreme point of $\Omega' = \{z: Rz = 0, z \geqq 0\}$. □

We can summarize the above procedure as follows.

13 **Procedure for computing adjacent extreme points.** Let $z_0 = \sum_{i \in \bar{J}(z_0)} z_0^i e_i$ be a basic solution to CLP (4.1), and let $\bar{J}(z_0)$ be an associated basis indicator set.

a. Find an index $j \in J(z_0)$ such that at least one α_j^i, with $i \in \bar{J}(z_0)$, in (2) is positive.

b. Compute θ_0 according to (5).

c. Compute the adjacent extreme point according to (8).

d. Compute the new basis-indicator set according to (9). □

14 **Remark.** Suppose that the extreme point z_1 was obtained from the extreme point z_0 by the above procedure. Referring to (9), we find that we can express this by saying "the extreme point z_1 was obtained from z_0 by exchanging the index $j \in J(z_0)$ for the index $k \in \bar{J}(z_0)$." □

It is important to note here that although z_0 and z_1, as computed above, are adjacent extreme points, it may very well be that

$z_0 = z_1$. To see why this is possible, let us return to expression (5),

$$\theta_0 = \min \left\{ \frac{z_0^i}{\alpha_j^i} : i \in \bar{J}(z_0),\ \alpha_j^i > 0 \right\}.$$

Now suppose that $z_0^k = 0$ for some $k \in \bar{J}(z_0)$ (that is, z_0 is a degenerate basic solution) and that $\alpha_j^k > 0$. Then, obviously, $\theta_0 = 0$, and according to (8), $z_1 = z_0$. If, however, $\theta_0 > 0$, then $z_1 \neq z_0$. It is common in mathematical programming literature to invoke a nondegeneracy assumption which precludes the occurrence of $\theta_0 = 0$ in (5). This assumption considerably simplifies the presentation of the simplex algorithm.

15 **Nondegeneracy assumption.** Every basic solution is a nondegenerate basic solution. □

16 **Remark.** When assumption (15) is satisfied, the vectors in the set $\{r_i : i \in \bar{I}(z_0)\}$ form a basis for E^m, and so $\bar{J}(z_0) = \bar{I}(z_0)$ in (2). Consequently, in (5), $z_0^i > 0$ for all $i \in \bar{J}(z_0)$, which means that $\theta > 0$, that is, that $z_1 \neq z_0$. □

After describing the simplex algorithm under the simplifying assumption (15), we shall examine a method for resolving degeneracies, i.e., for proceeding when some of the basic solutions are degenerate. In the meantime, to avoid confusion we shall state explicitly in theorems, remarks, etc., whether assumption (15) is required or not.

The following is one of the most important properties of procedure (13) when the nondegeneracy assumption applies. We shall make heavy use of this property in Section 6.11, where convergence of quadratic programming algorithms is considered.

17 **Theorem.** Suppose that all the basic solutions to the system $Rz = c$ and $z \geqq 0$ are nondegenerate. If the extreme point z_1 of the set $\{z : Rz = c,\ z \geqq 0\}$ was obtained from the extreme point z_0 by exchanging some index $\alpha \in I(z_0)$ for the index $\beta \in \bar{I}(z_0)$ [that is, $\bar{I}(z_1) = \bar{I}(z_0) + \{\alpha\} - \{\beta\}$], then z_0 is the unique extreme point which can be obtained from z_1 by exchanging the index $\beta \in I(z_1)$ for some index $\gamma \in \bar{I}(z_1)$ (that is, $\gamma = \alpha$). □

Since this is an easy theorem to establish, its proof is left as an exercise for the reader.

Now let us return to our initial basic solution introduced in (1). From (4) we define for $\theta \geqq 0$

18 $$z(\theta) = \sum_{i \in \bar{J}(z_0)} (z_0^i - \theta\alpha_j^i)e_i + \theta e_j,$$

where $j \in J(z_0)$ and the $\alpha_j{}^i$ are as in (2). Hence the cost associated with this vector is

19
$$\begin{aligned}\langle d, z(\theta)\rangle &= \sum_{i \in \bar{J}(z_0)} d^i(z_0{}^i - \theta\alpha_j{}^i) + \theta d^j \\ &= \langle d, z_0\rangle - \theta\Big(\sum_{i \in \bar{J}(z_0)} d^i\alpha_j{}^i - d^j\Big).\end{aligned}$$

To interpret (19) we must bring in a little more detail.

20 **Definition.** Given a basic solution z_0 to CLP (4.1) and its associated basis-indicator set $\bar{J}(z_0)$, we define $R_{\bar{J}(z_0)}$ to be the $m \times m$ nonsingular matrix whose columns are the linearly ordered vectors r_i for $i \in \bar{J}(z_0)$, $d_{\bar{J}(z_0)} \in E^m$ to be the vector whose components are the linearly ordered elements d^i for $i \in \bar{J}(z_0)$, and $\alpha_{\bar{J}(z_0)}$ for every $j \in J(z_0)$ to be the vector whose components are the linearly ordered coefficients $\alpha_j{}^i$ for $i \in \bar{J}(z_0)$, as determined by (2) (the ordering is on i). □

It follows immediately from (20) and (2) that

21
$$\alpha_{\bar{J}(z_0)} = R^{-1}_{\bar{J}(z_0)} r_j$$

and from (19) to (21) that

22
$$\sum_{i \in \bar{J}(z_0)} d^i\alpha_j{}^i = \langle d_{\bar{J}(z_0)}, \alpha_{\bar{J}(z_0)}\rangle = \langle (R^T_{\bar{J}(z_0)})^{-1} d_{\bar{J}(z_0)}, r_j\rangle.$$

Now let

23
$$\psi_{\bar{J}(z_0)} \triangleq (R^T_{\bar{J}(z_0)})^{-1} d_{\bar{J}(z_0)}.$$

Then, substituting from (23) into (22) and hence into (19), we obtain

24
$$\langle d, z(\theta)\rangle = \langle d, z_0\rangle - \theta(\langle \psi_{\bar{J}(z_0)}, r_j\rangle - d^j).$$

We now come to the following conclusions.

Case 1. For a given $j \in J(z_0)$ suppose that there is at least one $\alpha_j{}^i > 0$, as defined by (2), and $\langle \psi_{\bar{J}(z_0)}, r_j\rangle - d^j > 0$. Then z_1, as given by (8), is an extreme point adjacent to z_0, with equal or lower associated cost

25
$$\langle d, z_1\rangle = \langle d, z_0\rangle - \theta_0(\langle \psi_{\bar{J}(z_0)}, r_j\rangle - d^j) \leqq \langle d, z_0\rangle.$$

If z_0 is a nondegenerate basic solution, then, by remark (16), $\theta_0 > 0$ in (25), and strict inequality holds; that is, $\langle d, z_1\rangle < \langle d, z_0\rangle$. When z_0 is degenerate θ_0 may well be zero.

Case 2. For a given $j \in J(z_0)$ suppose that $\alpha_j{}^i \leqq 0$ for all $i \in \bar{J}(z_0)$ in (2) and that $\langle \psi_{\bar{J}(z_0)}, r_j \rangle - d^j > 0$. Then every vector on the ray $\{z(\theta): \theta \geqq 0\}$ defined by (19) is feasible [see (4) and (17)], and $\langle d, z(\theta) \rangle \to -\infty$ as $\theta \to \infty$, by (24). Hence CLP (4.1) has no solution (in the sense that we do not accept $-\infty$ as an optimal value).

Case 3. For every $j \in J(z_0)$ suppose that the conditions of case 2 do not arise and that

26 $$\langle \psi_{\bar{J}(z_0)}, r_j \rangle - d^j \leqq 0 \qquad \text{for all } j \in J(z_0).$$

Then z_0 is optimal, since (23), together with (26), is identical to (5.2).

27 **Remark.** The above result simply confirms the intuitively obvious fact that if the cost hyperplane $\{z: \langle d, z \rangle = \text{constant}\}$ touches the polyhedron $\Omega' = \{z: Rz = 0,\ z \geqq 0\}$ at a vertex z_0, and all the vertices adjacent to and rays emanating from z_0 are on the higher-cost side of this hyperplane, then the entire polyhedron Ω' must be on the higher-cost side, and hence z_0 must be optimal. □

5.9 THE SIMPLEX ALGORITHM

We now combine the procedures described in the preceding sections into an algorithm for solving the canonical linear programming problem (4.1).

1 **Initialization.** Find a basic solution to the system of equations and inequalities

2 $$Rz = c \qquad z \geqq 0.$$

If a basic solution is not readily available, use the simplex algorithm below to solve the linear programming problem:

3 $$\text{Minimize } \sum_{i=1}^{m} \xi^i \text{ subject to the constraints}$$

$$Rz + \xi = c \qquad z \geqq 0 \qquad \xi \geqq 0.$$

We may assume that $c \geqq 0$ without loss of generality.[1] As a basic solution to (3) we may take $z = 0$ and $\xi = c$. If $(\hat{z}, \hat{\xi})$ is an optimal solution to (3) obtained by means of the simplex algorithm, and if $\hat{\xi} = 0$, then $\hat{z}$ is a basic solution to system (2). If $\hat{\xi} \neq 0$, then CLP (4.1) has no feasible solutions. □

[1] We can always ensure that $c \geqq 0$ in (1) by multiplying the negative components of c, together with the corresponding rows of R, by -1.

4 **The simplex algorithm.** Let z_0 be a basic solution to CLP (4.1), and let $\bar{J}(z_0)$ be an associated basis-indicator set [see (6.8)].

Step 1. Compute $\psi_{\bar{J}(z_0)}$ according to

5 $$\psi_{\bar{J}(z_0)} = (R^T_{\bar{J}(z_0)})^{-1} d_{\bar{J}(z_0)},$$

where $R^T_{\bar{J}(z_0)}$ is an $m \times m$ nonsingular matrix with rows r_{i_k} for $k = 1, 2, \ldots, m$, with $i_k \in \bar{J}(z_0)$, and $d_{\bar{J}(z_0)}$ is an m vector whose components are d^{i_k} for $k = 1, 2, \ldots, m$, with $i_k \in \bar{J}(z_0)$ [see (8.20)].

Step 2. If $\langle r_j, \psi_{\bar{J}(z_0)}\rangle - d^j \leqq 0$ for all $j \in J(z_0)$, then stop, since z_0 is an optimal solution to CLP (4.1) [see (8.26)]. Otherwise let $j \in J(z_0)$ be the smallest (any) index such that $\langle r_j, \psi_{\bar{J}(z_0)}\rangle - d^j > 0$, and go to step 3.

Step 3. Determine the coefficients $\alpha_j{}^i$ for $i \in \bar{J}(z)$ satisfying

6 $$r_j = \sum_{i \in \bar{J}(z_0)} \alpha_j{}^i r_i,$$

where $j \in J(z_0)$ is the index obtained in step 2. Note that

7 $$\alpha_{\bar{J}(z_0)} = R^{-1}_{\bar{J}(z_0)} r_j,$$

where $\alpha_{\bar{J}(z_0)} = (\alpha_j{}^{i_1}, \alpha_j{}^{i_2}, \ldots, \alpha_j{}^{i_m})$ [see (8.21)]. If some $\alpha_j{}^i > 0$ for $i \in \bar{J}(z_0)$, go to step 4. Otherwise stop, since CLP (4.1) has no optimal solution.

Step 4. Determine θ_0 according to

8 $$\theta_0 = \min \left\{ \frac{z_0{}^i}{\alpha_j{}^i} : i \in \bar{J}(z_0),\ \alpha_j{}^i > 0 \right\} = \frac{z_0{}^k}{\alpha_j{}^k}.$$

If ties occur in (8), choose the smallest index k which satisfies (8). Set

9 $$z_1 = \sum_{i \in \bar{J}(z)} (z_0{}^i - \theta \alpha_j{}^i) e_i + \theta_0 e_j$$

and

10 $$\bar{J}(z_1) = \bar{J}(z_0) - \{k\} + \{j\}.$$

Then z_1 is a basic solution, and $\bar{J}(z_1)$ is an associated basis-indicator set. Set $z_0 = z_1$ and return to step 1. □

11 **Theorem.** Suppose that every basic solution to CLP (4.1) is a nondegenerate basic solution. Then the simplex algorithm reaches either the stop condition in step 2 (z_0 is an optimal solution) or the stop condition in step 3 (the problem has no solution) in a finite number of steps.

Proof. At each iteration, if z_0 is not an optimal solution, and if an edge $\{z(\theta): \theta \geqq 0\}$ of $\Omega' = \{z: Rz = 0, z \geqq 0\}$ is not encountered along which $\langle d,z(\theta)\rangle \rightarrow -\infty$ as $\theta \rightarrow \infty$ [that is, CLP (4.1) has no solution], then the simplex algorithm gives a procedure for generating a new extreme point z_1 of Ω', with $\langle d,z_1\rangle < \langle d,z_0\rangle$. It follows, therefore, that the algorithm is well defined and that it can never generate the same extreme point twice. Since there are only a finite number of extreme points of Ω', we conclude that the construction of new basic solutions must terminate in finitely many iterations either because the stop condition in step 2 is encountered, or because the stop condition in step 3 is encountered. □

The simplex algorithm (4) need not (but usually does) terminate in a finite number of steps when the nondegeneracy assumption is not satisfied. In the next section we shall describe a modified finite-step procedure which does not depend on the nondegeneracy assumption, but which is considerably more complex than the simplex algorithm and is rarely used.

5.10 RESOLUTION OF DEGENERACY

Let us suppose now that some of the basic solutions to the canonical linear programming problem (4.1) are in fact degenerate. Under these circumstances, a sequence of basic solutions $z_0, z_1, z_2, \ldots$ generated by the simplex algorithm (9.4) need not terminate after a finite number of vectors z_i. Indeed, since it is now possible to have $\langle d,z_i\rangle = \langle d,z_{i+1}\rangle$, the sequence $z_0, z_1, z_2, \ldots$ may cycle as follows: $z_0, z_1, \ldots, z_l, z_{l+1}, \ldots, z_p, z_l, z_{l+1}, \ldots, z_p, z_l, \ldots$ (for examples of such behavior see [3]). Although cycling is a phenomenon encountered only rarely in practice, it is nice to know that it can be avoided by means of a modification of the simplex algorithm (the procedure described below is due to Charnes [4]).

Consider again CLP (4.1):

1 Minimize $\langle d,z\rangle$ subject to the constraints

2 $$\sum_{i=1}^{n} z^i r_i = c, \qquad z \geqq 0,$$

(that is, $Rz = c$), and suppose that we have an initial basic solution z_0 to (2) such that $\bar{J}(z_0) = \{1,2, \ldots ,m\}$.† Now consider the perturbed linear programming problem:

3 Minimize $\langle d,z\rangle$ subject to the constraints

$$\sum_{j=1}^{n} z^j r_j = c + \sum_{j=1}^{n} \epsilon^j r_j \triangleq c + \rho(\epsilon) \qquad z \geqq 0,$$

where $\epsilon > 0$ is sufficiently small to make what follows valid and ϵ^j denotes ϵ to the power j. The fact that such an $\epsilon > 0$ exists, as well as that we need not know its value, will become clear later on.

4 **Properties of perturbed problem (3).** We shall show that:

a. For the perturbed problem (3) the simplex algorithm constructs a finite sequence of nondegenerate basic solutions $z_0(\epsilon), z_1(\epsilon), \ldots , z_N(\epsilon)$.

b. The original problem (1) has no solution if the perturbed problem (3) has no solution.

c. The vectors $z_i(\epsilon)$ for $i = 0, 1, \ldots$ are of the form $z_i(\epsilon) = z_i + \zeta_i(\epsilon)$, with z_i a basic but possibly degenerate solution to (2).

d. $\bar{I}(z_i(\epsilon)) = \bar{J}(z_i)$.

e. If $z_N(\epsilon) = z_N + \zeta_N(\epsilon)$ is an optimal solution to the perturbed problem (3), then z_N is an optimal solution to problem (1).

Furthermore, we shall see that we can calculate the successive index sets $\bar{I}(z_i(\epsilon)) = \bar{J}(z_i)$ without a knowledge of ϵ. Hence to obtain an optimal solution to the canonical linear programming problem (1) we need only establish the existence of a satisfactory $\epsilon > 0$.

Initialization. Recall that we already have a basic solution z_0 to (2), with $\bar{J}(z_0) = \{1,2, \ldots ,m\}$. Hence for each $j \in \{1,2, \ldots ,n\}$ there are scalars $\alpha_{0j}{}^i$ for $i \in \bar{J}(z_0)$ such that

5 $$r_j = \sum_{i\in\bar{J}(z_0)} \alpha_{0j}{}^i r_i.$$

Hence, since $\sum_{i\in\bar{J}(z_0)} z_0{}^i r_i = c$, we have

6 $$\sum_{i\in\bar{J}(z_0)} z_0{}^i r_i + \sum_{j=1}^{n} \epsilon^j r_j = \sum_{i\in\bar{J}(z_0)} \Big(z_0{}^i + \sum_{j=1}^{n} \alpha_{0j}{}^i \epsilon^j\Big) r_i = c + \rho(\epsilon).$$

† The requirement that $\bar{J}(z_0) = \{1,2, \ldots ,m\}$ is only to facilitate exposition; in practice we simply put the indices in $\bar{J}(z_0)$ into one-to-one correspondence with $1, 2, \ldots , m$ and then proceed.

Now, for $j \in \bar{J}(z_0)$, $\alpha_{0j}{}^i = 1$ if $i = j$ and $\alpha_{0j}{}^i = 0$ if $i \neq j$. Hence for $i \in \bar{J}(z_0)$

7 $$z_0{}^i(\epsilon) \triangleq z_0{}^i + \sum_{j=1}^{n} \alpha_{0j}{}^i \epsilon^j = z_0{}^i + \epsilon^i + \sum_{j \in J(z_0)} \alpha_{0j}{}^i \epsilon^j,$$

and therefore $z_0{}^i(\epsilon) \not\equiv z_0{}^j(\epsilon)$ for all $i \neq j$ in $\bar{J}(z_0)$. Since every $j \in J(z_0)$ is larger than every $i \in \bar{J}(z_0)$, by construction, there is an $\epsilon_0' > 0$ such that $z_0{}^i(\epsilon) > 0$ for all $\epsilon \in (0,\epsilon_0']$ and $i \in \bar{J}(z_0)$. We now define the vector $z_0(\epsilon)$ by

8 $$z_0{}^i(\epsilon) = \begin{cases} z_0{}^i + \sum_{j=1}^{n} \alpha_{0j}{}^i \epsilon^j & \text{if } i \in \bar{J}(z_0) \\ 0 & \text{if } i \in J(z_0). \end{cases}$$

Clearly, $z_0(\epsilon) \geqq 0$ for all $\epsilon \in (0,\epsilon_0']$, $\bar{I}(z_0(\epsilon)) = \bar{J}(z_0)$, and $\sum_{i \in \bar{I}(z_0(\epsilon))} z_0{}^i(\epsilon) r_i = c + \rho(\epsilon)$; that is, $z_0(\epsilon)$ is a nondegenerate basic solution to the perturbed problem (3) for all $\epsilon \in (0,\epsilon_0']$. Setting $\zeta_0{}^i(\epsilon) = \sum_{j=1}^{n} \alpha_{0j}{}^i \epsilon^j$ for $i \in \bar{J}(z_0)$ and zero otherwise, we obtain

9 $$z_0(\epsilon) = z_0 + \zeta_0(\epsilon)$$

10 $$\langle d,z_0(\epsilon)\rangle = \langle d,z_0\rangle + \langle d,\zeta_0(\epsilon)\rangle.$$

Computation of $z_1(\epsilon)$. We now proceed exactly as in Section 8. For $j \in J(z_0) = I(z_0(\epsilon))$ we multiply (5) by θ, add it to (6), and rearrange terms to obtain

11 $$\sum_{i \in \bar{J}(z_0)} \left(z_0{}^i + \sum_{s=1}^{n} \alpha_{0s}{}^i \epsilon^s - \theta \alpha_{0j}{}^i \right) r_i + \theta r_j = c + \rho(\epsilon).$$

With (11) defining $z(\theta)$, we find that

12 $$\begin{aligned} \langle d,z(\theta)\rangle &= \sum_{i \in \bar{J}(z_0)} d^i \left(z_0{}^i + \sum_{s=1}^{n} \alpha_{0s}{}^i \epsilon^s - \theta \alpha_{0j}{}^i \right) + d^j \theta \\ &= \langle d,z_0(\epsilon)\rangle - \theta(\langle r_j,\psi_{\bar{J}(z_0)}\rangle - d^j), \end{aligned}$$

where, as in Section 5.8,

13 $$\psi_{\bar{J}(z_0)} = (R^T_{\bar{J}(z_0)})^{-1} d_{\bar{J}(z_0)}.$$

Again there are three possibilities to be considered.

Case 1. $\langle r_j,\psi_{\bar{J}(z_0)}\rangle - d^j \leqq 0$ *for every* $j \in J(z_0)$. In this case $z_0(\epsilon)$ is an optimal solution to the perturbed problem (3), and since $\psi_{\bar{J}(z_0)}$ obviously does not depend on ϵ, z_0 is an optimal solution to problem (1), which proves *e*.

Case 2. $\langle r_j, \psi_{\bar{J}(z_0)} \rangle - d^j > 0$ *for some* $j \in J(z_0)$ *and* $\alpha_{0j}{}^i \leqq 0$ *for every* $i \in \bar{J}(z_0)$. In this case neither the perturbed problem (3) nor problem (1) has an optimal solution, since $\langle d, z(\theta) \rangle \to -\infty$ as $\theta \to +\infty$ in (12) [cf. (8.27)], which proves b.

Case 3. *There is an* $l \in J(z_0)$ *such that for some* $i \in \bar{J}(z_0)$, $\alpha_{0l}{}^i > 0$ *and* $\langle r_l, \psi_{\bar{J}(z_0)} \rangle - d^l > 0$. Now [cf. (9.8)] let

14 $$\theta(\epsilon) = \min \left\{ \frac{z_0{}^i + \sum_{s=1}^{n} \alpha_{0s}{}^i \epsilon^s}{\alpha_{0l}{}^i} : i \in \bar{J}(z_0),\ \alpha_{0l}{}^i > 0 \right\}.$$

Since $z_0{}^i + \sum_{s=1}^{n} \alpha_{0s}{}^i \epsilon^s > 0$ for all $i \in \bar{J}(z_0)$, it is clear that $\theta(\epsilon) > 0$.

Now each of the polynomials appearing in (14) contains a power of ϵ which cannot be found in any of the other polynomials in (14). Consequently, there exists an $\epsilon_0'' > 0$ such that for all $\epsilon \in (0, \epsilon_0'']$ one of these polynomials is strictly smaller than all the others. Therefore, for all $\epsilon \in (0, \epsilon_0'']$, $\theta(\epsilon)$ is attained at a unique index i, say $i = k \in \bar{J}(z_0)$, and therefore the vector $z_1(\epsilon)$ defined by

15 $$z_1{}^i(\epsilon) = \begin{cases} z_0{}^i + \sum_{s=1}^{n} \alpha_{0s}{}^i \epsilon^s - \theta(\epsilon) \alpha_{0l}{}^i & \text{if } i \in \bar{J}(z_0),\ i \neq k \\ \theta(\epsilon) & \text{if } i = l \\ 0 & \text{otherwise,} \end{cases}$$

is an improved nondegenerate basic solution to the perturbed problem (3).

16 **Remark.** To determine which ϵ-polynomial in (14) is the smallest, it is not necessary to choose a specific value of $\epsilon \in (0, \epsilon_0'']$. Indeed, for all $\epsilon \in (0, \epsilon_0'']$ and $i, j \in \bar{J}(z_0)$, $\left(z_0{}^i + \sum_{s=1}^{n} \alpha_{0s}{}^i \epsilon^s\right) / \alpha_{0l}{}^i < \left(z_0{}^j + \sum_{s=1}^{n} \alpha_{0s}{}^j \epsilon^s\right) / \alpha_{0l}{}^j$ if and only if $z_0{}^i / \alpha_{0l}{}^i < z_0{}^j / \alpha_{0l}{}^j$, or $z_0{}^i / \alpha_{0l}{}^i = z_0{}^j / \alpha_{0l}{}^j$ and $\alpha_{01}{}^i / \alpha_{0l}{}^i < \alpha_{01}{}^j / \alpha_{0l}{}^j$, etc. That is, we need only compare the coefficients of ϵ^s in (14), starting with the coefficient of ϵ^0. If we now set $\epsilon_0 = \min [\epsilon_0', \epsilon_0'']$, then for all $\epsilon \in (0, \epsilon_0]$ both $z_0(\epsilon)$ and $z_1(\epsilon)$ will be nondegenerate basic solution to problem (3), which proves the first part of a.

We shall now show that $z_1(\epsilon)$ can be expressed as $z_1(\epsilon) = z_1 + \zeta_1(\epsilon)$, with z_1 a basic solution to (2), and that $\bar{J}(z_1) = \bar{I}(z_1(\epsilon))$. Obviously, since $z_1(\epsilon)$ is a nondegenerate basic solution to (3), for each $j \in \{1,2, \ldots ,n\}$ there are coefficients α_{1j}^i for $i \in \bar{I}(z_1(\epsilon))$ such that

17 $$r_j = \sum_{i \in \bar{J}(_1(\epsilon))} \alpha_{1j}^i r_i.$$

Also, from (5), with k and l defined as in (15),

18 $$r_k = \frac{1}{\alpha_{0l}^k} r_l - \sum_{\substack{i \in \bar{J}(z_0) \\ i \neq k}} \frac{\alpha_{0l}^i}{\alpha_{0l}^k} r_i.$$

Substituting for r_k in (5), we obtain

19 $$\begin{aligned} r_j &= \sum_{\substack{i \in \bar{J}(z_0) \\ i \neq k}} \alpha_0{}^i r_i + \alpha_{0j}^k r_k \\ &= \sum_{\substack{i \in \bar{J}(z_0) \\ i \neq k}} \left(\alpha_{0j}^i - \alpha_{0j}^k \frac{\alpha_{0l}^i}{\alpha_{0l}^k} \right) r_i + \frac{\alpha_{0j}^k}{\alpha_{0l}^k} r_l. \end{aligned}$$

Since the coefficients in this representation must be unique, comparing (17) with (19) and recalling (16), we conclude that

20 $$\begin{aligned} \alpha_{1j}^i &= \alpha_{0j}^i - \alpha_{0j}^k \frac{\alpha_{0l}^i}{\alpha_{0l}^k} \qquad i \in \bar{J}(z_0),\ i \neq k \\ \alpha_{1j}^l &= \frac{\alpha_{0j}^k}{\alpha_{0l}^k}. \end{aligned}$$

Now, since

$$\theta(\epsilon) = \frac{z_0^k}{\alpha_{0l}^k} + \frac{\sum_{s=1}^{n} \alpha_{0s}^k \epsilon^s}{\alpha_{0l}^k},$$

we obtain from (15) that

21 $$\begin{aligned} z_1^i(\epsilon) &= \left(z_0^i - \alpha_{0l}^i \frac{z_0^k}{\alpha_{0l}^k} \right) + \sum_{s=1}^{n} \left(\alpha_{0s}^i - \alpha_{0l}^i \frac{\alpha_{0s}^k}{\alpha_{0l}^k} \right) \epsilon^s \\ &\qquad\qquad i \in \bar{J}(z_0),\ i \neq k \\ z_1^l(\epsilon) &= \frac{z_0^k}{\alpha_{0l}^k} + \sum_{s=1}^{n} \frac{\alpha_{0s}^k}{\alpha_{0l}^k} \epsilon^s. \end{aligned}$$

Defining the vector z_1 by

22 $$z_1^i = \begin{cases} z_0^i - \alpha_{0l}^i \dfrac{z_0^k}{\alpha_{0l}^k} & \text{if } i \in \bar{J}(z_0),\ i \neq k \\ z_0^k / \alpha_{0l}^k & \text{if } i = l \\ 0 & \text{otherwise,} \end{cases}$$

we find, making use of (20) and (21), that

23 $$z_1{}^i(\epsilon) = z_1{}^i + \sum_{s=1}^{n} \alpha_{1s}{}^i \epsilon^s \qquad i \in \bar{I}(z_1(\epsilon)).$$

Note that (17) and (23) are of the same form as (5), (7) [obviously, $z_1{}^i(\epsilon) = 0$ for $i \in I(z_1(\epsilon))$]. Now, since $z_1{}^i(\epsilon) > 0$ for all $i \in \bar{I}(z_1(\epsilon))$ and all $\epsilon \in (0,\epsilon_0]$, we must have $z_1{}^i \geqq 0$ for $i = 1, 2, \ldots, n$. Furthermore, it is easy to verify that

24 $$\sum_{i \in \bar{I}(z_1(\epsilon))} z_1{}^i r_i = c.$$

Thus z_1 is a basic solution to problem (1), and $\bar{J}(z_1)$ may be taken to be the set $\bar{I}(z_1(\epsilon))$, which proves c and d.

We may now repeat this construction with $0 < \epsilon \leqq \epsilon_1 \leqq \epsilon_0$, since each of the polynomials $z_1{}^i(\epsilon)$ for $i \in \bar{I}(z_1(\epsilon))$ contains a power of ϵ not appearing in the others, and, $z_1{}^i(\epsilon) > 0$ for all $i \in \bar{I}(z_1(\epsilon))$ and $\epsilon \in (0,\epsilon_0]$, since ties did not occur in computing $\theta(\epsilon)$ in (14). Because the cost of the perturbed problem (3) decreases a nonzero amount at each iteration, it is clear that no basis-indicator set can be repeated, and therefore after a finite number of iterations we shall either compute an optimal solution to the canonical linear programming problem or else we shall establish that it has no solution, which proves the second half of a. □

25 **Remark.** Note that in the above process we also generate a sequence of strictly positive numbers $\epsilon_0 \geqq \epsilon_1 \geqq \epsilon_2 \geqq \cdots \geqq \epsilon_N$, and provided $\epsilon \leqq \epsilon_N$ throughout the entire calculation, our arguments remain valid. Furthermore, $\theta(\epsilon)$ in (14) need not be computed; it is necessary only to compute the index k which leaves the original basis-indicator set; i.e., we need only know which k determines $\theta(\epsilon)$. As already pointed out, for sufficiently small $\epsilon > 0$ we can determine the smallest element in the set (14) simply by comparing the coefficients of ϵ^s for $s = 0, 1, 2, \ldots, n$ in the polynomials, and hence we need never know the value of ϵ_N. □

When the original canonical linear programming problem has nondegenerate basic solutions only, it is clear that the simplex algorithm applied to the perturbed problem yields exactly the same sequence of basic solutions as when it is applied directly to the original problem. When some of the basic solutions of the original problem are degenerate, the more complex rule for computing the index k implied by (14) is operative only at the degenerate basic solutions. Thus we see that whether the canonical linear programming problem has nondegenerate basic solutions only or not, it is still possible to use the simplex algorithm, with a slight modification, to obtain an optimal solution.

5.11 BOUNDED-VARIABLE LINEAR PROGRAMMING

In Section 5.4 we chose to take as our canonical linear programming problem (4.1) a linear programming problem (1.1) in which all the components of z were constrained to be nonnegative. However, we have seen that many optimal control problems, such as (4.2.48), reduce to linear programming problems in which the variables are bounded from above and from below. We have also seen (Section 4) that bounded-variable linear programming problems can be reduced to the form of CLP (4.1) by suitable transformations, but only at the expense of considerably increasing the number of equations and variables. The purpose of this section is to modify the simplex algorithm so that it can be applied directly to bounded-variable linear programming problems. Most of the details are left as exercises for the reader.

1 **The bounded-variable linear programming problem (BLP).** Given an $m \times n (m \leqq n)$ full-rank matrix R and vectors $c \in E^m$ and $d \in E^n$, find a vector $\hat{z} \in E^n$ which minimizes $\langle z,d \rangle$ subject to the constraints

2 $$Rz = c \qquad 0 \leqq z^i \leqq 1 \qquad i = 1, 2, \ldots, n. \quad \square$$

3 **Exercise.** Consider the linear programming problem: minimize $\langle x,d \rangle$ subject to the constraints

4 $$\tilde{R}x = \tilde{c}, \quad -\infty < \alpha^i \leqq x^i \leqq \beta^i < +\infty \qquad i = 1, 2, \ldots, n,$$

where $\tilde{R}$, $\tilde{d}$, and $\tilde{c}$ are $m \times n$ $(m \leqq n)$, $n \times 1$, and $m \times 1$ matrices, respectively. Assuming that $\tilde{R}$ has rank m, transform this problem into the canonical form (1) (this can be done without increasing the number of equations or variables). $\square$

Note that z is a feasible solution to BLP (1) if $Rz = c$ and $0 \leqq z^i \leqq 1$ for $i = 1, 2, \ldots, n$ or, equivalently, if $z \in \Omega' = \{z \colon Rz = c, 0 \leqq z^i \leqq 1, i = 1, 2, \ldots, n\}$.

5 **Definition.** Let $z \in E^n$ be a vector such that $0 \leqq z^i \leqq 1$ for $i = 1, 2, \ldots, n$. Then the index sets $\bar{I}(z)$, $L(x)$, and $U(x)$ are defined as follows:

6 $$\bar{I}(z) = \{i \in \{1,2, \ldots ,n\} : 0 < z^i < 1\}$$

7 $$L(z) = \{i \in \{1,2, \ldots ,n\} : z^i = 0\}$$

8 $$U(z) = \{i \in \{1,2, \ldots ,n\} : z^i = 1\}.$$

Consequently, if, for $i = 1, 2, \ldots, n$, we let $e_i = (0,0,1,0,0, \ldots ,0)$ be the usual unit basis vectors in E^n (the ith component of e_i is 1 and all the other components are zero), then for any $z \in E^n$ which is a feasible solution to BLP (1) we have

9 $$z = \sum_{i=1}^{n} z^i e_i = \sum_{i \in \bar{I}(z)} z^i e_i + \sum_{i \in U(z)} z^i e_i$$

and

10 $$Rz = \sum_{i=1}^{n} z^i r_i = \sum_{i \in \bar{I}(z)} z^i r_i + \sum_{i \in U(z)} z^i r_i = c.$$

Note that $I(z) = L(z) \cup U(z)$ is, as usual, the active-inequality-constraints index set.

11 **Definition.** A vector z is said to be a *basic solution* to BLP (1) if z is a feasible solution and the vectors $\{r_i: i \in \bar{I}(z)\}$ are linearly independent. □

12 **Definition.** A vector z is said to be a *nondegenerate basic solution* to BLP (1) if z is a basic solution and the vectors $\{r_i: i \in \bar{I}(z)\}$ form a basis for E^m. □

13 **Exercise.** Show that a basic solution to BLP (1) is an extreme point of the set $\Omega' = \{z: Rz = c, 0 \leqq z^i \leqq 1, i = 1, 2, \ldots ,n\}$. □

14 **Theorem.** If an optimal solution to BLP (1) exists, then there exists an optimal solution z which is an extreme point of Ω'. □

15 **Exercise.** Prove theorem (14). □

As in the case of the canonical linear programming problem (4.1), it is always possible to associate with any extreme point z of Ω' a set of m columns of R which form a basis for E^m.

16 **Definition.** Let z be a basic solution to BLP (1). We shall mean by a *basis-indicator set* any set $\bar{J}(z) \subset \{1,2, \ldots ,n\}$ with the following properties:

17 $\bar{I}(z) \subset \bar{J}(z)$, and vectors in the set $\{r_i: i \in \bar{J}(z)\}$ form a basis for E^m. □

18 **Lemma.** Suppose z is a basic solution of BLP (1). Then there exists a basis-indicator set $\bar{J}(z) \subset \{1,2, \ldots ,n\}$ satisfying (17). □

19 **Exercise.** Prove lemma (18). □

We can now describe an algorithm for solving the bounded-variable linear programming problem (1).

20 **Initialization.** Find a basic solution to the system of equations and inequalities

$$Rz = c \qquad 0 \leqq z^i \leqq 1 \qquad i = 1, 2, \ldots, n.$$

If a basic solution is not readily available, use the bounded-variable simplex algorithm below to solve the linear problem:

21 $$\text{Minimize } \sum_{i=1}^{m} \xi^i \text{ subject to the constraints}$$

22 $$\begin{aligned} &Rz + \xi = c \\ &0 \leqq z^i \leqq 1 \qquad i = 1, 2, \ldots, n \\ &0 \leqq \xi^i \leqq 1 \qquad i = 1, 2, \ldots, m. \end{aligned}$$

Assuming that we have multiplied all rows of R and all components of c by $1/\alpha$ or $-1/\alpha$, with $\alpha = \max |c^i|$, if necessary, we presume that $0 \leqq c^i \leqq 1$ for $i = 1, 2, \ldots, m$. Therefore, $z = 0$ and $\xi = c$ constitute a basic solution to (22). If $(\hat{z},\hat{\xi})$ is a solution to (22) obtained by means of the bounded-variable simplex algorithm and $\hat{\xi} = 0$, then $\hat{z}$ is a basic solution to (2). If $\hat{\xi} \neq 0$, then BLP (1) has no feasible solutions. □

23 **The bounded-variable simplex algorithm.** Let z_0 be a basic solution, and let $\bar{J}(z_0)$ be an associated basis-indicator set.

Step 1. Compute $\psi_{\bar{J}(z_0)}$ according to

24 $$\psi_{\bar{J}(z_0)} = (R^T_{\bar{J}(z_0)})^{-1} d_{\bar{J}(z_0)},$$

where $R^T_{\bar{J}(z_0)}$ is an $m \times m$ nonsingular matrix with whose kth row is r_{i_k} for $k = 1, 2, \ldots, m$ and $i_k \in \bar{J}(z_0)$ and $d_{\bar{J}(z_0)}$ is an m vector whose kth component is d^{i_k} for $k = 1, 2, \ldots, m$ and $i_k \in \bar{J}(z_0)$.

Step 2. If $\langle r_l, \psi_{\bar{J}(z_0)} \rangle - d^l \leqq 0$ for all $l \in L(z_0)$ *and* if $\langle r_u, \psi_{\bar{J}(z_0)} \rangle - d^u \geqq 0$ for all $u \in U(z_0)$, then stop, since z_0 is an optimal solution to BLP (1). Otherwise let $j \in L(z_0) \cup U(z_0)$ be the smallest (any) index such that

25 $$\langle r_j, \psi_{\bar{J}(z_0)} \rangle - d^j > 0 \qquad \text{if } j \in L(z_0)$$

26 $$\langle r_j, \psi_{\bar{J}(z_0)} \rangle - d^j < 0 \qquad \text{if } j \in U(z_0),$$

and proceed to step 3.

Step 3. Compute the coefficients α_j^i for $i \in \bar{J}(z_0)$ satisfying

27 $$r_j = \sum_{i \in \bar{J}(z_0)} \alpha_j^i r_i,$$

where $j \in L(z_0) \cup U(z_0)$ is the index determined in step 2. Note that

28 $$\alpha_{\bar{J}(z_0)} = R_{\bar{J}(z_0)}^{-1} r_j,$$

where $\alpha_{\bar{J}(z_0)} = (\alpha_j^{i_1}, \alpha_j^{i_2}, \ldots, \alpha_j^{i_m})$.

Step 4. Compute θ_0 as follows. If $j \in L(z_0)$, then

29 $$\theta_0 = \min \left\{ \min_{\substack{i \in \bar{J}(z_0) \\ \alpha_j^i > 0}} \frac{z_0^i}{\alpha_j^i}, \min_{\substack{i \in \bar{J}(z_0) \\ \alpha_j^i < 0}} \frac{z_0^i}{\alpha_j^i}, 1 \right\} \geqq 0.$$

If $j \in U(z)$, then

30 $$\theta_0 = \min \left\{ \min_{\substack{i \in \bar{J}(z_0) \\ \alpha_j^i < 0}} \frac{z_0^i}{\alpha_j^i}, \min_{\substack{i \in \bar{J}(z_0) \\ \alpha_j^i > 0}} \frac{z_0^i}{\alpha_j^i}, -1 \right\} \leqq 0.$$

Compute the adjacent extreme point

31 $$z_1 = \sum_{i \in \bar{J}(z_0)} (z_0^i - \theta_0 \alpha_j^i) e_i + \theta_0 e_j + \sum_{i \in (U(z_0)/U(z_0) \cap \bar{J}(z_0))} z_0^i e_i,$$

where $U(z_0)/U(z_0) \cap \bar{J}(z_0) = \{i: i \in U(z_0),\ i \notin \bar{J}(z_0)\}$. Determine the basis-indicator set $\bar{J}(z_1)$ associated with z_1 as follows. If $|\theta_0| = 1$, then set

32 $$J(z_1) = J(z_0).$$

If $|\theta_0| < 1$, and $k \in \bar{J}(z_0)$ is an index for which the minimum in (29) or in (30) occurred (if ties occur, take the smallest index k), then set

33 $$\bar{J}(z_1) = \bar{J}(z_0) - \{k\} + \{j\}.$$

Set $z_0 = z_1$ and return to step 1. □

34 **Theorem.** Suppose that every basic solution of BLP (1) is a nondegenerate basic solution. Then the bounded-variable simplex algorithm (23) determines an optimal solution to BLP (2) in a finite number of steps. □

35 **Exercise.** Prove theorem (34). [*Hint:* Show that the algorithm never repeats a basic solution, so that it stops after a finite number of iterations. Establish a necessary-and-sufficient-condition theorem analogous to (5.1) and show that it coincides with the stop conditions in step 2.] □

36 **Remark.** It is possible to give a subprocedure for resolving degeneracies in the above case similar to the one given in Section 5.10 when the simplex algorithm was used to solve the canonical linear programming problem (4.1). The derivation of such a subprocedure is left as an exercise for the interested reader; such a subprocedure is usually not required in practice. □

37 **Remark.** When BLP (1) is converted to the form of CLP (4.1), and simplex algorithm (9.4) is used to solve the resulting problem, it is necessary to work with $(n + m) \times (n + m)$ matrices (i.e., to solve a system of $n + m$ simultaneous equations) of each step. By comparison, we need only work with $m \times m$ matrices to solve BLP (1) with the algorithm (23). This, quite obviously, is considerably to our advantage. □

REFERENCES

1. G. B. Dantzig: Maximization of a Linear Function of Variables Subject to Linear Inequalities, chap. XXI in T. C. Koopmans (ed.), "Activity Analysis of Production and Allocation," Monograph 13 of the Cowles Commission, New York, N.Y., 1951.
2. G. B. Dantzig: "Linear Programming and Extensions," Princeton University Press, Princeton, N.J., 1963.
3. A. J. Hoffman: Cycling in the Simplex Algorithm, *Natl. Bur. Std. Rept.* 2974, December 16, 1953.
4. A. Charnes: Optimality and Degeneracy in Linear Programming, *Econometrica*, **20**:160–170 (1952).
5. G. B. Dantzig, A. Orden, and P. Wolfe: The Generalized Simplex Method for Minimizing a Linear Form under Linear Inequality constraints, *Pac. J. Math.*, **5**:183–195 (1955).

6

Optimal control and quadratic programming

6.1 FORMULATION OF THE GENERAL CONTROL PROBLEM WITH QUADRATIC COST AND TRANSFORMATION TO A QUADRATIC PROGRAMMING PROBLEM

We shall now consider a class of discrete optimal control problems for which the corresponding Basic Problem [see (1.4.1)] is a quadratic programming problem of the form:

1 Minimize $\frac{1}{2}\langle z,Qz\rangle + \langle d,z\rangle$ subject to $Rz = c$, $Pz \leqq \nu$, and $\alpha \leqq z \leqq \beta$,

where d, α, and β are in E^n, Q is an $n \times n$ symmetric (usually positive-semidefinite) matrix, R is an $m \times n$ matrix, P is an $l \times n$ matrix, and $c \in E^m$ and $\nu \in E^l$ (we shall always assume that $\alpha^i < \beta^i$ for $i = 1, 2, \ldots, n$ and that it is possible to have $\alpha^i = -\infty$ and $\beta^j = \infty$ for any i and j in $\{1,2, \ldots ,n\}$).

Our formulation of this class of problems is intended to be sufficiently general to include all the discrete optimal control problems with quadratic costs which are discussed in the literature. However, the possible variations on such problems are so extensive that it is virtually impossible to formulate a class general enough to include all possible cases. Some examples of control problems outside our formulation which reduce to quadratic programming problems are included in the exercises; the reader can probably generate others. The following formulation is the simplest one that will include all the standard problems.

2 **The quadratic control problem (QCP).** Consider a dynamical system described by the linear difference equation

3 $$x_{i+1} - x_i = Ax_i + Bu_i \qquad i = 0, 1, \ldots, k-1,$$

where $x_i \in E^n$ is the system state at time i, $u_i \in E^m$ is the system input at time i, A is an $n \times n$ matrix, and B is an $n \times m$ matrix. Find a control sequence $\hat{\mathfrak{U}} = (\hat{u}_0, \hat{u}_1, \ldots, \hat{u}_{k-1})$ and a corresponding trajectory $\hat{\mathfrak{X}} = (\hat{x}_0, \hat{x}_1, \ldots, \hat{x}_k)$, determined by (3), which minimize the quadratic cost function

4 $$\tfrac{1}{2}\langle z, Qz\rangle + \langle d, z\rangle,$$

where $z \triangleq (\mathfrak{X}, \mathfrak{U}) = (x_0, x_1, \ldots, x_k, u_0, u_1, \ldots, u_{k-1})$, Q is a $[(k+1)n + km] \times [(k+1)n + km]$ symmetric positive-semi-definite matrix, and $d \in E^{(k+1)n+km}$. The minimization is subject to the constraints

5 $$u_i \in U_i = \{u\colon F_i u_i \leqq w_i\} \qquad i = 0, 1, \ldots, k-1$$

6 $$x_i \in X_i' = \{x\colon H_i x \leqq v_i\} \qquad i = 0, 1, \ldots, k,$$

and in addition, x_0 and x_k are required to satisfy

7 $$G_0 x_0 = c_0 \qquad G_k x_k = c_k,$$

where the F_i and w_i for $i = 0, 1, \ldots, k$, the H_i and v_i for $i = 0, 1, \ldots, k-1$, and G_0, G_k, c_0, and c_k are appropriate matrices and vectors [some of the matrices in (4) to (7) may be zero]. □

We now reduce the QCP (2) to a Basic Problem by making the usual identifications (see Section 1.5). Let z be defined as in (4) and let f and r defined by

8 $$f(z) = \tfrac{1}{2}\langle z, Qz\rangle + \langle d, z\rangle$$

9 $$r(z) = \begin{bmatrix} x_1 - x_0 - Ax_0 - Bu_0 \\ \cdot \\ \cdot \\ \cdot \\ x_k - x_{k-1} - Ax_{k-1} - Bu_{k-1} \\ G_0 x_0 - c_0 \\ G_k x_k - c_k \end{bmatrix} = Rz - c,$$

where c is of the form $c \triangleq (0, \ldots, 0, c_0, c_k)$. Le Ω be defined by

10
$$\Omega = X'_0 \times X'_1 \times X'_2 \times \cdots \times X'_k \times U_0 \times U_1 \times \cdots \times U_{k-1};$$

hence Ω is of the form

11
$$\Omega = \{z \colon Pz \leqq \nu,\ \alpha \leqq z \leqq \beta\},$$

where P, ν, α and β are derived from (5) and (6).

Obviously, with f, r, and Ω defined by (8), (9), and (11), respectively, we have reduced problem (2) to the form of problem (1).

12 **Remark.** We saw in Section 5.2 that there is an alternative method for transcribing control problems into a Basic Problem which leads to a reduced number of unknown variables. This method entails solving the difference equation (3) for each of the states x_i, with $i = 1, \ldots, k$, in terms of the initial state x_0 and the control sequence $\mathcal{U} = (u_0, u_1, \ldots, u_{k-1})$, and then eliminating these states from the problem by substituting for them in the cost function and the constraints. □

13 **Exercise.** Transcribe QCP (2) into a quadratic programming problem by means of the method indicated in (12). □

Note that not only the number of variables, but also the number of equality constraints, is reduced when the alternative method for transcribing QCP into Basic Problem form is used. We shall make this transcription for a number of important special cases of the quadratic control problem when we discuss these problems in detail.

6.2 THE EXISTENCE OF AN OPTIMAL SOLUTION TO THE QUADRATIC PROGRAMMING PROBLEM

Let us now turn our attention to the question of when an optimal solution to the quadratic programming problem (1.1) exists. In this section we shall see that we need only a minimum of additional assumptions to guarantee the existence of an optimal solution. First, however, we introduce a form of the quadratic programming problem (1.1) which will facilitate our task, and some terminology:

1 **The quadratic programming problem (QP).** Minimize $f(z) = \frac{1}{2}\langle z, Qz\rangle + \langle d, z\rangle$ subject to the constraints $Rz = c$ and $\alpha \leqq z \leqq \beta$, where Q is an $n \times n$ symmetric positive-semidefinite matrix, $d \in E^n$, R is an

$m \times n$ matrix, and α and β are vectors in E^n whose components may take on the values $\pm\infty$. □

2 **Exercise.** Transcribe the quadratic programming problem (1.1) into the form (1). By definition, (1) is already of the form (1.1). (*Hint:* See section (5.4) on canonical linear programming problems.) □

Again it will be recollected that a vector z which satisfies the constraints $Rz = c$ and $\alpha \leqq z \leqq \beta$ of problem (1) is a *feasible solution* to the problem.

We now state and prove a theorem concerning the existence of an optimal solution to QP (1).

3 **Theorem.** If $\langle d,z \rangle = 0$ for every $z \in E^n$ satisfying $Qz = 0$ and $Rz = 0$ and there exists a feasible solution to QP (1), then there exists an optimal solution to QP (1).

Proof. Let $\Omega' = \{z\colon Rz = c,\ \alpha \leqq z \leqq \beta\}$; that is, Ω' is the set of feasible solutions to QP (1). Ω' is nonempty, by assumption. We shall prove the theorem in two parts. First we shall show that $f(z)$ is bounded from below for $z \in \Omega'$, and hence that there exists a finite number γ which is the *infimum* of $f(z)$ for $z \in \Omega'$. Then we shall show that there exists a $z^* \in \Omega'$ such that $f(z^*) = \gamma$.

To begin, let us denote by $\mathfrak{N}(R)$ and $\mathfrak{N}(Q)$ the null spaces of R and Q, respectively. By assumption, $d \in [\mathfrak{N}(R) \cap \mathfrak{N}(Q)]^\perp$, the orthogonal complement of $\mathfrak{N}(R) \cap \mathfrak{N}(Q)$. This is equivalent to saying that

$$d \in \left[\mathfrak{N}\left(\begin{bmatrix} Q \\ \hdashline R \end{bmatrix}\right)\right]^\perp,$$

where $\begin{bmatrix} Q \\ \hdashline R \end{bmatrix}$ is the $(n + m) \times n$ matrix, with Q and R as submatrices, as indicated. Since d is orthogonal to the null space of $\begin{bmatrix} Q \\ \hdashline R \end{bmatrix}$, it must be contained in the range of $\begin{bmatrix} Q \\ \hdashline R \end{bmatrix}^T = [Q \,\vdots\, R^T]$. Therefore we must have

4 $$d = Q\mu + R^T\nu,$$

where μ and ν are some vectors in E^n and E^m, respectively. Substituting (4) into the expression for $f(z)$, we obtain

5 $$\begin{aligned} f(z) &= \langle z,Qz \rangle + \langle Q\mu + R^T\nu, z \rangle \\ &= \langle z,Qz \rangle + \langle \mu,Qz \rangle + \langle \nu,Rz \rangle. \end{aligned}$$

Now, we are interested only in those vectors $z \in E^n$ which satisfy $Rz = c$. It follows, therefore, that

6 $$f(z) = \langle z + \mu, Qz \rangle + \langle \nu, c \rangle \qquad \text{for all } z \in \Omega'.$$

Since Q is symmetric and positive semidefinite, we obtain for Q the spectral expansion

7 $$Q = \sum_{i=1}^{n} \lambda^i \xi_i \rangle \langle \xi_i,$$

where the $\lambda^i \geqq 0$ for $i = 1, 2, \ldots, n$ are the eigenvalues of Q, the $\xi_i = (\xi_i^1, \xi_i^2, \ldots, \xi_i^n)$ are a corresponding set of orthonormal eigenvectors of Q, and $\xi_i \rangle \langle \xi_i$ is the $n \times n$ (dyad) matrix whose lkth element is $\xi_i^l \xi_i^k$. Hence

8 $$\langle z + \mu, Qz \rangle = \sum_{i=1}^{n} \lambda^i (\langle \xi_i, z \rangle^2 + \langle \xi_i, \mu \rangle \langle \xi_i, z \rangle),$$

where the quantities in the parentheses,

$$\langle \xi_i, z \rangle^2 + \langle \xi_i, \mu \rangle \langle \xi_i, z \rangle \qquad i = 1, 2, \ldots, n,$$

are of the form $x^2 + ax$, which has a finite minimum for every finite value of a. Since $\lambda^i \geqq 0$ for $i = 1, 2, \ldots, n$, we can conclude that $\langle z + \mu, Qz \rangle$ must be bounded from below for all z. We have already seen that $f(z) = \langle z + \mu, Qz \rangle + \langle \nu, c \rangle$ for all $z \in \Omega'$. Hence $f(z)$ is bounded from below on Ω'. Let γ be the greatest lower bound of $f(z)$ for $z \in \Omega'$; that is,

9 $$\gamma = \inf_{z \in \Omega'} f(z) > -\infty.$$

This completes the first half of the proof.

Since γ is the infimum of f over Ω', it follows that there exists a sequence of points $\{z_i\}_{i=1}^{\infty}$ in Ω' such that $f(z_i) \to \gamma$. If $\{z_i\}_{i=1}^{\infty}$ is convergent, or even if it has a convergent subsequence, we are done, since the limit point of this sequence would be in Ω' and would give the required value for f. However, this sequence need not be bounded, since Ω' need not be bounded, and hence it need not have a convergent subsequence. What we shall do now is project Ω' and the sequence $\{z_i\}_{i=1}^{\infty}$ onto a subspace in such a way that we can obtain a bounded sequence with certain nice properties. Note that since Q is symmetric, the orthogonal complement of $\mathfrak{N}(Q)$, the null space of Q, is $\mathfrak{R}(Q)$, the range of Q. Let P be an $n \times n$ matrix such that $Px = 0$ for all $x \in \mathfrak{N}(Q)$ and $Px = x$ for all $x \in \mathfrak{R}(Q)$; that is, P is an orthogonal-projection matrix. Let $\{z_i\}_{i=1}^{\infty}$ be a sequence in Ω' such that $f(z_i) \to \gamma$, and let

10 $$y_i = Pz_i \qquad i = 1, 2, \ldots .$$

Also let

11 $$\hat{\Omega}' = \{y \in E^n : y = Qz,\ z \in \Omega'\}.$$

Clearly, $y_i \in \hat{\Omega}$ for every i. Furthermore, if we define $h\colon E^n \to E^1$ by

12 $$h(z) = \langle z + \mu, Qz \rangle,$$

then

13 $$h(y_i) = h(z_i) = f(z_i) - \langle \nu, c \rangle \qquad \text{for all } i,$$

since, by definition of y_i,

14 $$z_i = y_i + x_i,$$

where $x_i \in \mathfrak{N}(Q)$. It follows that

15 $$h(y_i) \to \gamma - \langle \nu, c \rangle$$

and therefore that the sequence $\{h(y_i)\}$ is bounded. Furthermore, Q restricted to $\mathfrak{R}(Q)$ is positive definite, and hence $\{h(y_i)\}_{i=1}^{\infty}$ is bounded if and only if $\{y_i\}_{i=1}^{\infty}$ is bounded. We therefore conclude from (15) that there exists at least one limit point y^* to which a subsequence of $\{y_i\}_{i=1}^{\infty}$ converges. If $\hat{\Omega}'$ is closed, we are done, since then y^* belongs to $\hat{\Omega}'$, and any corresponding vector $z^* \in \Omega'$ for which $y^* = Pz^*$ satisfies $f(z^*) = \gamma$.

Since it is not true in general that the image of a closed set under a linear map is closed, we must appeal to the special nature of the set Ω', namely, to the fact that it is a convex polyhedral set. The following representation theorem is stated here without proof, (for a proof see Goldman [4], theorem 1, p. 44).

16 **Theorem.** Any closed nonempty convex polyhedral set S in E^n of the form

17 $$S = \{x : Ax \leqq b\}$$

can be expressed as the vector sum

18 $$C^{\Delta} + D^{L} = \{x = x_1 + x_2 : x_1 \in C^{\Delta},\ x_2 \in D^{L}\}$$

of a closed and bounded convex polyhedron C^{Δ} of the form

19 $$C^{\Delta} = \{x : x = Cu,\ u \geqq 0,\ \Sigma u_i = 1\}$$

and a closed convex polyhedral cone D^L of the form

20 $$D^L = \{x : x = Dw,\ w \geqq 0\}.$$

Conversely, any nonempty set of the form $C^\Delta + D^L$ is a closed convex polyhedral set.

If we represent S as $C^\Delta + D^L$, it is easy to see that the image of $C^\Delta + D^L$ under a linear transformation P is a set of the same form, that is, $P[C^\Delta + D^L] = \hat{C}^\Delta + \hat{D}^L$, where

21 $$\hat{C}^\Delta = \{y : y = (PC)u,\ u \geqq 0,\ \Sigma u_i = 1\}$$
22 $$\hat{D}^L = \{y : y = (PD)w,\ w \geqq 0\}.$$

From the converse of theorem (16) we now conclude that $\hat{C}^\Delta + \hat{D}^L$ is a closed convex polyhedral set.

Although our set Ω' does not have the specific form of S in the theorem, it may easily be verified that these forms are equivalent, and hence that $\hat{\Omega}'$ is a closed convex polyhedron. □

There are several special cases of this theorem, stated here in the form of corollaries.

23 **Corollary.** If $d = 0$ and there exists a feasible solution to QP (1), then there exists an optimal solution to QP (1). □

24 **Corollary.** If Q is positive definite and there exists a feasible solution to QP (1), then there exists an optimal solution to QP (1). □

25 **Corollary.** If R is nonsingular and there exists a feasible solution to QP (1), then there exists an optimal solution to QP (1). □

26 **Corollary.** If $\mathfrak{N}(R) \cap \mathfrak{N}(Q) = \{0\}$ and there exists a feasible solution to QP (1), then there exists an optimal solution to QP (1). □

This last corollary is of particular interest, since, as we shall see in the next section, the condition $\mathfrak{N}(R) \cap \mathfrak{N}(Q) = \{0\}$ is also a sufficient condition for the optimal solution to QP (1) to be unique.

As a final note, it should be emphasized that the conditions of theorem (3) are only sufficient conditions for the existence of an optimal solution. Optimal solutions may, in fact, exist even if these conditions are not satisfied. Indeed, referring to the proof of theorem (3), we see that the assumption

$$d \in \left[\mathfrak{N}\left(\begin{bmatrix} Q \\ \hdashline R \end{bmatrix}\right)\right]^\perp$$

was needed only in order to show that $f(z)$ is bounded from below for $z \in \Omega'$. Consequently, we may substitute for theorem (2) the following more general result.

27 **Theorem.** If $f(z)$ is bounded from below for $z \in \Omega'$ and Ω' is not empty, then there exists an optimal solution to QP (1). □

This concludes our discussion of conditions ensuring the existence of solutions to the quadratic programming problem.

6.3 A SUFFICIENT CONDITION FOR A UNIQUE OPTIMAL SOLUTION TO THE QUADRATIC PROGRAMMING PROBLEM

In this section we shall always assume that an optimal solution to the quadratic programming problem [see (1.1) or (2.1)] exists, and we shall seek to establish conditions which will guarantee that there is a unique optimal solution. As we shall see later in the chapter, the quadratic programming problem is considerably easier to solve when there is a unique optimal solution.

There does not appear to be any set of conditions which are both necessary and sufficient for the quadratic programming problem to have a unique solution. Of the many possible sets of sufficient conditions, we shall examine one set which not only has the advantage of being relatively straightforward to check, but also immediately implies the nonsingularity of certain matrices which appear in algorithms for the solution of the quadratic programming problem. We now state these conditions in the form of a theorem. The terminology is the same as in Section 2.

1 **Theorem.** If $\mathcal{N}(Q) \cap \mathcal{N}(R) = \{0\}$ and the QP (2.1) has a feasible solution, then it has a unique optimal solution.

Proof. Note first that if a feasible solution to QP (2.1) exists, then an optimal solution exists by corollary (2.26). Therefore we need only show that there cannot be two distinct optimal solutions.

We prove this by contradiction. Suppose that z_1 and z_2, where $z_1 \neq z_2$, are both optimal solutions to QP (2.1). Then $z_2 = z_1 + z_0$ for some $z_0 \neq 0$, and $z_0 \in \mathcal{N}(R)$. Again denoting the set of all feasible solutions by Ω', we find that

$$z(\lambda) = \lambda z_1 + (1 - \lambda)z_2 \in \Omega' \qquad \text{for every } \lambda \in [0,1]$$

because Ω' is a convex set. Thus $z(\lambda)$ is a feasible solution to QP (2.1) for every $\lambda \in [0,1]$. We shall show that for all $\lambda \in (0,1)$, $f(z(\lambda)) <$

$f(z_1) = f(z_2)$, which is a contradiction of the assumption that z_1 and z_2 are both optimal. First note that

2 $$f(z_1) = f(z_2) = f(z_1 + z_0) = f(z_1) + f(z_0) + \langle z_1, Qz_0 \rangle,$$

and hence that

3 $$f(z_0) = -\langle z_1, Qz_0 \rangle.$$

After some tedious algebraic manipulation it can be shown that

4 $$f(z(\lambda)) = f(z_1) + (1 - \lambda)[\langle z_1, Qz_0 \rangle + \tfrac{1}{2}(1 - \lambda)\langle z_0, Qz_0 \rangle + \langle z_0, d \rangle].$$

Using (3), we reduce this to

5 $$f(z(\lambda)) = f(z_1) - \frac{\lambda(1 - \lambda)}{2} \langle z_0, Qz_0 \rangle.$$

Since $\mathfrak{N}(R) \cap \mathfrak{N}(Q) = \{0\}$ and $z_0 \neq 0$ belongs to $\mathfrak{N}(R)$, we conclude that $z_0 \notin \mathfrak{N}(Q)$, that is, that $\langle z_0, Qz_0 \rangle > 0$ (this follows upon writing Q in spectral-expansion form). Therefore $f(z(\lambda)) < f(z_1)$ for all $\lambda \in (0,1)$. □

The condition that the null spaces of Q and R have only the zero vector in common is relatively easy to check, since it is equivalent to verifying that the $(n + m) \times n$ matrix $\begin{bmatrix} Q \\ R \end{bmatrix}$ has rank n. If we make the not unreasonable restriction that R have rank m, that is, that the equality constraints form a linearly independent set of equations, we get an even stronger result, which is stated below in the form of a theorem.

6 **Theorem.** Suppose that the matrix R has rank m; then $\mathfrak{N}(Q) \cap \mathfrak{N}(R) = \{0\}$ if and only if the $(n + m) \times (n + m)$ matrix

7 $$D = \begin{bmatrix} -Q & R^T \\ R & 0 \end{bmatrix}$$

is nonsingular.

Proof. Every vector $u \in E^n \times E^m$ can be partitioned into two components, $u = (x,v)$, where $x \in E^n$ and $v \in E^m$. If D is nonsingular, then for every vector u of the form $u = (x,0)$, with $x \neq 0$, we have

8 $$Du = \begin{bmatrix} -Qx \\ Rx \end{bmatrix} \neq 0,$$

which implies that $\mathfrak{N}(Q) \cap \mathfrak{N}(R) = \{0\}$.

Conversely, suppose that $\mathfrak{N}(Q) \cap \mathfrak{N}(R) = \{0\}$ and that $u^* = (x^*,v^*)$ satisfies $Du^* = 0$. Then, from (7),

9 $$R^T v^* = Qx^*$$
10 $$Rx^* = 0.$$

Using equations (9) and (10), we obtain

11 $$\langle x^*,Qx^*\rangle = \langle x^*,R^T v^*\rangle = \langle Rx^*,v^*\rangle = 0,$$

and hence $x^* \in \mathfrak{N}(Q)$. This, together with (10), implies that $x^* = 0$, since $\mathfrak{N}(Q) \cap \mathfrak{N}(R) = \{0\}$. We therefore conclude from (9) that

12 $$R^T v^* = 0.$$

Since R has rank m, $R^T v^* = 0$ implies that $v^* = 0$. Therefore the only solution to $Du^* = 0$ is $u^* = 0$, and hence D is nonsingular. □

On the surface, this result may not appear to be any more significant than the previously noted fact that $\begin{bmatrix} Q \\ R \end{bmatrix}$ must have rank n. However, the matrix D in (7) plays a prominent role when we apply necessary and sufficient conditions for optimality to the quadratic programming problem, and the fact that it is nonsingular under the assumptions stated above is highly useful.

6.4 NECESSARY AND SUFFICIENT CONDITIONS OF OPTIMALITY FOR THE QUADRATIC PROGRAMMING PROBLEM

For the purpose of deriving algorithms it is convenient to restrict ourself to one of the following two canonical forms of the quadratic programming problem (1.1):

1 Minimize $\frac{1}{2}\langle z,Qz\rangle + \langle d,z\rangle$ subject to $Rz = c$ and $\alpha \leqq z \leqq \beta$.
2 Minimize $\frac{1}{2}\langle z,Qz\rangle + \langle d,z\rangle$ subject to $Rz = c$ and $z \geqq 0$.

3 **Exercise.** Show that by adding variables we can transcribe the form (1) into the form (2) [(2) is a special case of (1)]. □

When applied to problem (1), the necessary-and-sufficient conditions theorems (3.3.5) and (3.6.1) combine to give the following result.

4 **Theorem.** If $\hat{z}$ is a feasible solution to problem (1), then $\hat{z}$ is an optimal solution if and only if there exists a vector $\psi = (\psi^1, \ldots ,\psi^m) \in E^m$ such that for $i = 1, 2, \ldots , n$

5
$$\begin{aligned} \langle r_i,\psi\rangle - \langle q_i,\hat{z}\rangle - d^i &= 0 && \text{if } \alpha^i < \hat{z}^i < \beta^i \\ \langle r_i,\psi\rangle - \langle q_i,\hat{z}\rangle - d^i &\leqq 0 && \text{if } \hat{z}^i = \alpha^i \\ \langle r_i,\psi\rangle - \langle q_i,\hat{z}\rangle - d^i &\geqq 0 && \text{if } \hat{z}^i = \beta^i, \end{aligned}$$

where for $i = 1, 2, \ldots, n$, r_i is the ith column of R, q_i is the ith column of Q, and d^i is the ith component of d. □

6 **Exercise.** Prove theorem (4). □

6.5 APPLICATIONS TO UNBOUNDED CONTROL PROBLEMS

We shall now consider several special cases of the quadratic control problem (1.2) which have no inequality constraints. The corresponding quadratic programming problems also have no inequality constraints. These problems have been chosen not because of their great practical significance, but because they are among the few which have closed-form solutions. This permits us to compare and evaluate various methods of attack. The observations we shall make in this section will also be pertinent to more general forms of the quadratic control problem.

As a first example, we shall consider the following special case of the quadratic control problem.

1 **The minimum-energy problem: two-point-boundary form.** Consider a dynamical system described by the linear difference equation

2 $$x_{i+1} - x_i = Ax_i + Bu_i \qquad i = 0, 1, \ldots, k-1,$$

where $x_i \in E^n$ is the system state at time i, $u_i \in E^m$ is the system input at time i, A is an $n \times n$ matrix, and B is an $n \times m$ matrix. Find a control sequence $\hat{\mathfrak{u}} = (\hat{u}_0, \hat{u}_1, \ldots, \hat{u}_{k-1})$ which transfers system (2) from the initial state $\hat{x}_0 = c_0$ to the terminal state $\hat{x}_k = c_k$ and minimizes

3 $$f(\mathfrak{u}) = \sum_{i=0}^{k-1} \langle u_i, u_i \rangle = \sum_{i=0}^{k-1} \|u_i\|^2 \quad \square$$

4 **Assumption.** $k \geqq n$. □

5 **Assumption.** System (2) is completely controllable; i.e., the $(n \times nm)$-dimensional matrix $[B \mid (I + A)B \mid \cdots \mid (I + A)^{n-1}B]$ has rank n. □

Solution of (1) by Direct Transcription

Obviously, problem (1) is a special case of the quadratic control problem, and we may therefore reduce it to a quadratic programming problem of the following form:

6 Minimize $\frac{1}{2}\langle z, Qz\rangle$ subject to the constraint $Rz = c$, where $z = (x_0, x_1, \ldots, x_k, u_0, u_1, \ldots, u_{k-1})$,

7 $$Q = \begin{bmatrix} 0 & 0 \\ 0 & 2I \end{bmatrix}$$

is a $[(k+1)n + km] \times [(k+1)n + km]$ in which I is the $km \times km$ identity matrix,

8 $$R = \begin{bmatrix} -(I+A) & I & 0 & \cdots & 0 & -B & 0 & \cdots & \cdots & 0 \\ 0 & -(I+A) & I & 0 & 0 & 0 & -B & 0 & \cdots & 0 \\ \cdots & \cdots & \cdots & \cdots & \cdots & \cdots & \cdots & \cdots & \cdots & \cdots \\ 0 & \cdots & 0 & -(I+A) & I & 0 & 0 & \cdots & 0 & -B \\ I & 0 & \cdots & \cdots & 0 & 0 & \cdots & \cdots & \cdots & 0 \\ 0 & \cdots & \cdots & \cdots & I & 0 & \cdots & \cdots & \cdots & 0 \end{bmatrix}$$

is a $(k+2)n \times [(k+1)n + km]$ matrix and

9 $$c = (0, 0, \ldots, c_0, c_k) \in E^{(k+2)n}. \quad \square$$

Note that there is no linear term in the cost function of problem (6), and hence an optimal solution to (6) exists whenever a feasible solution exists [corollary (2.23)]. Since there are no constraints in (6) of the form $\alpha^i \leqq z^i \leqq \beta^i$, a feasible solution exists if R has rank $(k+2)n$.

10 **Exercise.** Show that assumptions (4) and (5) imply that R has rank $(k+2)n$. $\square$

The only question we might wish to investigate before attempting to solve problem (6) is whether it has a unique optimal solution.

11 **Lemma.** Problem (6) [and hence problem (1)] has a unique optimal solution.

Proof. According to theorem (3.1), we need only show that $\mathfrak{N}(Q) \cap \mathfrak{N}(R) = \{0\}$. Clearly, the null space of Q is the set of vectors $\tilde{z}$ of the form $\tilde{z} = (x_0, x_1, \ldots, x_k, 0, \ldots, 0)$. Thus we must examine the equation

$$R\tilde{z} = \begin{bmatrix} -(I+A) & I & 0 & \cdots & \cdots & 0 \\ 0 & -(I+A) & I & 0 & \cdots & 0 \\ \cdots & \cdots & \cdots & \cdots & \cdots & \cdots \\ 0 & \cdots & \cdots & \cdots & -(I+A) & I \\ I & 0 & \cdots & \cdots & \cdots & 0 \\ 0 & \cdots & \cdots & \cdots & 0 & I \end{bmatrix} \begin{bmatrix} x_0 \\ x_1 \\ \cdot \\ \cdot \\ \cdot \\ x_k \end{bmatrix} = 0.$$

Note that the next-to-the-bottom block of rows in (12) yield

13 $$x_0 = 0.$$

We may now start with the top block of rows and successively determine that

14
$$\begin{aligned} x_1 &= (I + A)x_0 = 0 \\ x_2 &= (I + A)x_1 = 0 \\ &\cdots\cdots\cdots\cdots \\ x_k &= (I + A)x_{k-1} = 0. \end{aligned}$$

Consequently, $\mathfrak{N}(Q) \cap \mathfrak{N}(R) = \{0\}$, which is sufficient to guarantee that (6) has a unique optimal solution. □

We now apply theorem (4.4) to obtain a set of equations from which the optimal solution $\hat{z}$ to problem (6) can be computed. Since for this case $\alpha^i = -\infty$ and $\beta^i = +\infty$ for $i = 1, 2, \ldots, (k+1)n + km$, we obtain from (4.4) that a vector $\hat{z}$ satisfying

15
$$R\hat{z} = c$$

is optimal if and only if there exists a vector $\psi \in E^{(k+1)n+km}$ such that

16
$$\langle r_i,\psi\rangle - \langle q_i,\hat{z}\rangle = 0 \qquad i = 1, 2, \ldots, (k+1)n + km.$$

We may write (16) in matrix form as

17
$$R^T\psi - Q\hat{z} = 0.$$

Combining (15) and (17), we see that a solution $(\hat{z},\psi)$ to the matrix equation

18
$$\begin{bmatrix} -Q & R^T \\ R & 0 \end{bmatrix} \begin{bmatrix} \hat{z} \\ \psi \end{bmatrix} = \begin{bmatrix} 0 \\ c \end{bmatrix}$$

will yield the desired optimal solution $\hat{z}$. It should now be clear why we stopped to establish the rank of R and the uniqueness of the optimal solution $\hat{z}$ to problem (6), for it now follows immediately from theorem (3.6) that the matrix on the left-hand side of (18) is nonsingular. Therefore we obtain

19
$$\begin{bmatrix} \hat{z} \\ \psi \end{bmatrix} = \begin{bmatrix} -Q & R^T \\ R & 0 \end{bmatrix}^{-1} \begin{bmatrix} 0 \\ c \end{bmatrix}.$$

The actual computation of $\hat{z}$ requires the inversion of a matrix whose dimensions can be quite large even for a relatively simple problem. However, this matrix contains many zeros, which helps in the numerical inversion. The following example should give some idea of the degree of difficulty involved in solving the problem by this method.

20 **Example.** Let $n = 2$, $m = 1$, and $k = 4$, and let system (2) be of the specific form

21 $$x_{i+1} - x_i = \begin{bmatrix} -1 & 1 \\ -2 & -2 \end{bmatrix} x_i + \begin{bmatrix} 0 \\ 1 \end{bmatrix} u_i.$$

The initial state is taken as $c_0 = (2,2)$, and the terminal state is taken as $c_4 = (0,0)$. It is easily verified that (21) is a completely controllable system.

In this case R is the (12×14)-dimensional matrix

22 $$R = \left[\begin{array}{cc|cc|cc|cc|cc|c|c|c|c|c}
0 & -1 & 1 & 0 & 0 & 0 & 0 & 0 & 0 & 0 & 0 & 0 & 0 & 0 \\
2 & 1 & 0 & 1 & 0 & 0 & 0 & 0 & 0 & 0 & -1 & 0 & 0 & 0 \\
\hline
0 & 0 & 0 & -1 & 1 & 0 & 0 & 0 & 0 & 0 & 0 & 0 & 0 & 0 \\
0 & 0 & 2 & 1 & 0 & 1 & 0 & 0 & 0 & 0 & 0 & -1 & 0 & 0 \\
\hline
0 & 0 & 0 & 0 & 0 & -1 & 1 & 0 & 0 & 0 & 0 & 0 & 0 & 0 \\
0 & 0 & 0 & 0 & 2 & 1 & 0 & 1 & 0 & 0 & 0 & 0 & -1 & 0 \\
\hline
0 & 0 & 0 & 0 & 0 & 0 & 0 & -1 & 1 & 0 & 0 & 0 & 0 & 0 \\
0 & 0 & 0 & 0 & 0 & 0 & 2 & 1 & 0 & 1 & 0 & 0 & 0 & -1 \\
\hline
1 & 0 & 0 & 0 & 0 & 0 & 0 & 0 & 0 & 0 & 0 & 0 & 0 & 0 \\
0 & 1 & 0 & 0 & 0 & 0 & 0 & 0 & 0 & 0 & 0 & 0 & 0 & 0 \\
\hline
0 & 0 & 0 & 0 & 0 & 0 & 0 & 0 & 1 & 0 & 0 & 0 & 0 & 0 \\
0 & 0 & 0 & 0 & 0 & 0 & 0 & 0 & 0 & 1 & 0 & 0 & 0 & 0
\end{array}\right].$$

The matrix

23 $$\begin{bmatrix} -Q & R^T \\ R & 0 \end{bmatrix}$$

is 26×26 and would require such a large space to write down that it is omitted here. The interested reader may pursue this to verify that the optimal control sequence is

24 $$\hat{u} = (-\tfrac{14}{23}, \tfrac{10}{23}, \tfrac{22}{23}, \tfrac{28}{23}). \quad \square$$

It is clear from this example that even simple problems become fairly cumbersome with this approach. One reason is that no account has been taken of the particular nature of the equality constraints. We have already pointed out in (1.12) that it may sometimes be more convenient to use an alternative approach for converting a control problem into Basic Problem form. We shall now see what simplifications can be achieved by taking into account the structure of the system equation.

SUBST OF STATE EQN INTO DIFF INDEX

Solution of (1) by Alternative Transcription

Solving problem (2) for x_k, with $x_0 = c_0$, we obtain

25
$$x_k = (I + A)^k c_0 + \sum_{i=0}^{k-1} (I + A)^{k-i-1} Bu_i,$$

and problem (1) is now seen to be equivalent to the problem:

26   Minimize $\tfrac{1}{2}\langle \mathfrak{u}, Q\mathfrak{u} \rangle$ subject to the constraint $R\mathfrak{u} = c$, where $Q = 2I$, I being the $km \times km$ identity matrix

27     $$R = [(I + A)^{k-1}B | (I + A)^{k-2}B | \cdots | (I + A)B | B],$$

and

28     $$c = c_k - (I + A)^k c_0. \qquad \square$$

Problem (26) is clearly of the form of QP (2.1).

Note the several significant differences in this reformulation. First (since $k \geqq n$), the matrix appearing in the assumption of complete controllability (5) is a submatrix of R, as given by (27). It follows immediately that R has rank n. Thus a feasible solution to this problem always exists. Second, Q is a positive-definite matrix, and so the optimal solution exists and is unique. Obviously, these facts are now much easier to establish than they were previously.

Now consider the solution of this problem. It can easily be verified from (4.4) that a necessary and sufficient condition for a control sequence $\hat{\mathfrak{u}}$ to be optimal is that there exist a vector ψ such that

NO MATRIX FORM

29
$$\begin{bmatrix} -Q & R^T \\ R & 0 \end{bmatrix} \begin{bmatrix} \hat{\mathfrak{u}} \\ \psi \end{bmatrix} = \begin{bmatrix} 0 \\ c \end{bmatrix}$$

is satisfied. As in (18), the matrix in (29) is nonsingular, and hence it may be inverted to find $\hat{\mathfrak{u}}$. Note, however, the dimension of the matrix in (29) is $(km + n) \times (km + n)$, which is significantly lower than $[km + (2k + 3)n] \times [km + (2k + 3)n]$, the dimension of the matrix in (18). For example (20) this works out to be 6×6 in comparison with 26×26 in (22).

However, we still have not taken full advantage of the structure of the problem. Since $Q = 2I$, we may solve the first set of equations in (29) for $\hat{\mathfrak{u}}$, which yields

30     $$\hat{\mathfrak{u}} = \tfrac{1}{2} R^T \psi.$$

This, in turn, may be substituted into the second set of equations in (29) to obtain

31     $$R\hat{\mathfrak{u}} = \tfrac{1}{2} R R^T \psi = c.$$

Since R has full row rank, the matrix RR^T is positive definite[1] and hence is nonsingular. Therefore

32 $$\psi = 2(RR^T)^{-1}c,$$

and substitution into (30) yields

33 $$\hat{\mathfrak{u}} = R^T(RR^T)^{-1}c.$$

Thus by taking full advantage of the structure of this problem we need only invert the $n \times n$ matrix RR^T to obtain the optimal solution $\hat{\mathfrak{u}}$. This is indeed a significant improvement over the previous approach, since the dimension RR^T is independent of k. To illustrate the difference let us again solve the problem in example (20).

34 **Example.** Let $n = 2$, $m = 1$, and $k = 4$, and let system (2) be of the specific form

$$x_{i+1} - x_i = \begin{bmatrix} -1 & 1 \\ -2 & -2 \end{bmatrix} x_i + \begin{bmatrix} 0 \\ 1 \end{bmatrix} u_i,$$

with $c_0 = (2,2)$ and $c_4 = (0,0)$.

Evaluating R and c, we obtain

35 $$R = \begin{bmatrix} 7 & 3 & 1 & 0 \\ 15 & 7 & 3 & 1 \end{bmatrix} \qquad c = (-2,-2).$$

Consequently,

36 $$RR^T = \begin{bmatrix} 59 & 129 \\ 129 & 284 \end{bmatrix}$$

and

37 $$\hat{\mathfrak{u}} = (-14/23, 10/23, 22/23, 28/23). \quad \square$$

Thus, while the alternative transcription of an optimal control problem into Basic Problem form may not always be practical for nonlinear problems, it does offer significant advantages for many problems with linear dynamics.

Before we leave the miminum-energy problem (1), however, we must consider one more approach to its solution.

The Control Approach to the Minimum-energy Problem

By the "control approach" to the mimimum-energy problem (1) we shall mean the examination of this problem by means of the neces-

[1] For any $x \neq 0$ the quadratic form $\langle x, RR^Tx\rangle = \|R^Tx\|^2 > 0$, since $R^Tx \neq 0$, by the rank assumption.

sary conditions for optimality developed in Sections 4.1 and 4.2 [which can also be shown to be sufficient for problem (1)]. We may use either theorem (4.1.17) or theorem (4.2.34), for, as we shall see shortly, the hypotheses of both theorems are satisfied. For no reason other than to demonstrate its application, we shall use theorem (4.2.34), the discrete *maximum principle.*

Recall that in order to apply theorem (4.2.34) we must first examine the sets $\mathbf{f}_i(x_i,U_i)$ for $i = 0, 1, \ldots, k-1$, which for problem (1) are given by

38 $$\mathbf{f}_i(x,U_i) = \{\mathbf{v} = (v^0,v): v^0 = \|u_i\|^2, \quad v = Ax + Bu \text{ for some } u \in U_i\}.$$

It may be verified that for every $x \in E^n$ these sets are b_0-directionally convex [see (4.2.1)], where $b_0 = (-1,0, \ldots ,0) \in E^{n+1}$, as required in assumption (4.2.11). All the other assumptions made in Section 4.1 are obviously satisfied. Therefore we may apply the necessary-conditions theorem (4.2.34) to problem (1).

39 **Exercise.** Show that in applying theorem (4.2.34) to problem (1) we must take $p^0 \neq 0$, and hence we may choose $p^0 = -1$. [*Hint:* See (4.1.45). What role does controllability play here?] □

40 **Exercise.** Show that if a feasible control sequence for problem (1) satisfies the conditions of theorem (4.2.34) with $p_i^0 = -1$ for $i = 0, 1, \ldots, k$, then it must be optimal; i.e., the maximum principle (4.2.34) is also a sufficient condition of optimality for this problem [*Hint:* Adapt corollary (3.6.9)]. □

Applying theorem (4.2.34), together with the results in (39) and (40), to problem (1), we find that a control sequence $\hat{\mathfrak{u}} = (\hat{u}_0,\hat{u}_1, \ldots ,\hat{u}_{k-1})$ and the corresponding trajectory $\hat{\mathfrak{X}} = (\hat{x}_0,\hat{x}_1, \ldots ,\hat{x}_k)$ are optimal if and only if $\hat{x}_0 = c_0$, $\hat{x}_k = c_k$, and there exist n-dimensional costate vectors $p_0, p_1, \ldots, p_k$ satisfying

41 $$p_i - p_{i+1} = A^T p_{i+1} \qquad i = 0, 1, \ldots, k-1$$

such that

42 $$H(\hat{x}_i,\hat{u}_i,p_{i+1},p^0,i) = \max_{u_i \in U_i} H(\hat{x}_i,u_i,p_{i+1},p^0,i) \qquad i = 0, 1, \ldots, k-1,$$

where for this case the hamiltonian $H(\hat{x}_i,u_i,p_{i+1},p^0,i) = -\|u_i\|^2 + \langle p_{i+1}, A\hat{x}_i + Bu_i\rangle$, since $p^0 = -1$.

Since the hamiltonian $H(\hat{x}_i,u_i,p_{i+1},-1,i)$ consists of a negative-definite quadratic form in u_i and of a linear term in u_i, it is concave in u_i. Thus, since u_i is unconstrainted, $\hat{u}_i$ must satisfy

43 $$\frac{\partial}{\partial u} H(\hat{x}_i,\hat{u}_i,p_{i+1},-1,i) = -2\hat{u}_i + B^T p_{i+1} = 0 \qquad i = 0, 1, \ldots, k-1.$$

Consequently,

44 $$\hat{u}_i = \tfrac{1}{2}B^T p_{i+1} \qquad i = 0, 1, \ldots, k-1.$$

To obtain the optimal control sequence $\hat{\mathfrak{u}} = (\hat{u}_0,\hat{u}_1, \ldots ,\hat{u}_{k-1})$ we now solve equations (2), (41), and (44), with the boundary conditions $x_0 = c_0$ and $x_k = c_k$.

Substituting (41) in (2), we obtain

45 $$\hat{x}_{i+1} - \hat{x}_i = A\hat{x}_i + \tfrac{1}{2}BB^T p_{i+1} \qquad i = 0, 1, \ldots, k-1.$$

Solving (41) for p_{i+1} in terms of p_k, we have

46 $$p_{i+1} = [(I + A)^T]^{k-i-1}p_k \qquad i = 0, 1, \ldots, k-1.$$

We may now use (46) to eliminate p_{i+1} in (45), obtaining

47 $$\hat{x}_{i+1} - \hat{x}_i = A\hat{x}_i + \tfrac{1}{2}BB^T[(I + A)^T]^{k-i-1}p_k$$

Next we solve (47) for $\hat{x}_k$ in terms of $\hat{x}_0$ and $\hat{p}_k$ and obtain

48 $$\hat{x}_k = (I + A)^k\hat{x}_0 + \tfrac{1}{2}\sum_{i=0}^{k-1} (I + A)^{k-i-1}BB^T[(I + A)^{k-i-1}]^T p_k.$$

If we let

49 $$M = \tfrac{1}{2}\sum_{i=0}^{k-1} (I + A)^{k-i-1}BB^T[(I + A)^{k-i-1}]^T$$

and substitute for $\hat{x}_k$ and $\hat{x}_0$ in (48), we arrive at the following equation for p_k:

50 $$Mp_k = c_k - (I + A)^k c_0.$$

It is left as an exercise to verify that equation (50) is equivalent to equation (31) (with $\psi = p_k$); that is to say,

$$M = \tfrac{1}{2}RR^T,$$

where R is as defined in (27). Therefore M is invertible, and

$$p_k = M^{-1}c,$$

where $c = c_k - (I + A)^k c_0$. From (46) and (44) we now determine that

51 $$\hat{u}_i = \tfrac{1}{2}B^T[(I + A)^T]^{k-i-1}M^{-1}c \qquad i = 0, 1, \ldots, k-1.$$

52 **Exercise.** Consider the dynamical system

$$* \quad x_{i+1} - x_i = f_i(x_i,u_i),\ i = 0, 1, \ldots, k-1,$$

with $x_i \in E^n$, $u_i \in E^m$, and the $f_i(\cdot,\cdot)$ continuously differentiable in both arguments. Suppose that $\hat{x}_0, \hat{x}_1, \ldots, \hat{x}_k$ is the nominal trajectory which the system is required to follow and that this trajectory can be achieved by applying the control sequence $\hat{u}_0, \hat{u}_1, \ldots, \hat{u}_{k-1}$ to (*), with $x_0 = \hat{x}_0$. Now suppose that there are some difficulties in setting the initial state of (*) and that we must accept $x_0 = \hat{x}_0 + \delta\hat{x}_0$, where $\delta\hat{x}_0$ is measured precisely and is known to be small. To account for this discrepancy in the initial state, the entire control sequence must be trimmed to a new set of values $\hat{u}_0 + \delta\hat{u}_0$, $\hat{u}_1 + \delta\hat{u}_1, \ldots, \hat{u}_{k-1} + \delta\hat{u}_{k-1}$. A set of control corrections $\delta\hat{u}_0, \ldots, \delta\hat{u}_{k-1}$, can be computed to first order accuracy by solving the following problem:

$$** \quad \text{Minimize } \tfrac{1}{2}\sum_{i=0}^{k-1} \langle \delta u_i, Q_i \delta u_i\rangle + \tfrac{1}{2}\sum_{i=1}^{k} \langle \delta x_i, R_i \delta x_i\rangle, \text{ subject to}$$

$$\delta x_{i+1} - \delta x_i = A_i\delta x_i + B_i\delta u_i \qquad i = 0, \ldots, k-1,$$

$$\delta x_0 = \delta\hat{x}_0,$$

where $A_i = \partial f_i(\hat{x}_i,\hat{u}_i)/\partial x_i$, $B_i = \partial f_i(\hat{x}_i,\hat{u}_i)/\partial u_i$, and Q_i, R_i are positive definite, symmetric matrices which can be used as a design parameter.

Show that the optimal control sequence $\delta\hat{u}_0, \delta\hat{u}_1, \ldots, \delta\hat{u}_{k-1}$ for (**) is unique, and if $\delta\hat{x}_0, \delta\hat{x}_1, \ldots, \delta\hat{x}_k$ is the corresponding optimal trajectory, then, provided all the inverses used exist,

$$\delta\hat{u}_i = Q_i^{-1}B_i^T K_{i+1}(I - B_iQ_i^{-1}B_i^TK_{i+1})^{-1}(A_i + I)\delta\hat{x}_i,$$

$$i = 0, 1, \ldots, k-1,$$

where for $i = 0, 1, \ldots, k-1$, K_{i+1} is an $n \times n$ matrix defined by the Riccati type equation

$$K_i = -R_i + (A_i + I)^T K_{i+1}(I - B_iQ_i^{-1}B_i^TK_{i+1})^{-1}(A_i + I)$$

$$K_k = R_k.$$

Thus, for problem (**), the control approach yields the optimal control sequence in linear feedback form. □

It is clear from the preceding that for the minimum energy problem, the control approach works as well as the better of the two approaches discussed before it. This is also true for the particular minimum-quadratic-cost problem which was presented in exercise (52). The control approach depends entirely on our ability to express the optimal controls $\hat{u}_i$ in terms of the optimal states $\hat{x}_i$ and of the costates p_i. When the elimination of the controls $\hat{u}_i$ from the necessary conditions equations cannot be performed readily, as in problem (53), the control approach cannot be applied.

53 **The minimum-quadratic-cost problem.** Consider the dynamical system governed by the difference equation

54 $$x_{i+1} - x_i = Ax_i + Bu_i \qquad i = 0, 1, \ldots, k-1,$$

where the notation is the same as before. The initial state x_0 is required to belong to a linear manifold described by

55 $$G_0 x_0 = c_0,$$

where G_0 is an $l_0 \times n$ matrix of rank l_0 and $c_0 \in E^{l_0}$ is a fixed vector, and the terminal state x_k must belong to the linear manifold

56 $$G_k x_k = c_k,$$

where G_k is an $l_k \times n$ matrix of rank l_k and $c_k \in E^{l_k}$ is a fixed vector. Find a control sequence $\hat{\mathfrak{U}} = (\hat{u}_0, \hat{u}_1, \ldots, \hat{u}_k)$ and a corresponding trajectory $\hat{\mathfrak{X}} = (\hat{x}_0, \hat{x}_1, \ldots, \hat{x}_k)$ which minimize

57 $$\tfrac{1}{2}\langle \mathfrak{X}, Q_x \mathfrak{X} \rangle + \tfrac{1}{2}\langle \mathfrak{U}, Q_u \mathfrak{U} \rangle,$$

subject to the constraints (54) to (56), where Q_x and Q_u are symmetric positive-semidefinite matrices. □

As in the minimum-energy problem (1), we shall make the following assumptions:

58 **Assumption.** $k \geqq n$. □

59 **Assumption.** System (54) is completely controllable. □

Obviously, problem (53) is a special case of the quadratic control problem (1.2). The matrix Q in (1.4) assumes for this case the form

60 $$Q = \begin{bmatrix} Q_x & 0 \\ 0 & Q_u \end{bmatrix}.$$

The conversion of problem (53) into a quadratic programming problem should by now be routine. Thus the cost function becomes

61 $$f(z) = \tfrac{1}{2}\langle z, Qz \rangle,$$

where $z = (x_0, x_1, \ldots, x_k, u_0, u_1, \ldots, u_{k-1})$ and Q is as given in (60). The equality constraints become

62 $$Rz = c,$$

where R is the matrix

63
$$R = \left[\begin{array}{cccccc|ccccc} -(I+A) & I & 0 & \cdots & \cdots & 0 & -B & 0 & \cdots & \cdots & 0 \\ 0 & -(I+A) & I & 0 & \cdots & 0 & 0 & -B & 0 & \cdots & 0 \\ 0 & \cdots & \cdots & \cdots & -(I+A) & I & 0 & \cdots & \cdots & 0 & -B \\ G_0 & 0 & \cdots & \cdots & \cdots & 0 & 0 & \cdots & \cdots & \cdots & 0 \\ 0 & \cdots & \cdots & \cdots & 0 & G_k & 0 & \cdots & \cdots & \cdots & 0 \end{array}\right]$$

and $c = (0,0, \ldots ,0,c_0,c_k)$.

Since there is no linear term in the cost function, it follows immediately from corollary (2.23) that an optimal solution to this problem exists whenever a feasible solution exists. Moreover, assumptions (58) and (59), together with the fact that there are no inequality constraints present, guarantee that a feasible solution exists. Hence an optimal solution to this problem always exists.

There is very little that can be said about uniqueness of the optimal solutions to problem (53) other than that we can check the conditions of theorem (3.1); that is, we must show that $\mathfrak{N}(Q) \cap \mathfrak{N}(R) = \{0\}$. This may be done by examining the matrix

64
$$\begin{bmatrix} Q \\ \hdashline R \end{bmatrix}$$

to see if it has full rank. Alternatively, since R has full rank [because of assumptions (58) and (59), together with the full-rank assumption on G_0 and G_k], we may, as a consequence of theorem (2.6), determine if the matrix

$$\begin{bmatrix} Q & R^T \\ R & 0 \end{bmatrix}$$

is nonsingular.

Because of the special form of Q [see (60)], the rank of (64) becomes easier to check when either Q_x or Q_u is positive definite. For instance, if Q_u is positive definite, then the rank of the matrix in (64) is the same as the rank of the matrix

65
$$\begin{bmatrix} & & Q_x & & \\ \hdashline -(I+A) & I & 0 & \cdots & 0 \\ \cdots & \cdots & \cdots & \cdots & \cdots \\ 0 & \cdots & \cdots & -(I+A) & I \\ G_0 & \cdots & \cdots & \cdots & 0 \\ 0 & \cdots & \cdots & \cdots & G_k \end{bmatrix}$$

Solution of (53) by Direct Transcription

The solution of the quadratic programming problem formulated above is so similar in procedure to the corresponding solution of the minimum-energy problem (1) that we shall not repeat it. Suffice it to say that we eventually arrive at the point where we must solve the equation

66 $$\begin{bmatrix} -Q & R^T \\ R & 0 \end{bmatrix} \begin{bmatrix} \hat{z} \\ \psi \end{bmatrix} = \begin{bmatrix} 0 \\ c \end{bmatrix}.$$

Consequently, whenever the optimal solution to problem (53) is unique, we can solve (66) by inverting the matrix on the left-hand side.

It is appropriate to note that (66) may be solved for an optimal $\hat{z}$ even when the matrix appearing on the left-hand side is singular. The existence of an optimal solution to problem (53), together with the fact that (66) expresses a necessary and sufficient condition for optimality, guarantees that (66) has at least one solution. Furthermore, every solution of (66) is also an optimal solution to (53).

Solution of (53) by Alternative Transcription

In the alternate transcription of problem (53) into a quadratic programming problem, we eliminate all the x_i vectors other than x_0 by solving for them by means of (54). In the minimum-energy problem (1) this was very easy to do because only the terminal constraint involved any of these x_i. Now, however, the x_i also appear in the cost function, which makes the conversion to a quadratic programming problem much more complicated.

As before, we solve (54) for the x_i vectors, obtaining

67 $$x_i = (I + A)^i x_0 + \sum_{j=0}^{i-1} (I + A)^{i-j-1} B u_j \qquad i = 1, 2, \ldots, k.$$

If we define the vector z in E^{km+n} to be

68 $$z = (x_0, u_0, u_1, \ldots, u_{k-1}),$$

then expression (67) becomes

69 $$x_i = M_i z \qquad i = 1, 2, \ldots, k,$$

where M_i is the $n \times (km + n)$ matrix

70 $$M_i = [(I + A)^i \,\vdots\, (I + A)^{i-1} B \,\vdots\, \cdots \,\vdots\, (I + A) B \,\vdots\, B \,\vdots\, 0 \cdots \vdots\, 0 \,\vdots\,] \qquad \text{for } i = 1, 2, \ldots, k.$$

Hence the trajectory $\mathfrak{X} = (x_0, x_1, \ldots, x_k)$ is given by

71 $$\mathfrak{X} = Mz,$$

where M is the $(k+1)n \times (km+n)$ matrix

72 $$M = \begin{bmatrix} I \;\; 0 \;\; \cdots \;\; 0 \\ M_1 \\ M_2 \\ \cdots\cdots\cdots \\ M_k \end{bmatrix} = \begin{bmatrix} I & 0 & \cdots & \cdots & \cdots & 0 \\ I+A & B & 0 & \cdots & \cdots & 0 \\ (I+A)^2 & (I+A)B & B & 0 & \cdots & 0 \\ \cdots & \cdots & \cdots & \cdots & \cdots & \cdots \\ (I+A)^k & (I+A)^{k-1}B & & \cdots & \cdots & B \end{bmatrix}.$$

The cost function (57) becomes

73 $$\langle \mathfrak{X}, Q_x \mathfrak{X} \rangle + \langle \mathfrak{U}, Q_u \mathfrak{U} \rangle = \langle z, Pz \rangle,$$

where

74 $$P = M^T Q_x M + N$$

and

$$N = \begin{bmatrix} 0 & 0 \\ 0 & Q_u \end{bmatrix}.$$

It is easily verified that P is a symmetric positive-semidefinite matrix.

The boundary constraints may now be reformulated in terms of z. The initial constraint manifold (55) becomes

75 $$G_0 M_0 z = c_0,$$

where M_0 is the $n \times (km+n)$ matrix

76 $$M_0 = [I \vdots 0 \vdots \;\cdots\; \vdots 0].$$

The terminal constraint manifold (56), together with (69), yields

77 $$G_k M_k z = c_k,$$

where M_k is as defined in (70).

The matrix M_0 is clearly of rank n, and assumptions (58) and (59) guarantee that M_k has rank n. It may be verified that $G_0 M_0$ and $G_k M_k$ have rank l_0 and l_k, respectively, as a consequence.

From this point we proceed to minimize (73) subject to the equality constraints (75) and (77). It should be clear that we shall once again arrive at the expression

78 $$\begin{bmatrix} -P & R^T \\ R & 0 \end{bmatrix} \begin{bmatrix} \hat{z} \\ \psi \end{bmatrix} = \begin{bmatrix} 0 \\ c \end{bmatrix},$$

where $\hat{z}$ is the optimal solution, ψ is the corresponding multiplier, R is the $(l_0 + l_k) \times (km+n)$ matrix given by

79 $$R = \begin{bmatrix} G_0 M_0 \\ \hdashline G_k M_k \end{bmatrix},$$

and $c = (c_0, c_k)$.

Note that it is not immediately obvious that a unique solution to optimization problem (53) implies the nonsingularity of the matrix in (78), since R may not have full rank.

80 **Exercise.** Show that the uniqueness of the optimal solution to problem (53) implies that R in (79) has rank $(l_0 + l_k)$. [*Hint:* Show that $\mathfrak{N}(G_0) \cap \mathfrak{N}(G_k(I + A)^k) = \{0\}$ follows from the uniqueness of the optimal solution and is sufficient for full rank of R.] $\square$

There will not, in general, be any way to further decompose (78), as we did in the minimum-energy problem. Hence the solution will require the inversion of a $(km + n + l_0 + l_k) \times (km + n + l_0 + l_k)$-dimensional matrix. This is still quite a reduction in dimension in comparison with the previous approach.

We conclude this section with a summary of some of our observations concerning the relative advantages and disadvantages of various approaches to solving unconstrained quadratic control problems.

The approach which is based on a direct transcription into an equivalent quadratic programming problem has the disadvantage that the dimensions of the matrices involved may get quite large, even for a relatively simple problem. However, these matrices have many zeros, and there are currently being developed methods of handling sparse matrices which may at least partially negate this disadvantage. This method has the advantage that the quadratic programming problem is set up and solved in a very straightforward manner which does not vary with the particular form of the control problem. It can also be applied to the general case of QCP (1.2).

The alternative method for setting up the quadratic programming problem entails first eliminating the state variables x_i for $i = 1, 2, \ldots, k$ by solving for them from the difference equation. In the two classes of problems considered in this section, this approach substantially reduced the dimensions of the resulting problem. As was demonstrated in the second class of problems, in some cases the initial setting up of the quadratic programming problem may be somewhat complicated. However, if computation speed is a critical factor, this disadvantage is greatly outweighed by the reduction in the dimensions of the problem. This approach can also be applied to the general case of QCP (1.2).

The control approach takes advantage of the specialized form of the necessary conditions which were developed for control problems. While the control approach is very useful for solving simple, unconstrained problems, it is not a satisfactory tool for dealing with problems that include state space constraints, or problems with control constraints and cost functions depending on the states, etc. Since this text is primarily concerned with constrained minimization problems, we leave to the reader the extension of the results indicated in (52) to more general situations.

6.6 QUADRATIC CONTROL PROBLEMS WITH INEQUALITY CONSTRAINTS

In Section 6.1 it was shown that the most general form of the quadratic control problem can be reduced to a quadratic programming problem. Section 6.5 contained some examples of how we would proceed if there were no inequality constraints. The remainder of this chapter will be devoted to the presentation of an algorithm for solving the quadratic programming problem (under suitable assumptions, which will be stated later) in the case when inequality constraints are present. However, before we proceed, let us consider the nature of the quadratic programming problems resulting from different special cases of the quadratic control problem. For our purposes, the two classes of problems considered in Section 6.5, with some additional inequality constraints, will serve nicely.

1 **The constrained minimum-energy problem.** (Compare with problem (5.1).) Consider a dynamical system described by

2 $$x_{i+1} - x_i = Ax_i + Bu_i \qquad i = 0, 1, \ldots, k-1,$$

with the initial and terminal constraints

3 $$x_0 = c_0 \qquad \text{and} \qquad x_k = c_k,$$

and with the control constraints

4 $$|u_i^j| \leqq 1 \qquad j = 1, 2, \ldots, m, \; i = 0, 1, \ldots, k-1,$$

where $u_i = (u_i^1, u_i^2, \ldots, u_i^m)$ for $i = 0, 1, \ldots, k-1$. (The bound on the components of the control variables has been set at unity, but this is not really important, since we can always normalize a finite bound to unity.) Find a control sequence $\hat{\mathfrak{u}} = (\hat{u}_0, \hat{u}_1, \ldots, \hat{u}_{k-1})$ which minimizes

5 $$\sum_{i=0}^{k-1} \langle u_i, u_i \rangle,$$

subject to (2), (3) and (4). □

6 **Assumption.** $k \geqq n$. □

7 **Assumption.** System (2) is completely controllable. □

The transformation of problem (1) into a quadratic programming problem may again be accomplished by first eliminating the x_i for $i = 1, 2, \ldots, k$ by means of the difference equation, as was worked out in detail in Section 5. The resulting equivalent quadratic programming problem has the form

8 Minimize $\frac{1}{2}\langle \mathcal{U}, Q\mathcal{U} \rangle$ subject to the constraints

9 $R\mathcal{U} = c$

10 $-1 \leqq u^j \leqq 1 \qquad j = 1, 2, \ldots, km,$

where $Q = 2I$,

11 $$R = [(I + A)^{k-1}B \vdots (I + A)^{k-2}B \vdots \cdots \vdots (I + A)B \vdots B],$$

and

12 $$c = c_k - (I + A)^k c_0. \quad \square$$

Note that (8) differs from (5.6) only by the inequality constraints (10).

There are two points about this problem which are significant with respect to the algorithms for solving quadratic programming problems. First, the variables in this problem are all bounded [see (10)]. Second, the matrix R appearing in (9) has rank n, as is easily deduced from (7). This is an assumption which is required by the algorithms discussed later.

Now let us consider what happens to the minimum-quadratic-cost problem (5.53) when we add bounds for the control variables.

13 **The constrained minimum-quadratic-cost problem.** Consider a dynamical system governed by the difference equation

14 $$x_{i+1} - x_i = Ax_i + Bu_i \qquad i = 0, 1, \ldots, k - 1,$$

with initial and terminal constraints

15 $$G_0x_0 = c_0 \qquad G_kx_k = c_k,$$

where G_0 is an $l_0 \times n$ matrix of rank l_0 and G_k is an $l_k \times n$ matrix of rank l_k; with control constraints

16 $$|u_i^j| \leqq 1 \qquad j = 1, 2, \ldots, m, i = 0, 1, \ldots, k - 1,$$

where $u_i = (u_i^1, u_i^2, \ldots, u_i^m)$, and with cost function

17 $$\langle \mathcal{X}, Q_x\mathcal{X} \rangle + \langle \mathcal{U}, Q_u\mathcal{U} \rangle,$$

where Q_x and Q_u are symmetric positive-semidefinite matrices, $\mathcal{X} = (x_0,x_1, \ldots ,x_k)$ and $\mathcal{U} = (u_0,u_1, \ldots ,u_{k-1})$. Find a control sequence $\mathcal{U}$ which minimizes (17) subject to (14), (15), and (16). □

18 **Assumption.** $k \geqq n$. □

19 **Assumption.** System (14) is completely controllable. □

We convert this problem to a quadratic programming problem by the alternative transcription method described in Section 5, beginning with equation (67). It can easily be verified that if we define

20 $$z \triangleq (x_0,u_1, \ldots ,u_{k-1}),$$

then the resulting quadratic programming problem is:

21 Minimize $\langle z,Pz\rangle$ subject to the constraints

22 $$Rz = c$$

23 $$|z^i| \leqq 1 \qquad i = n+1, n+2, \ldots , n+km,$$

where P, R, and c are as defined in (5.74) and (5.79). □

Note that it is no longer true that all the variables are bounded, even though the controls are bounded. Specifically, the first n components of z corresponding to x_0 are unbounded. In general, then, not all quadratic programming problems which arise from a control problem have all variables bounded.

In the following sections we shall derive two algorithms for solving quadratic programming problems. Like the simplex algorithm, these algorithms are combinational in nature, and they either determine an optimal solution or determine that an optimal solution does not exist.

6.7 OPTIMALITY CONDITIONS FOR THE CANONICAL QUADRATIC PROGRAMMING PROBLEM

The algorithms we are about to discuss apply to quadratic programming problems of the following form.

1 **The canonical quadratic programming problem (CQP).** Given an $m \times n (m \leqq n)$ full-rank matrix R, an $n \times n$ symmetric positive-semidefinite matrix Q, and vectors $c \in E^m$ and $d \in E^n$, find a $\hat{z} \in E^n$ which minimizes

2 $$\tfrac{1}{2}\langle z,Qz\rangle + \langle z,d\rangle$$

subject to the constraints

3 $$Rz = c \qquad z \geqq 0. \quad \square$$

4 **Remark.** It follows from exercises (2.6) and (4.2) that the quadratic programming problem (1.1) can be reduced to the above canonical form. □

For the purpose of describing the algorithms for the solution of (1), the necessary and sufficient conditions for optimality as stated in theorems (3.3.5) and (3.6.1) are more convenient to work with than theorem (4.1). Thus, combining (3.3.5) and (3.6.1), we obtain the following result.

5 **Theorem.** A vector $z \in E^n$ is an optimal solution to CQP (1) if and only if there exist multipliers $\psi = (\psi^1,\psi^2, \ldots ,\psi^m)$ and $\xi = (\xi^1,\xi^2, \ldots ,\xi^n)$ such that

6
$$\begin{gathered} Qz + R^T\psi - \xi + d = 0 \qquad Rz - c = 0 \\ z \geqq 0 \qquad \xi \geqq 0 \qquad \langle z,\xi\rangle = 0. \end{gathered}$$
□

The above system of equations and inequalities can be written in a more symmetric form by decomposing the vector ψ into a positive part, which we denote by ψ_+, and a negative part, which we denote by $-\psi_-$. Thus let

7
$$\psi = \psi_+ - \psi_-,$$

with the restriction that

8
$$\psi_+ \geqq 0 \qquad \psi_- \geqq 0,$$

9
$$\psi_+^i\psi_-^i = 0 \qquad i = 1, 2, \ldots , m.$$

Note that (9) permits either ψ_+^i or ψ_-^i to be strictly positive, but not both at the same time. Because of (8), (9) can be written more compactly as

10
$$\langle\psi_+,\psi_-\rangle = 0.$$

Substituting from (7), (8), and (10) into (6) leads to the following system of equations and inequalities:

11
$$\begin{gathered} Qz - R^T\psi_- - \xi + R^T\psi_+ = -d \qquad Rz = c \\ z \geqq 0 \qquad \psi_- \geqq 0 \qquad \xi \geqq 0 \qquad \psi_+ \geqq 0 \\ \langle z,\xi\rangle = \langle\psi_+,\psi_-\rangle = 0. \end{gathered}$$

6.8 THE DERIVED MINIMIZATION PROBLEM

The effect of theorem (7.5) was to reduce the problem of solving the canonical quadratic programming problem (7.1) to that of solving system (7.11). In turn, a solution to this system can be obtained by solving the derived minimization problem stated below. It might be noted at this point that it is common practice in mathematical programming to find solutions to systems of equations and inequalities by solving a related optimization problem for which there exist efficient algorithms. As a case in point, we shall see later that a slight modification of the simplex algorithm can be used to solve the problem we are about to define, and hence to obtain a solution to CQP (7.1).

1 **The derived problem.** Minimize the linear form $\langle l,y \rangle$ subject to the constraints

2 $$Ax = g \qquad x \geqq 0$$
3 $$\langle v,w \rangle = 0,$$

where

$$x = (z,\psi_-,\xi,\psi_+,y) = (v,w,y) \in E^{2(n+m)+n}$$
$$v = (z,\psi_-) \in E^{n+m}, \qquad w = (\xi,\psi_+) \in E^{n+m}$$

4 $$A = \begin{bmatrix} Q & -R^T & -I & R^T & K \\ R & 0 & 0 & 0 & 0 \end{bmatrix} \qquad (n+m) \times [2(n+m)+n]$$

$$g = (-d,c) \in E^{n+m} \qquad l = (1,1, \ldots ,1) \in E^n$$

The matrices Q, R, d, and b are as defined in (7.1); the $n \times n$ matrix K will be specified in (9.2). □

In the remainder of this chapter we shall be using the terms *basic solution*, *nondegenerate basic solution*, etc., which are all defined and discussed in Section 5.6. The reader is strongly urged to review this section as well as Section 5.8, in which the procedure for generating adjacent extreme points is described.

5 **Definition.** A vector x is said to be a *usable basic solution* to the derived problem (1) if x is a basic solution to (2) and, in addition, satisfies (3). A usable basic solution which is a nondegenerate basic solution to (2) will be called a *usable nondegenerate basic solution.* □

6 **Remark.** Clearly, every usable basic solution x to problem (1) is a feasible solution; that is,

$$x \in \Omega' = \Omega \cap \{x: \langle v,w \rangle = 0\},$$

where

7 $$\Omega = \{x: Ax = g, x \geqq 0\}. \quad \square$$

8 **Lemma.** Suppose that the system of equations and inequalities (7.11) has a solution. Then $\hat{x} = (\hat{v},\hat{w},\hat{y})$ is an optimal solution for the derived problem (1) if and only if $(\hat{v},\hat{w})$ satisfies system (7.11).

Proof. For every $x \in \Omega'$, $\langle l,y \rangle \geq 0$. Furthermore, $\langle l,y \rangle = 0$ if and only if $y = 0$. The claimed result then follows. □

9 **Exercise.** Show that there is an extreme point of Ω, defined as in (7), at which the objective function $\langle l,y \rangle$ of the derived problem (1) attains its minimum. [*Hint:* The proof is almost identical to the proof of theorem (5.5.6).] □

The importance of exercise (9) lies in the fact that to find a solution to the derived problem we need only search over the extreme points of Ω. Since the simplex algorithm can be used to explore extreme points, the possibility of using a modification of the simplex algorithm readily comes to mind.

6.9 THE SIMPLEX ALGORITHM FOR QUADRATIC PROGRAMMING

We shall now consider an algorithm due to Wolfe [1] for solving the canonical quadratic programming problem (7.1). The popularity of this algorithm is unquestionably due to the ease with which it lends itself to computer coding. It is somewhat restricted in that it converges (demonstrably) only if the matrices appearing in the statement of CQP (7.1) satisfy the following additional condition:

1 **Assumption.** $\langle d,\eta \rangle = 0$ for every $\eta \in E^n$ satisfying $Q\eta = 0$ and $R\eta = 0$. □

Several sufficient conditions for the satisfaction of assumption (1) were given in Sections 6.2 and 6.3. Recall that, by theorem (2.3), this is a sufficient condition for CQP (7.1) to have an optimal solution.

We are now ready to consider the algorithm.

2 **Initialization.** First we must obtain a usable basic solution x_0 to the derived problem (8.1). This is done in two steps. We use the simplex algorithm (5.9.4) to obtain a basic feasible solution to the system

$$Rz = c \qquad z \geqq 0.$$

Let z_0 be the basic solution thus obtained, and let $\bar{J}(z_0) \subset \{1,2, \ldots ,n\}$ be the associated basis-indicator set [see (5.6.5)]. We can now define the remaining components of x_0, as well as the $n \times n$ *diagonal matrix* $K = [k_{ii}]$ appearing in (8.4), as follows:

For $i = 1, 2, \ldots, n$, $\xi_0^i = 0$.
For $i = 1, 2, \ldots, m$, $\psi_{-0}^i = \psi_{+0}^i = 0$.
For $i = 1, 2, \ldots, n$

$$k_{ii} = \begin{cases} \delta^i \triangleq (-d - Qz_0 + R^T\psi_{-0} + \xi_0 - R^T\psi_{+0})^i & \text{if } \delta^i \neq 0 \\ 1 & \text{if } \delta^i = 0. \end{cases}$$

$$y_0^i = \begin{cases} 1 & \text{if } \delta^i \neq 0 \\ 0 & \text{if } \delta^i = 0. \end{cases}$$

3 **Exercise.** Let x_0 and K be as defined above. Show that x_0 is a usable basic solution to the derived problem (8.1) and that $\bar{J}(x_0) = \bar{J}(z_0) \cup \{2(n + m) + 1, \ldots, 2(n + m) + n\}$ is an associated basis-indicator set. □

4 **The simplex algorithm for quadratic programming.** Suppose that x_N is a usable basic solution to the derived problem (8.1). Let $\bar{J}(x_N) \subset \{1, 2, \ldots, 2(n + m) + n\}$ be the basis-indicator set associated with x_N.

Step 1. Use the basic solution x_N in the simplex algorithm (5.9.4)† to compute an improved basic solution x_{N+1} to the problem:

5 Minimize $\langle l,y\rangle$, subject to the constraints $Ax = g \quad x \geqq 0$, with the following side condition:

6 If $j \in \bar{J}(x_N) \cap \{1, 2, \ldots, n + m\}$ do not admit $j + n + m$ into the basis-indicator set $\bar{J}(x_{N+1})$ for x_{N+1} and if $j \in \bar{J}(x_N) \cap \{n + m + 1, \ldots, 2(n + m)\}$ do not admit $j - (n + m)$ into the basis-indicator set $\bar{J}(x_{N+1})$.

If a basic feasible solution x_{N+1} cannot be constructed in accordance with (6), then stop; otherwise proceed to step 2. Note that x_{N+1} is a usable basic solution.

Step 2. If $\langle l,y_{N+1}\rangle = 0$, then stop. If $\langle l,y_{N+1}\rangle > 0$, set $x_N = x_{N+1}$ and return to step 1. □

To summarize, algorithm (4) can reach a stop command in one of two ways.

7 **Stop 1.** The algorithm, under condition (6), does not yield an improved basic solution to problem (5). □

8 **Remark.** We shall see later that whenever assumption (1) is satisfied, stop condition (7) coincides with the following stop condition. □

9 **Stop 2.** At some iteration $\langle l,y_N\rangle = 0$. In this case x_N is an optimal solution to the derived problem (8.1). The first n components of x_N, that is, z_N^i for $i = 1, 2, \ldots, n$, are an optimal solution to the canonical quadratic programming problem. □

10 **Exercise.** Show that algorithm (4) generates a finite sequence of usable basic solutions to the derived problem (8.1); that is, one of the

† Use the procedure in Section 5.10 whenever cycling occurs because of degeneracies.

stop commands must be executed in a finite number of steps. [*Hint:* First eliminate the possibility of obtaining an unbounded ray, $\{x(\theta): \theta \in [0,\infty)\}$, of the polyhedron Ω (8.7).] □

By exercise (10), algorithm (4) generates a finite number of usable basic solutions to the derived problem. The generation of new usable basic solutions stops when either condition (7) or condition (9) is reached. If condition (9) occurs, we are done. We shall now see that whenever condition (7) occurs, condition (9) occurs at the same time.

11 **Theorem.** Suppose that assumption (1) is satisfied. Let $\hat{x} = (\hat{z},\hat{\psi}_-,\hat{\xi},\hat{\psi}_+,\hat{y})$ be the last usable basic solution generated by algorithm (4) at which condition (7) has occurred. Then $\hat{y} = 0$, and $\hat{z}$ is an optimal solution to CQP (7.1).

Proof. Consider the linear programming problem:

12 Minimize $\langle l,y\rangle$ subject to the constraints

$$Ax = g \qquad \langle \hat{z},\xi\rangle = \langle \hat{\xi},z\rangle = \langle \hat{\psi}_+,\psi_-\rangle = \langle \hat{\psi}_-,\psi_+\rangle = 0$$
$$x \geqq 0,$$

where A, g, and x are as defined in (8.4). Expanding (12), we get:

13 Minimize $\langle l,y\rangle$ subject to the constraints

14
$$\begin{bmatrix} Q & -R^T & -I & R^T & K \\ R & 0 & 0 & 0 & 0 \\ \hat{\xi} & \hat{\psi}_+ & \hat{z} & \hat{\psi}_- & 0 \end{bmatrix} \begin{bmatrix} z \\ \psi_- \\ \xi \\ \psi_+ \\ y \end{bmatrix} = \begin{bmatrix} -d \\ c \\ 0 \end{bmatrix}$$

$$z \geqq 0 \qquad \psi_- \geqq 0 \qquad \xi \geqq 0 \qquad \psi_+ \geqq 0 \qquad y \geqq 0,$$

where $\hat{\xi}$, $\hat{\psi}_+$, $\hat{z}$, and $\hat{\psi}_-$ are considered to be row matrices.

Since algorithm (4) has examined all usable basic solutions to (5) which are adjacent to $\hat{x}$ and satisfy (6), and has found none of lower cost, we conclude that $\hat{x}$ must be an optimal solution to (14). We shall now see that this implies that $\hat{y} = 0$.

Because $\hat{x}$ is optimal for (14), there must exist, by theorem (5.5.1), multiplier vectors λ_1, λ_2, λ_3, and μ_1, μ_2, μ_3, μ_4, μ_5, of appropriate dimensions, such that

15 *a.* $Q\lambda_1 + R^T\lambda_2 + \hat{\xi}\lambda_3 - \mu_1 = 0$

b. $-R\lambda_1 + \hat{\psi}_+\lambda_3 - \mu_2 = 0$

c. $-\lambda_1 + \hat{z}\lambda_3 - \mu_3 = 0$

d. $R\lambda_1 + \hat{\psi}_-\lambda_3 - \mu_4 = 0$

e. $l + K^T\lambda_1 - \mu_5 = 0$

and

16 $a.\quad \mu_1 \geqq 0 \qquad \langle \mu_1, \hat{z} \rangle = 0$
$b.\quad \mu_2 \geqq 0 \qquad \langle \mu_2, \hat{\psi}_- \rangle = 0$
$c.\quad \mu_3 \geqq 0 \qquad \langle \mu_3, \hat{\xi} \rangle = 0$
$d.\quad \mu_4 \geqq 0 \qquad \langle \mu_4, \hat{\psi}_+ \rangle = 0$
$e.\quad \mu_5 \geqq 0 \qquad \langle \mu_5, \hat{y} \rangle = 0.$

Note that $\hat{y} = 0$ if and only if $\langle l, \hat{y} \rangle = 0$. We shall now see that $\langle l, \hat{y} \rangle = 0$ whenever the following identities hold:

17 $$Q\lambda_1 = 0$$
18 $$R\lambda_1 = 0$$
19 $$\langle \lambda_1, \hat{\xi} \rangle = 0.$$

Note that (17) and (18), with assumption (1), imply that

20 $$\langle d, \lambda_1 \rangle = 0.$$

Indeed, suppose that equations (17) to (19) hold. Then, taking the scalar product of both sides of (15*e*) with the vector $\hat{y}$, we obtain [with (16*e*)]

21 $$\langle \hat{y}, l \rangle = -\langle K\hat{y}, \lambda_1 \rangle.$$

Since $\hat{x}$ is a feasible solution, $A\hat{x} = g$; that is,

22 $$Q\hat{z} - R^T\hat{\psi}_- - \hat{\xi} + R^T\hat{\psi}_+ + K\hat{y} = -d.$$

Substituting $K\hat{y}$ in (21) from (22) and making use of (17) to (20), we obtain

23 $$\langle \hat{y}, l \rangle = 0.$$

Therefore we shall now prove (17) to (19). Taking the scalar product of both sides of (15*b*) and (15*d*) with $\hat{\psi}_-$ and $\hat{\psi}_+$, respectively, and recalling that $\langle \hat{\psi}_+, \hat{\psi}_- \rangle = 0$, we obtain [with the use of (16*b*) and (16*d*)]

24 $$\langle \hat{\psi}_+, R\lambda_1 \rangle = \langle \hat{\psi}_-, R\lambda_1 \rangle = 0.$$

Now, taking the scalar product of the left-hand side of (15*b*) with (15*d*) and making use of (16) and (24), we obtain

25 $$-\langle R\lambda_1, R\lambda_1 \rangle + \langle R\lambda_1, \mu_4 - \mu_2 \rangle + \langle \mu_2, \mu_4 \rangle = 0.$$

Subtracting (15*b*) from (15*d*), we obtain

26 $$2R\lambda_1 + (\hat{\psi}_- - \hat{\psi}_+)\lambda_3 - \mu_4 + \mu_2 = 0.$$

Now, substituting for $\mu_4 - \mu_2$ from (26) into (25) and using (24), we obtain

27 $$\langle R\lambda_1,R\lambda_1\rangle + \langle \mu_2,\mu_4\rangle = 0.$$

Since $\mu_2 \geqq 0$ and $\mu_4 \geqq 0$, it follows that $\langle R\lambda_1,R\lambda_1\rangle \leqq 0$, and hence that $R\lambda_1 = 0$, which proves (18).

Taking the scalar product of both sides of (15c) with $\hat{\xi}$ and making use of (16c) and the fact that $\langle \hat{z},\hat{\xi}\rangle = 0$, we obtain (19).

Finally, taking the scalar product of both sides of (15a) with λ_1 and making use of (18) and (19), we obtain

28 $$\langle \lambda_1,Q\lambda_1\rangle = \langle \mu_1,\lambda_1\rangle.$$

Now, from (15c) and (16a), we obtain

29 $$\langle \mu_1,\lambda_1\rangle + \langle \mu_1,\mu_3\rangle = 0,$$

and since $\mu_1 \geqq 0$ and $\mu_3 \geqq 0$, we have $\langle \mu_1,\lambda_1\rangle \leqq 0$, and therefore $\langle \lambda_1,Q\lambda_1\rangle \leqq 0$. But Q is symmetric and positive semidefinite, which implies that $Q\lambda_1 = 0$, that is, that (17) holds. □

6.10 A FURTHER GENERALIZATION

The purpose of this section is to indicate how algorithm (9.4) can be generalized so that it applies to the canonical quadratic programming problem (7.1) independently of whether or not assumption (9.1) is satisfied. Furthermore, an initial feasible solution will not be required. The reader who is already familiar with the quadratic programming algorithms of Dantzig and Cottle [2] and Lemke [3] will readily see the similarity between their algorithms and the one we are about to discuss here.

The first step toward our goal is to make a deceptively simple observation. Suppose that instead of introducing n variables y^i for $i = 1, 2, \ldots, n$, as we did for the derived problem (8.1), we introduce only one variable, which we again denote by y. Thus, instead of original derived problem, consider the new derived problem:

1 Minimize y subject to the constraints

2 $$Ax = g \qquad x \geqq 0 \qquad \langle v,w\rangle = 0,$$

where now

3 $$A = \begin{bmatrix} Q & -R^T & -I & R^T & k_1 \\ R & 0 & 0 & 0 & k_2 \end{bmatrix} \qquad (n+m) \times [2(n+m)+1]$$

and, as before,

4 $$x = (z,\psi_-,\xi,\psi_+,y) = (v,w,y) \in E^{2(n+m)+1}$$
$$v = (z,\psi_-) \qquad w = (\xi,\ \psi_+) \qquad g = (-d,c). \ \square$$

In the above formulation k_1 is an $n \times 1$ matrix and k_2 is an $m \times 1$ matrix. If, for the moment, we assume that k_2 is identically zero, then the only difference in formulation between the derived problem (8.1) and problem (1) is that we have collapsed the $n \times n$ diagonal matrix K in (8.4) into an $n \times 1$ matrix k_1. Eventually we shall assign specific values to k_1 and k_2 to facilitate the initialization of the algorithm.[1]

Since the restriction $\langle v,w \rangle = 0$ in (2) requires us to examine the components of v and w in pairs, we find that the discussion is considerably simplified by the following notation.

5 **Definition.** Given a usable basic solution $x = (v,w,y)$ to (2), with an associated basis-indicator set $\bar{J}(x)$, we shall say that v^i for $i \in \{1, 2, \ldots, n+m\}$ is a *basic variable* if $i \in \bar{J}(x)$ and that w^i for $i \in \{1, 2, \ldots, n+m\}$ is a *basic variable* if $i + n + m \in \bar{J}(x)$. $\square$

Clearly, algorithm (9.4) can be applied to the new derived problem (1) without modification. However, an important simplification occurs in the procedure, which, together with a new set of stop rules, results in an important generalization, or extension of algorithm (9.4).

Thus suppose that x_N is a usable basic solution to (2), with $y_N > 0$, such that

6 v_N^i and w_N^i for $i = 1, 2, \ldots, n+m$ are not both basic variables. $\square$

That is, if v_N^i is basic, then w_N^i is not, and vice versa. Note that because of condition (9.6), algorithm (9.4) generates a sequence of usable basic solutions for the new derived problem (1) which satisfy condition (6). Since, by assumption, $y_N > 0$ and x_N is a usable basic solution, there are exactly $n + m - 1$ basic variables among the $2(n + m)$ variables of v_N and w_N. Furthermore, in view of (6), there is only one index $j \in \{1, 2, \ldots, n+m\}$ with the property that neither v_N^j nor w_N^j is a basic variable. Now, to construct an improved usable basic solution x_{N+1} in accordance with step 1 of algorithm (9.4), we use the simplex algorithm (5.9.4) with side condition (9.6):

7 For $i = 1, 2, \ldots, n+m$, if v_N^i is a basic variable, then w_{N+1}^i may not be a basic variable, and if w_N^i is a basic variable, then v_{N+1}^i may not be a basic variable. $\square$

[1] It will be seen that by using the vector k_2 we avoid the need for finding a basic solution to $Rz = c$ and $z \geqq 0$, which was required to initialize the algorithm in the preceding section.

Consequently, the construction of x_{N+1} requires us to make either v^j_{N+1} or w^j_{N+1} a basic variable [that is, j or $j + n + m$ are the *only* elements in $J(x_N)$ which can be transferred into $\bar{J}(x_{N+1})$; there are no other possibilities]. We could determine which of these variables should be made basic by routinely following steps 1 and 2 of the simplex algorithm (5.9.4). However, a little reflection shows that these calculations are not necessary, because in the sequence of usable basic solutions $x_0, x_1, \ldots, x_{N-1}, x_N$, which we have implicitly assumed to have been constructed by algorithm (9.4), one of the following two situations must have occurred:

a. v^j_{N-1} was a basic variable.

b. w^j_{N-1} was a basic variable.

The conclusion should now be obvious. If v^j_{N-1} (w^j_{N-1}) was a basic variable, then make w^j_{N+1} (v^j_{N+1}) a basic variable.

Thus we see that in applying algorithm (9.4) to problem (1) we can eliminate the calculations involved in steps 1 and 2 of the simplex algorithm (5.9.4). Note, however, that the stop conditions of algorithm (9.4) become inoperative in this process. Thus, while algorithm (9.4) was originally conceived with the idea of reducing the value of a linear form at each step, the above-indicated modification results in a purely combinatorial procedure which makes no use at all of the values of this linear form. Our description of the new algorithm is still incomplete, since we have not yet stated the stop conditions which are to replace those of (9.4). As we shall see, it is the change in the stop conditions that increases the range of applicability of the new algorithm. Before we state our new algorithm with its stop conditions, let us consider how to initialize it. One method which readily comes to mind is to place an upper bound on the variable y whose optimal value should be zero. If we take this bound to be 1, problem (1) transforms into the following one:

8 Minimize y subject to the constraints

9 $$Ax = g \qquad x \geqq 0 \qquad \langle v,w \rangle = 0,$$

where x has been augmented by one component over the x in (2) and A and g have also been suitably modified. Thus

$$x = (z,\psi_-,\xi,\psi_+,y,s) = (v,w,y,s) \in E^{2(n+m)+2}$$

$$v = (z,\psi_-) \qquad w = (\xi,\psi_+)$$

10 $$g = (-d,b,1) \in E^{n+m+1}$$

$$A = \begin{bmatrix} Q & -R^T & -I & R^T & k_1 & 0 \\ R & 0 & 0 & 0 & k_2 & 0 \\ 0 & 0 & 0 & 0 & 1 & 1 \end{bmatrix} \qquad \begin{matrix} (n+m+1) \\ \times [2(n+m)+2] \end{matrix} \quad \square$$

Note that, by (9) and (10), $y + s = 1$, $s \geqq 0$, and $y \geqq 0$, and we have $0 \leqq y \leqq 1$.

For reasons which will become clear later [see theorem (11.33)], we shall henceforth assume that *no column of the matrix*

$$\begin{bmatrix} Q \\ R \\ 0 \end{bmatrix}$$

is zero. This is not a restriction, for if, say, the ith column were zero, then $r_i = 0$ and $q_i = 0$, and consequently, without loss in generality, we may assume that $d^i = 0$ and restate CQP (7.1) with one less variable [note that if $d^i < 0$, then CQP (7.1) has no solution, since $d^i z^i \to -\infty$ as $z^i \to +\infty$].

11 **Initialization.** We must obtain a usable basic solution to system (9). Since R has rank m, by assumption, we may assume that the columns of R are arranged so that its first m columns are linearly independent. Set

12 $$x_0 = (v_0, w_0, y_0, s_0),$$

with

$$z_0^i = \begin{cases} 1 & i = 1, 2, \ldots, m \\ 0 & i = m+1, \ldots, n \end{cases}$$

$$\xi_0^i = \begin{cases} 0 & i = 1, 2, \ldots, m \\ 1 & i = m+1, \ldots, n \end{cases}$$

$$\psi_{-0}^i = 0 \qquad i = 1, 2, \ldots, m$$

$$\psi_{+0}^i = 1 \qquad i = 1, 2, \ldots, m$$

$$y_0 = 1 \qquad s_0 = 0,$$

and let the vectors $k_1 \in E^n$ and $k_2 \in E^m$ be defined by

13 $$k_1 = -Qz_0 + R^T\psi_{0-} + \xi_0 - R^T\psi_{0+} - d \qquad k_2 = -Rz_0 + c.$$

14 **Exercise.** Let k_1 and k_2 be defined as in (13). Show that x_0, defined as in (12), is a usable nondegenerate basic solution to (9).

As is our convention, let $\bar{I}(x_0) = \{i: x_0^i > 0\}$. Since x_0 is a nondegenerate basic solution to (9), $\bar{I}(x_0)$ is a basis-indicator set [see (5.6.5)]. We now use procedure (5.8.13) for computing adjacent extreme points to construct a new usable basic solution x_1 by exchanging the index $2(n + m) + 2 \in I(x_0)$ for some index in $\bar{I}(x_0)$ which will result in s_1 being a basic variable.[1] If $y_1 = 0$, then the

[1] We find it convenient at this point to extend definition (5) as follows: given a usable basic solution x to (9), with basis-indicator set $\bar{J}(x)$, we shall say that a component x^i of x is *basic variable* if $i \in \bar{J}(x)$.

This step is in keeping with the spirit of algorithm (9.4), since the linear form y will necessarily decrease due to the constraint $y + s = 1$.

first n components of x_1, that is, the vector z_1, is an optimal solution to the canonical quadratic programming problem (7.1). Otherwise x_1 is a usable basic solution satisfying the following conditions:

15 $0 < y_1 < 1.$

16 For $i = 1, 2, \ldots, n$, if $v_1{}^i$ is a basic variable, then $w_1{}^i$ is not, and if $w_1{}^i$ is a basic variable, then $v_1{}^i$ is not.

This concludes the initialization. □

17 **Algorithm.** Suppose that $x_0, x_1, \ldots, x_N$, with x_0 and x_1 as constructed in (11), are usable basic solutions generated by the algorithm such that for $j = 1, 2, \ldots, N$

18 $0 < y_j < 1;$

19 For $i = 1, 2, \ldots, n$, if $v_j{}^i$ is a basic variable, then $w_j{}^i$ is not, and if $w_j{}^i$ is a basic variable, then $v_j{}^i$ is not.

Step 1. Note that there is a unique index $h \in \{1, 2, \ldots, n + m\}$ such that neither $w_N{}^h$ nor $v_N{}^h$ is a basic variable. Since a similar situation must also hold for x_{N-1} for with $N = 2, 3, \ldots$, we are left with two alternatives:

a. If v_{N-1}^h was a basic variable, use procedure (5.8.13) for computing adjacent extreme points to make w_{N+1}^h basic; i.e., attempt to exchange the index $h + n + m \in J(x_N)$ for some index in the basis indicator set $\bar{J}(x_N)$. Go to step 2.

b. If w_{N-1}^h was a basic variable, use procedure (5.8.13) to make v_{N+1}^h basic; i.e., attempt to exchange the index $h \in J(x_N)$ for some index in $\bar{J}(x_N)$. Go to step 2.

Step 2. There are two possible outcomes for step 1:

a. A new usable basic solution x_{N+1} was obtained in step 1. If either $y_{N+1} = 0$ or $y_{N+1} = 1$, then stop. Otherwise $0 < y_{N+1} < 1$; set $N = N + 1$ and return to step 1.

b. A new usable basic solution was not obtained in step 1; that is, an infinite ray $\{x(\theta) \colon \theta \in [0, \infty)\}$ of the polyhedron $\Omega' = \{x \colon Ax = g,\ x \geqq 0\}$ was encountered.[1] In this case stop. □

Termination. Algorithm (17) incorporates three stop conditions.

20 **Stop 1.** $x_{N+1}{}^{2(n+m)+1} = y_{N+1} = 0$. In this case the first n components of x_{N+1}, that is, the vector z_{N+1}, are an optimal solution to CQP (7.1).

[1] This corresponds to all the coefficients $\alpha_j{}^i$ being nonpositive in (5.8.5). See also (5.8.27).

21 **Stop 2.** At some step N an infinite ray of the polyhedron Ω was obtained. We shall see in the next section that in this case CQP (7.1) does not have a solution, either because it has no feasible solution or because the constrained infimum of the cost function is $-\infty$.

22 **Stop 3.** At some step $N \geqq 1$, $x_{N+1}{}^{2(n+m)+1} = 1$, that is, $y_{N+1} = 1$. We shall see in the next section that as long as the cost function of CQP (7.1) is a positive-semidefinite quadratic form, this stop condition can never occur. Thus $0 \leqq y_N < 1$ for every $N \geqq 1$. This stop command is included to eliminate the need for establishing whether the matrix Q is positive semidefinite or not (usually a difficult task), and the stop on $y_N = 1$ is designed to ensure that calculations will stop after a finite number of iterations. Note that when Q is not positive semidefinite, an optimal solution to the new derived problem (1) yields only a feasible solution to the quadratic programming problem, satisfying the necessary conditions for optimality. □

6.11 CONVERGENCE

In this section we shall prove that algorithm (10.17) must reach one of the stop conditions (10.20) to (10.22) and must therefore terminate after a finite number of iterations. In doing so, we shall prove that stop condition (10.22) never occurs in solving the canonical quadratic programming problem (7.1); that is, for each $N \geqq 1$ $0 \leqq y_N < 1$. Finally, we shall prove that if algorithm (10.17) terminates on stop condition (10.21), then CQP (7.1) does not have a solution.

It is interesting to note that in the convergence proofs of the algorithms we have seen so far we have relied heavily on the fact that the cost function is reduced at every iteration. This device is not available to us now. Indeed, it is not hard to generate examples for which the scalar y_N, formally the cost function for algorithm (9.4), increase at some iterations and decreases at others, due to the fact that the stop conditions of algorithm (10.17) are different from those of (9.4). For this reason the convergence proof becomes intricate. However, our task can be simplified somewhat by invoking a nondegeneracy assumption.

1 **Nondegeneracy assumption.** Every usable basic solution to the system

2 $$Ax = g \qquad x \geqq 0 \qquad \langle v,w \rangle = 0$$

is a usable nondegenerate basic solution. □

Recall that a similar assumption (5.8.16) was made when the simplex algorithm was described in Chapter 5, and later a rule was given for resolving degeneracy, thus putting the algorithm on a firm theoretical foundation. It will subsequently become clear that the degeneracies (or ties) which arise in algorithm (10.17) can be resolved in the same manner as for the simplex algorithm (see Section 5.10).

As a consequence of this assumption, recall from definition (5.6.5) that if x is a basic solution to (2), then $\bar{I}(x) = \{i: x^i > 0\}$ is the basis-indicator set for x.

3 **Theorem.** Suppose that assumption (1) is satisfied by problem (10.1). Let $x_0, x_1, x_2, \ldots$ be a sequence of usable basic solutions to (10.9) generated by algorithm (10.17). Then $x_i \neq x_j$ for $i \neq j$, with $i,j = 0, 1, 2, \ldots$.

Proof. Suppose the theorem is false. Then some x_i must be repeated in the sequence $x_0, x_1, x_2, \ldots$. Let x_k be the first element in this sequence, with the property that there exists an x_l, with $l > k + 1$,† such that $x_l = x_k$ and $x_i \neq x_j$ for $i, j \in \{k + 1, k + 2, \ldots, l - 1\}$. Obviously, such an element x_k must exist. We shall consider two cases.

Case 1. $k = 0$. Recall that, by construction of x_0 in (10.11), the index $2(n + m) + 2$ is not in $\bar{I}(x_0)$; that is, s_0 is not a basic component. Also, none of the stop conditions for algorithm (10.17) were encountered at $x_1, x_2, \ldots, x_{l-1}$, for otherwise the sequence $x_0, x_1, \ldots, x_l$ could not have been constructed. Consequently, for $i = 1, 2, \ldots, l - 1$ we must have $0 < y_i < 1$ and $0 < s_i < 1$; that is, indices $2(n + m) + 1$ and $2(n + m) + 2$ must both belong to $\bar{I}(x_i)$ for $i = 1, 2, \ldots, l - 1$. Now, since $x_l = x_0$ and the index $2(n + m) + 2$ is in $\bar{I}(x_{l-1})$ but not in $\bar{I}(x_l)$, we must have [see (5.8.13) and (5.8.9)]

4 $$\bar{I}(x_0) = \bar{I}(x_l) = \bar{I}(x_{l-1}) + \{\alpha_{l-1}\} - \{2(n + m) + 2\},$$

where α_{l-1} is some index in $I(x_{l-1})$. By theorem (5.8.13), since all the x_i for $i = 0, 1, 2, \ldots$ are supposed to be usable nondegenerate basic solutions, x_{l-1} must be the unique adjacent extreme point resulting from procedure (5.8.13) [see (5.8.14)] when the index $2(n + m) + 2$ is exchanged for some index in $\bar{I}(x_0)$. But this is exactly how we constructed x_1; hence $x_1 = x_{l-1}$, which contradicts the assumption that $x_i \neq x_j$ for $i, j \in \{1, 2, \ldots, l - 1\}$.

† It is clear from the algorithm, with the nondegeneracy assumption, that $x_k = x_{k+1}$ cannot hold.

Case 2. $k > 0$. Since no stop conditions were reached at x_k, we must have $0 < y_k < 1$ and $0 < s_k < 1$; that is, both are basic. Hence there exists a unique index $j_v \in \{1, 2, \ldots, n + m\}$ such that neither j_v nor $j_w = j_v + (n + m)$ is in $\bar{I}(x_k)$. Furthermore, it is clear from step 1 of algorithm (10.17) that either j_v or j_w must belong to $\bar{I}(x_{k-1})$. So, without loss of generality, let us suppose that $j_v \in \bar{I}(x_{k-1})$; that is,

5 $$\bar{I}(x_k) = \bar{I}(x_{k-1}) + \{\alpha_{k-1}\} - \{j_v\},$$

where α_{k-1} is some index in $I(x_{k-1})$. To construct x_{k+1} according to (10.17), since $j_v \in \bar{I}(x_{k-1})$, we must exchange the index j_v for some index β_k in $\bar{I}(x_k)$; that is,

6 $$\bar{I}(x_{k+1}) = \bar{I}(x_k) + \{j_w\} - \{\beta_k\}.$$

Now, since $x_k = x_l$, by the same argument as above, either the index j_v or the index j_w must also belong to $\bar{I}(x_{l-1})$. If $j_v \in \bar{I}(x_{l-1})$ and we exchange the index $j_v \in I(x_l)$ for some index in $\bar{I}(x_l)$ according to procedure (5.8.13), then, by theorem (5.8.18), the resulting usable solution is unique and must be x_{l-1}. But, by (5), this operation should yield the point x_{k-1}, and hence if $j_v \in \bar{I}(x_{l-1})$, we must have $x_{k-1} = x_{l-1}$. Obviously, this contradicts the assumption that x_k was the first repeated point with the properties stated.

Consequently, let us suppose that $j_w \in \bar{I}(x_{l-1})$. Then we must be able to reconstruct x_{l-1} from x_k by exchanging the index $j_w \in I(x_l)$ for some index β_k' in $\bar{I}(x_l)$. Since, by (5.8.13), this process yields a unique result, we must conclude from (6) that $\beta_k = \beta_k'$ and $x_{k+1} = x_{l-1}$, which again contradicts the assumptions on x_k, in particular that $x_i \neq x_j$ for $i, j \in \{k + 1, k + 2, \ldots, l - 1\}$. □

7 **Corollary.** Algorithm (10.17) terminates in a finite number of steps; i.e., one of stop conditions (10.20) to (10.22) is encountered after a finite number of steps.

Proof. With every usable basic solution to (10.2) there are associated $n + m + 1$ linearly independent columns of the matrix A. Since A has a finite number of columns, it follows that there are a finite number of usable basic solutions. Hence, since the algorithm never repeats a usable basic solution and will construct a new one unless a stop condition is reached, it must reach one of stop conditions (10.20) to (10.22) after a finite number of steps. □

8 **Theorem.** Let k_1 and k_2 be as defined in (10.13), with x_0 as given by (10.12). If we set $s = 0$, then x_0 is the unique solution to the system of equations and inequalities (10.2).

Proof. Clearly, with s fixed at zero, $y_0 = 1$ is the only value of y which satisfies

9 $$y_0 + s = 1 \qquad y_0 \geqq 0.$$

Consequently, we need only show that $(z_0,\psi_{-_0},\xi_0,\psi_{+_0})$ is the only solution to the system

10 $$\begin{aligned} &Qz - R^T\psi_- - \xi + R^T\psi_+ = -k_1 - d \qquad Rz = -k_2 + c \\ &z \geqq 0 \qquad \psi_- \geqq 0 \qquad \xi \geqq 0 \qquad \psi_+ \geqq 0 \\ &\langle z,\xi\rangle = \langle \psi_+,\psi_-\rangle = 0 \end{aligned}$$

Suppose that $(\tilde{z},\tilde{\psi}_-,\tilde{\xi},\tilde{\psi}_+)$ also satisfies (10). Then, by subtraction, we obtain

11 $$Q(z_0 - \tilde{z}) - R^T(\psi_{-_0} - \tilde{\psi}_-) - (\xi_0 - \tilde{\xi}) + R^T(\psi_{+_0} - \tilde{\psi}_+) = 0$$

12 $$R(z_0 - \tilde{z}) = 0.$$

Taking the scalar product of both sides of (11) with the vector $z_0 - \tilde{z}$, we obtain

13 $$\langle (z_0 - \tilde{z}), Q(z_0 - \tilde{z})\rangle + \langle (z_0 - \tilde{z}), R^T(\psi_{+_0} - \psi_{-_0} - \tilde{\psi}_+ + \tilde{\psi}_-)\rangle - \langle (z_0 - \tilde{z}), (\xi_0 - \tilde{\xi})\rangle = 0.$$

Since the second term in (13) is zero, by (12), this reduces to

14 $$\langle (z_0 - \tilde{z}), Q(z_0 - \tilde{z})\rangle + \langle z_0,\tilde{\xi}\rangle + \langle \xi_0,\tilde{z}\rangle - \langle z_0,\xi_0\rangle - \langle \tilde{z},\tilde{\xi}\rangle = 0.$$

Now, the first term in (14) is nonnegative, since Q is a positive-semidefinite matrix, and the last two terms are zero, by (10). It follows that

15 $$\langle z_0,\tilde{\xi}\rangle + \langle \xi_0,\tilde{z}\rangle \leqq 0.$$

But each term in (15) is nonnegative, so that

16 $$\langle z_0,\tilde{\xi}\rangle = 0 \qquad \langle \xi_0,\tilde{z}\rangle = 0.$$

Keeping in mind the definitions of z_0 and ξ_0 as given in (10.11), we conclude that

17 $$\tilde{\xi}^i = 0 \qquad i = 1, 2, \cdots, m$$

18 $$\tilde{z}^i = 0 \qquad i = m + 1, \cdots, n$$

Now, the first m components of z_0 are positive, and the remaining components of z_0 are zero. Hence, by (10) and (18),

19 $$\sum_{i=1}^{m} (z_0{}^i - \tilde{z}^i)r_i = 0,$$

where r_i is the ith column of R. Since the first m columns of R were assumed to be linearly independent, it follows that $z_0{}^i = \tilde{z}^i$ for $i = 1, 2, \ldots, m$, and hence that $z_0 = \tilde{z}$. Equation (11) now becomes

20 $$R^T([(\psi_{+_0} - \psi_{-_0}) - (\tilde{\psi}_+ - \tilde{\psi}_-)]) = (\xi_0 - \tilde{\xi}).$$

The first m components of ξ_0 are zero; consequently, by (17) the first m components of $\tilde{\xi}$ are zero. Hence

21 $$\langle r_i, [(\psi_{+_0} - \psi_{-_0}) - (\tilde{\psi}_+ - \tilde{\psi}_-)]\rangle = 0 \qquad i = 1, 2, \ldots, m.$$

Again, since the vectors r_i for $i = 1, 2, \ldots, m$ are a basis for E^m, we conclude that

22 $$\psi_{+_0} - \psi_{-_0} = \tilde{\psi}_+ - \tilde{\psi}_-.$$

But $\psi_{-_0} = 0$ and $\psi_{+_0}{}^i = 1$ for $i = 1, 2, \ldots, m$, so that

23 $$\tilde{\psi}_+{}^i - \tilde{\psi}_-{}^i = 1 \qquad i = 1, 2, \ldots, m.$$

Since $\tilde{\psi}_+{}^i$ and $\tilde{\psi}_-{}^i$ cannot both be positive, by (10), we have

24 $$\tilde{\psi}_-{}^i = 0 \qquad i = 1, 2, \ldots, m$$

25 $$\tilde{\psi}_+{}^i = 1 \qquad i = 1, 2, \ldots, m.$$

Therefore $\tilde{\psi}_+ = \psi_{+_0}$ and $\tilde{\psi}_- = \psi_{-_0}$, and hence, from (20), $\xi_0 = \tilde{\xi}$. □

26 **Corollary.** Let x_N for $N = 0, 1, 2, \ldots$ be the sequence of usable basic solutions generated by algorithm (10.17). Then for $N \geqq 1$, $x_N{}^{2(n+m)+1} = y_N < 1$; that is, stop condition (10.22) is never executed.

Proof. Suppose the corollary is false. Then for some $N \geqq 1$, $x_N{}^{2(n+m)+1} = y_N = 1$. Hence

27 $$x_N = (v_N, w_N, y_N, s_N) \qquad s_N = 0$$

28 $$x_0 = (v_0, w_0, y_0, s_0) \qquad s_0 = 0.$$

It now follows from the above theorem that $x_N = x_0$, which is a contradiction of theorem (3). □

We are now left with showing that the canonical quadratic programming problem (7.1) does not have a solution if stop condition (10.21) occurs. Toward this goal, the following lemmas will prove useful.

29 **Lemma.** If the system $Rz = c$ and $z \geqq 0$ has a solution, then every vector $\eta \in E^m$ satisfying the system of inequalities $R^T\eta \geqq 0$ also satisfies $\langle \eta, c\rangle \geqq 0$. □

30 **Exercise.** Prove lemma (29). □

31 **Lemma.** Suppose that CQP (7.1) has a feasible solution, i.e., that the system $Rz = c$ and $z \geqq 0$ has a solution. If there is a vector $\eta \in E^n$ such that

$$R\eta = 0 \qquad Q\eta = 0 \qquad \eta \geqq 0 \qquad \langle d,\eta\rangle < 0,$$

then the constrained infimum of the cost function in CQP (7.1) is $-\infty$. □

32 **Exercise.** Prove lemma (31). □

33 **Theorem.** Suppose that algorithm (10.17) terminates on stop command (10.21). Then either CQP (7.1) does not have a feasible solution, or else the constrained infimum of its cost function is $-\infty$.

Proof. The proof is by contradiction. Suppose that CQP (7.1) has a feasible solution, that the constrained infimum of its cost function is finite, and that stop condition (10.21) is encountered at some iteration, say, N. Referring to procedure (5.8.13) for computing adjacent extreme points, and in particular to equation (5.8.2), we conclude that there exist scalars $\alpha^i_{P_{N-1}}$ for $i \in \bar{I}(x_N)$, *not all zero,*[1] and a column $a_{P_{N-1}}$ of the matrix A in (10.10), with $P_{N-1} \in I(x_N)$, such that

34
$$a_{P_{N-1}} = \sum_{i \in \bar{I}(x_N)} \alpha^i_{P_{N-1}} a_i$$
$$\alpha^i_{P_{N-1}} \leqq 0 \qquad \text{for all } i \in \bar{I}(x_N).$$

Using the definition of the matrix A in (10.9), we conclude that there is a non zero vector $\delta x = (\delta z,\delta\psi_-,\delta\xi,\delta\psi_+,\delta y,\delta s)$, made up of the $\alpha^i_{P_{N-1}}$, such that

35
$$Q\,\delta z - R^T\,\delta\psi_- - \delta\xi + R^T\,\delta\psi_+ + k_1\,\delta y = 0$$
$$R\,\delta z + k_2\,\delta y = 0 \qquad \delta y + \delta s = 0 \qquad \delta x \geqq 0.$$

In addition, we have

36
$$\langle\delta z,\delta\xi\rangle = \langle\delta\psi_-,\delta\psi_+\rangle = \langle\delta\xi,z_N\rangle = \langle\delta z,\xi_N\rangle = 0,$$

[1] If $\alpha^i_{P_{N-1}} = 0$ for all $i \in \bar{I}(x_N)$, then the column $a_{P_{N-1}}$ of A is identically zero. An examination of the matrix A in (10.10) shows that this column is either a column of $\begin{bmatrix} R^T \\ 0 \\ 0 \end{bmatrix}$, which is impossible, since R has rank m, or a column of $\begin{bmatrix} Q \\ R \\ 0 \end{bmatrix}$, which is not allowed [see the discussion in (10.11)].

where $x_N = (z_N, \psi_{-_N}, \xi_N, \psi_{+_N}, \lambda_N, \sigma_N)$ is the usable basic solution determined at iteration N. Using (35) and (36), we can easily deduce the following, in the order given:

37 $$\delta y = \delta s = 0$$

38 $$R\,\delta z = 0 \qquad \delta z \geqq 0$$

39 $$Q\,\delta z = 0$$

40 $$R^T \delta\psi = \delta\xi \geqq 0 \qquad \delta\psi \triangleq (\delta\psi_+ - \delta\psi_-).$$

In obtaining (39) we first deduced from (37), (38), and the first equation in (35) that $\langle \delta z, Q\,\delta z\rangle = 0$.

Since x_N is a usable basic solution,

41 $$\begin{aligned} &Qz_N - R^T\psi_{-_N} - \xi_N + R^T\psi_{+_N} + k_1 y_N = -d \\ &Rz_N + k_2 y_N = c \\ &y_N + s_N = 1 \\ &x_N \geqq 0 \end{aligned}$$

and

42 $$\langle z_N, \xi_N\rangle = \langle \psi_{-_N}, \psi_{+_N}\rangle = 0$$

(note that $0 < y_N < 1$).

Taking the scalar product of the first equation in (41) with the vector δz and using (36), (38), and (39), we obtain

43 $$\langle \delta z, k_1\rangle y_N = -\langle d, \delta z\rangle.$$

From the definition of k_1 in (10.13) this reduces to

44 $$y_N\langle \delta z, \xi_0\rangle = (y_N - 1)\langle \delta z, d\rangle,$$

where, it is recalled, $x_0 = (z_0, \psi_{-_0}, \xi_0, \psi_{+_0}, y_0, s_0)$ is the initial usable basic solution used in algorithm (10.17). Since $\delta z \geqq 0$, $\xi_0 \geqq 0$, $y_N > 0$, and $(y_N - 1) < 0$, it follows that $\langle \delta z, d\rangle \leqq 0$. But by (38) and (39), $R\delta z = 0$, $Q\delta z = 0$, and $\delta z \geqq 0$, and so if the constrained infimum of the cost function of CQP (7.1) is finite, then $\langle \delta z, d\rangle \geqq 0$, by lemma (31). Consequently, we must have $\langle \delta z, d\rangle = 0$, and so

45 $$\langle \delta z, \xi_0\rangle = 0.$$

Next, taking the scalar product of the second equation in (41) with the vector $\delta\psi = (\delta\psi_+ - \delta\psi_-)$ and using (36), (40), and the definition of k_2 in (10.13), we obtain

46 $$y_N\langle z_0, \delta\xi\rangle = (y_N - 1)\langle \delta\psi, c\rangle.$$

Since $y_N > 0$, $\delta\xi \geqq 0$, $z_0 \geqq 0$, and $(y_N - 1) < 0$, it follows that $\langle \delta\psi, b\rangle \leq 0$. But, by (40), $R^T\delta\psi \geq 0$, and so if CQP (7.1) has a feasible solution, then we must have $\langle \delta\psi, b\rangle \geqq 0$, by Lemma (29). Hence $\langle \delta\psi, b\rangle = 0$, and so

47 $$\langle \delta\xi, z_0\rangle = 0.$$

Now, the first m components of z_0 are positive [see (10.12)], so that, by (47), the first m components of $\delta\xi$ are zero. Thus, by (40), we have

$$\langle r_i, \delta\psi_+ - \delta\psi_-\rangle = 0 \qquad i = 1, 2, \ldots, m,$$

where r_i is the ith column of R. Again recall that the first m columns of R were so arranged that they were linearly independent vectors; hence

48 $$\delta\psi_+ = \delta\psi_-,$$

which implies that

49 $$\delta\psi_+ = \delta\psi_- = 0,$$

since $\delta\psi_+ \geqq 0$, $\delta\psi_- \geqq 0$, and $\langle \delta\psi_+, \delta\psi_-\rangle = 0$.

The proof is now almost complete, for with (45), (47), and (49) we shall deduce that there are two solutions to the system of equations and inequalities (2) when $s = 0$, in contradiction to theorem (8). By construction, $x_0 = (z_0, \psi_{0-}, \xi_0, \psi_{0+}, y_0, s_0)$, with $y_0 = 1$, is a solution to (2) [see (10.11)]. We shall show that $x_0 + \theta\,\delta x$ is also a solution to this system when $y_0 = 1$, for any value of $\theta > 0$.

First, note that $x_0 + \theta\,\delta x \geqq 0$ for all $\theta > 0$, since $\delta x \geqq 0$. Next, we see from (36), (45), and (47) that

50 $$\langle z_0 + \theta\,\delta z, \xi_0 + \theta\,\delta\xi\rangle = \langle z_0, \xi_0\rangle + \theta(\langle \delta z, \xi_0\rangle + \langle \delta\xi, z_0\rangle) + \theta^2\langle \delta\xi, \delta z\rangle = 0$$

and from (49) that

51 $$\langle \psi_{+_0} + \theta\,\delta\psi_+, \psi_{-_0} + \theta\,\delta\psi_-\rangle = \langle \psi_{+_0}, \psi_{-_0}\rangle = 0.$$

Thus it only remains to show that

52 $$\begin{aligned} Q(z_0 + \theta\,\delta z) - R^T(\psi_{-_0} + \theta\,\delta\psi_-) - (\xi_0 + \theta\,\delta\xi) \qquad & \\ + R^T(\psi_{+_0} + \theta\,\delta\psi_+) + (y_0 + \theta\,\delta y)k_1 &= -d \\ R(z_0 + \theta\,\delta z) + (y_0 + \theta\,\delta y)k_2 &= c \\ (y_0 + \theta\,\delta y) + (s_0 + \theta\,\delta s) &= 1 \end{aligned}$$

and that

53 $$y_0 + \theta\,\delta y = 1.$$

But (52) follows immediately from (35) and the fact that x_0 is a usable basic solution, and (53) follows from the fact that $\delta y = 0$ and $y_0 = 1$. □

54 **Corollary.** If CQP (7.1) has a feasible solution and the constrained infimum of its cost function is finite, then it has an optimal solution [cf. theorem (2.27)].

Proof. Under the hypothesis of this corollary, stop command (10.21) is never executed. By corollary (26), stop command (10.22) is never executed. Hence, by corollary (7), stop command (10.20) is executed in a finite number of steps; that is, CQP (7.1) has an optimal solution. □

This completes the proof of convergence for algorithm (10.17), as well as our discussion of quadratic programming problems.

REFERENCES

1. P. Wolfe: The Simplex Method for Quadratic Programming, *Econometrica*, **27**:382–397 (1959).
2. G. B. Dantzig and R. W. Cottle: Positive (Semi-) Definite Programming, in "Nonlinear Programming," J. Abadie (ed), North-Holland Publishing Company, Amsterdam, 1968.
3. C. E. Lemke: Bimatrix Equilibrium Points and Mathematical Programming, *Management Science*, **11**:681–689 (1965).
4. A. J. Goldman: Resolution and Separation Theorems for Polyhedral Convex Sets, *Ann. Math. Studies* 38, pp. 41–51, Princeton University Press, Princeton, N.J., 1956.
5. E. M. L. Beale: On Quadratic Programming, *Naval Res. Logistics Quart.*, **6**:227–243 (1959).

7
Convex programming algorithms

7.1 INTRODUCTION

This chapter will be devoted primarily to nonlinear programming problems of the following form.

1 **The convex programming problem.** Minimize $f(z)$ subject to $r(z) = 0$ and $q(z) \leqq 0$, where $f(\cdot)$ is a continuously differentiable, real valued, convex function defined on E^n, $r: E^n \to E^m$ is affine, and $q: E^n \to E^k$ is a continuously differentiable function whose components, $q^i(\cdot)$, are convex. □

We shall consider a few representative algorithms for dealing with problem (1), and we shall discuss how, and to what extent, these algorithms can be applied to the general nonlinear programming problem (3.1.1). In discussing the algorithms it will occasionally be convenient to depart from the notation we have used thus far. This departure from our standard notation will be clearly indicated whenever it occurs.

A number of the algorithms we are about to examine require the knowledge of an initial feasible solution to problem (1). We shall now show that such a solution can be obtained by solving another convex programming problem for which an initial solution is trivially constructed. Note that since the function $r(\cdot)$ in problem (1) is affine, we must have $r(z) = Rz - c$, where $c \in E^m$ and R is an $m \times n$ matrix. Thus let us consider the set

2 $$\Omega' = \{z: q(z) \leqq 0, Rz = c\}.$$

If the functions $q^i(\cdot)$ for $i = 1, 2, \ldots, k$ are affine, then the simplex algorithm can be used to determine (in a finite number of steps) either a point $z_0 \in \Omega'$ or whether Ω' is empty. Let us assume, therefore, that at least one of the functions $q^i(\cdot)$ is nonlinear.

Consider the following nonlinear programming problem:

3 Minimize σ subject to the constraints

4 $$\begin{aligned} &q^i(z) - \sigma l^i \leqq 0 \qquad i = 1, 2, \ldots, k \\ &\langle r^j,z\rangle - c^j - \sigma e^j = 0 \qquad j = 1, 2, \ldots, m \\ &\sigma \geqq 0, \end{aligned}$$

where l^i for $i = 1, 2, \ldots, k$ and e^j for $j = 1, 2, \ldots, m$ are scalars and r^j for $j = 1, 2, \ldots, m$ denotes the jth row of R. □

Suppose that the $m \times n$ matrix R has rank m. Assuming that the first m columns of the matrix R are linearly independent, and denoting this submatrix by $\tilde{R}$, we may define

5 $$\begin{aligned} &z_0{}^i = (\tilde{R}^{-1}c)^i \qquad i = 1, 2, \ldots, m \\ &z_0{}^i = 0 \qquad i = m + 1, \ldots, n. \end{aligned}$$

Thus $Rz_0 = c$. Now let

6 $$\begin{aligned} &e^j = 0 \qquad j = 1, 2, \ldots, m \\ &l^i = \begin{cases} 0 & \text{if } q^i(z_0) \leqq 0 \\ 1 & \text{if } q^i(z_0) > 0 \end{cases} \\ &\sigma_0 = \max_i q^i(z_0). \end{aligned}$$

Note that if $\sigma_0 \leqq 0$, then $z_0 \in \Omega'$. Otherwise, (z_0,σ_0) is a feasible solution to system (4), with e^j and l^i as defined above.

Thus problem (3) is a convex programming problem with an initial feasible solution (σ_0,z_0), as in (5) and (6). If the set Ω' is not empty, then for any $z' \in \Omega'$ system (4) is satisfied with $\sigma = 0$. Since $\sigma \geqq 0$, problem (3) must have an optimal solution $\hat{\sigma} = 0$ and $\hat{z} \in \Omega'$; that is, we can find a point in Ω' by solving problem (3).

7 **Remark.** Suppose that there is a point z in Ω' such that $q^i(z) < 0$ for $i = 1, 2, \ldots, k$. Then, if we remove the restriction in (4) that $\sigma \geqq 0$, we obtain a new problem whose optimal solution is $\hat{\sigma} < 0$. Since the procedures we shall consider start with the initial value $\sigma_0 > 0$ and produce a sequence σ_i for $i = 0, 1, 2, \ldots$ converging to

the value $\hat{\sigma} < 0$, there will be an integer p such that $\sigma_i < 0$ for all $i \geqq p$; that is, the corresponding vectors z_i for $i \geqq p$ will be in Ω'. Thus it will be possible to compute an initial feasible solution $\tilde{z} \in \Omega'$ in a finite number of steps. □

In the event that R does not have maximum rank, we can avoid the calculation defined by (5) as follows. Take any point z_0 in E^n, and for $i = 1, 2, \ldots, k$ set

8 $$l^i = \begin{cases} 0 & \text{if } q^i(z_0) \leqq 0 \\ 1 & \text{if } q^i(z_0) > 0 \end{cases}$$

in (4). Now set

9 $$\sigma_0 = \begin{cases} 1 & \text{if } q^i(z_0) \leqq 0 \text{ for every } i = 1, 2, \ldots, k \\ \max\limits_i q^i(z_0) & \text{otherwise} \end{cases}$$

and

10 $$e^j = \frac{\langle r^j, z_0 \rangle - c^j}{\sigma_0}.$$

Then (σ_0, z_0) is an initial feasible solution for problem (3), with the e^j and l^i defined as above (of course, now z_0 does not necessarily satisfy the equality constraint $Rz_0 = c$). Again, if there is at least one vector $z \in \Omega'$, problem (3) will have an optimal solution $(\hat{\sigma}, \hat{z})$, with $\hat{\sigma} = 0$ and $\hat{z} \in \Omega'$.

We now proceed to a few of the better-known convex programming algorithms.

7.2 METHODS OF FEASIBLE DIRECTIONS

Let us consider an algorithm, or, to be more precise, a family of algorithms introduced by Zoutendijk [1] for solving convex programming problems. These algorithms can also be applied to the nonlinear programming problem (3.1.1) [minimize $f(z)$ subject to the constraints $r(z) = 0$ and $q(z) \leqq 0$], when the equality constraint function $r(\cdot)$ is affine, to compute points $\hat{z}$ satisfying necessary conditions of optimality. Obviously, in this case there is no guarantee that the algorithms will determine a global minimum. However, under some mild assumptions, it can be shown that they will compute a local minimum. Zoutendijk called these algorithms *methods of feasible directions*. Because they can be brought to bear on such a wide class of problems, we shall not assume in what follows that the cost function $f(\cdot)$ or the inequality-constraint functions $q^i(\cdot)$ are convex. Let us begin by defining the class of problems which we shall consider in this section.

1 **Problem.** Given $k+1$ real-valued continuously differentiable functions $q^i(\cdot)$ for $i = 0, 1, \ldots, k$ defined on E^n and an affine function $r(z) = Rz - c$, where R is an $m \times n (m \leqq n)$ full-rank matrix and $c \in E^n$, find a vector $\hat{z} \in E^n$ satisfying

2 $$q^i(\hat{z}) \leqq 0 \qquad i = 1, 2, \ldots, k$$
3 $$r(\hat{z}) = 0$$

such that for all vectors $z \in E^n$ satisfying (2) and (3)

4 $$q^0(\hat{z}) \leqq q^0(z). \quad \square$$

5 **Remark.** Note that the cost function in (4) is denoted by $q^0(\cdot)$ rather than by $f(\cdot)$, as has been our practice until now. We shall see that this device enables us to simplify notation. $\square$

Concerning notation, we shall again denote by Ω' the set of feasible solutions to the nonlinear programming problem (1), that is,

6 $$\Omega' = \{z: q^i(z) \leqq 0, i = 1, 2, \ldots, k, r(z) = 0\},$$

and for any $z \in \Omega'$ the functions $q^i(\cdot)$ for $i \in I(z)$ are the active constraints at z; that is,

7 $$I(z) = \{i: q^i(z) = 0, i \in \{1,2, \ldots, k\}\}.$$

Finally, we shall assume that the functions defining Ω' satisfy the following constraint qualification:†

8 **Assumption.** For every $z \in \Omega'$ the *internal cone* to Ω' at z, defined by

9 $$IC(z,\Omega') = \{h: Rh = 0, \langle \nabla q^i(z),h \rangle < 0 \text{ for all } i \in I(z)\} \cup \{0\},$$

contains some point other than the origin. $\square$

10 **Remark.** By corollary (3.4.31), under assumption (8), theorem (3.4.22) provides a necessary condition for optimality, with $\psi^0 < 0$, for the nonlinear programming problem (1). $\square$

11 **Exercise.** Referring to problem (1), suppose that the functions $q^i(\cdot)$ for $i = 1, 2, \ldots, k$ are convex, and that for every $i \in \{1,2 \ldots, k\}$ there exists a point $z \in \Omega'$, possibly depending on i, such that $q^i(z) < 0$. Show that assumption (8) is satisfied. [*Hint:* First show that there exists a $z \in \Omega'$ such that $q^i(z) < 0$ for every $i = 1, 2, \ldots, k$, and then examine the proof of theorem (2.3.30).] $\square$

† When some of the functions q^i for $i \in I(z)$ are affine, it suffices to require that there exist a vector $h \in E^n$ such that $\langle \nabla q^i(z),h \rangle \leqq 0$ for these functions and $\langle \nabla q^i(z),h \rangle < 0$ for the remaining functions q^i, with $i \in I(z)$, and that $Rh = 0$.

As might be suspected, there are no known algorithms for finding optimal solutions to the quite general programming problem (1). About all that can be said concerning the algorithms which can be brought to bear on problem (1) is that they compute a point where the necessary conditions for optimality are satisfied. As a practical matter, therefore, we shall consider instead the following problem.

12 **Problem: determination of a point where the necessary conditions are satisfied.** Given $k + 1$ continuously differentiable real-valued functions $q^i(\cdot)$ for $i = 0, 1, \ldots, k$ defined on E^n and an affine function $r(z) = Rz - c$, where R is an $m \times n (m \leqq n)$ full-rank matrix, find a vector $\hat{z} \in E^n$ and multiplier vectors $\psi = (\psi^1, \psi^2, \ldots, \psi^m) \in E^m$ and $\mu = (\mu^1, \mu^2, \ldots, \mu^k) \in E^k$ such that

13 $$\hat{z} \in \Omega'$$

14 $$-\nabla q^0(\hat{z}) + \sum_{i=1}^{k} \mu^i \nabla q^i(\hat{z}) + R^T\psi = 0$$

15 $$\mu \leqq 0, \qquad \mu^i q^i(\hat{z}) = 0 \qquad i = 1, 2, \ldots, k. \quad \square$$

16 **Remark.** Relations (13) to (15) are a restatement of the necessary conditions for optimality [theorem (3.4.22), with $\psi^0 < 0$]. By remark (10), if $\hat{z}$ is a solution to the nonlinear programming problem (1) and assumption (8) is satisfied, then there exist multiplier vectors ψ and μ satisfying (13) to (15). Conversely, if $(\hat{z}, \psi, \mu)$ satisfy (13) to (15), then $\hat{z}$ may be a global minimum for problem (1) [see theorems (3.6.1) and (3.6.22)], or if $\nabla q^0(\hat{z}) \neq 0$, then $\hat{z}$ may be a local minimum or a local saddle point, or if $\nabla q^0(\hat{z}) = 0$, then $\hat{z}$ may be a local minimum, a local maximum, or a local saddle point. $\square$

For the purpose of describing the methods of feasible directions and proving their convergence, it is convenient to restate problem (12) in an alternative form. First, however, let us introduce some new notation.

17 **Definition.** Let $z \in \Omega'$ and $\epsilon \geqq 0$ be given. We shall define the *index set* $I_\epsilon(z) \subset \{0, 1, \ldots, k\}$ by

18 $$I_\epsilon(z) = \{0\} \cup \{i: q^i(z) + \epsilon \geqq 0, i \in \{1, 2, \ldots, k\}\}. \quad \square$$

For $\epsilon = 0$ the index set $I_0(z)$ may be expressed as

19 $$I_0(z) = \{0\} \cup I(z),$$

where $I(z)$ is as defined in (7).

20 **Definition.** We shall denote by S any subset of E^n of the form

21 $$S = S' \cap S'',$$

where S' is a *compact convex subset of* E^n *containing the origin in its interior* and S'' is the *linear subspace* of E^n defined by

$$S'' = \{h: Rh = 0\}. \quad \square$$

22 **Remark.** S is a compact convex subset of E^n containing the origin, and it is the choice of S that distinguishes one algorithm from another in the family of methods of feasible directions. $\square$

23 **Theorem.** Suppose that assumption (8) is satisfied. Then a vector $\hat{z} \in \Omega'$, together with multiplier vectors $\psi \in E^m$ and $\mu \in E^k$, solves problem (12) if and only if

24 $$\min_{h \in S} \max_{i \in I_0(\hat{z})} \langle \nabla q^i(\hat{z}), h \rangle = 0$$

for every subset S defined as in (20).

Proof. Suppose that $(\hat{z}, \psi, \mu)$ satisfies the necessary conditions of optimality (13) to (15), and suppose that (24) does not hold at $\hat{z}$ for some subset S defined as in (20). Now, $0 \in S$, from which it follows that if (24) does not hold, then

$$\min_{h \in S} \max_{i \in I_0(\hat{z})} \langle \nabla q^i(\hat{z}), h \rangle < 0.$$

Hence there exists a vector $h^* \in S$ such that

25 $$\langle \nabla q^i(\hat{z}), h^* \rangle < 0 \text{ for all } i \in I_0(\hat{z}) = \{0\} \cup I(\hat{z}).$$

From the definition of the set S in (20), and from (15), the expression obtained after taking the scalar product of both sides of (14) with the vector h^* simplifies to

26 $$-\langle \nabla q^0(\hat{z}), h^* \rangle + \sum_{i \in I(\hat{z})} \mu^i \langle \nabla q^i(\hat{z}), h^* \rangle = 0.$$

Since $\mu \geqq 0$, this is clearly in contradiction to equation (25).

Conversely, suppose that condition (24) holds for some vector $\hat{z} \in \Omega'$ and any set S as in (20). Then for all $h \in S$

$$\max_{i \in I_0(\hat{z})} \langle \nabla q^i(\hat{z}), h \rangle \geqq 0.$$

In particular, since, by assumption (8), $IC(\hat{z}, \Omega) \neq \{0\}$, we must have

27 $$\langle \nabla q^0(\hat{z}), h \rangle \geqq 0 \qquad \text{for all } h \in \overline{IC}(\hat{z}, \Omega') = \{h: \langle \nabla q^i(\hat{z}), h \rangle \leqq 0,\ i \in I(\hat{z}),\ Rh = 0\}.$$

We now conclude from Farkas' lemma (A.5.34) that there exist multiplier vectors $\psi \in E^m$ and $\mu \in E^k$ such that $(\hat{z},\psi,\mu)$ satisfies (13) to (15). □

Thus problem (12) is equivalent to the following problem:

28 **Problem.** Given $k + 1$ continuously differentiable functions $q^i(\cdot)$ for $i = 0, 1, \ldots, k$ defined on E^n and an affine function $r(z) = Rz - c$ mapping E^n into E^m, with R having rank m, find a vector $\hat{z} \in \Omega'$ such that

29
$$\min_{h \in S} \max_{i \in I_0(\hat{z})} \langle \nabla q^i(\hat{z}),h \rangle = 0,$$

where S and $I_0(\hat{z})$ are as defined in (20) and (19), respectively. □

It is problem (28) to which we address ourselves from now on. Accordingly, *we shall not impose assumption* (8) unless we wish to use theorem (23) to relate the solutions of (28) to the solutions of (12). The reader may well ask at this point how to interpret condition (29) in the absence of assumption (8). This is the content of the following lemma and exercises.

30 **Lemma.** A vector $\hat{z} \in \Omega'$ solves problem (28) if and only if there exist multiplier vectors $\psi \in E^m$ and $\mu \in E^k$ and a scalar $\psi^0 \leqq 0$, not all zero, such that

31
$$\psi^0 \nabla q^0(\hat{z}) + \sum_{i=1}^{k} \mu^i \nabla q^i(\hat{z}) + R^T\psi = 0$$
$$\mu \geqq 0 \qquad \mu^i q^i(\hat{z}) = 0 \qquad i = 1, 2, \ldots, k. \quad □$$

32 **Exercise.** Prove lemma (30). [*Hint:* If assumption (8) is satisfied, then lemma (30) is a slightly weaker statement than theorem (23). Show that (31) holds trivially (with $\psi^0 = 0$) when assumption (8) is not satisfied.] □

33 **Exercise.** Let z be any point in Ω' such that $IC(z,\Omega') = \{0\}$. Show that

$$\min_{h \in S} \max_{i \in I_0(z)} \langle \nabla q^i(z),h \rangle = 0. \quad □$$

34 **Remark.** In view of lemma (30), problem (28) is equivalent to finding a point where the generalized necessary conditions for optimality [theorem (3.5.11)] are satisfied. Recall that these conditions are very weak, and that even for convex programming problems their satisfaction at a point z may have little or no bearing on the optimality of that point. This was made abundantly clear in exercise (33). □

Let us now see what has been gained by transcribing problem (12) into form (28). Suppose we are given a point $z_0 \in \Omega'$ and we wish to determine whether or not z_0 solves problem (12). By theorem (23), this is equivalent to determining whether or not

35 $$\min_{h \in S} \max_{i \in I_0(z_0)} \langle \nabla q^i(z_0), h \rangle = 0.$$

Consider the following nonlinear programming subproblem:

36 **Subproblem.** Given a $z_0 \in \Omega'$, find a real σ_0 and a vector $h_0 \in E^n$ which minimize the linear form σ subject to the constraints

$$\langle \nabla q^i(z_0), h \rangle \leqq \sigma \qquad \text{for all } i \in I_0(z_0)$$
$$h \in S = S' \cap \{h\colon Rh = 0\},$$

where S' is *any* compact convex subset of E^n containing the origin in its interior. □

37 **Exercise.** Show that if (σ_0, h_0) is an optimal solution to (36) for some set S', then

38 $$\min_{h \in S} \max_{i \in I_0(z_0)} \langle \nabla q^i(z_0), h \rangle = \sigma_0.$$

Conversely, show that if (38) holds for the above S', then there exists a vector h_0 such that (σ_0, h_0) solves (36). □

39 **Exercise.** Show that subproblem (36) always has an optimal solution, as we have already tacitly assumed. Hence a (σ_0, h_0) satisfying (38) always exists. □

Thus to determine whether or not (35) holds we must solve subproblem (36). In turn, since the set S' in (20) is quite arbitrary, subproblem (36) is made tractable by a proper selection of S'. If we let

40 $$S' = \{h. = (h^1, h^2, \ldots, h^n)\colon |h^i| \leqq 1,\ i = 1, 2, \ldots, n\},$$

i.e., if S' is the unit hypercube in E^n, then S' satisfies all the properties stipulated in definition (20), and subproblem (36) becomes a linear programming problem. When transcribed into canonical form by appropriate substitutions, it can be solved by either the simplex algorithm (5.9.4) or the bounded-variable simplex algorithm (5.10.23). The reader can no doubt generate other examples of sets S' for which subproblem (36) reduces to a linear programming problem. Theoretically, of course, we have a great deal of freedom in choosing S'. Other simple choices of S' which lead to a tractable form of (36) are

$$S' = \{h: \langle h,h\rangle \leqq 1\} \qquad S' = \Big\{h: \sum_{i=1}^{n} |h^i| \leqq 1\Big\}.$$

41 **Exercise.** Transform the linear programming problem: minimize $\{\sigma: \langle \nabla q^i(z_0),h\rangle \leqq \sigma,\ i \in I_0(z_0),\ Rh = 0,\ |h^i| \leqq 1,\ i = 1, 2, \ldots, n\}$ into a bounded-variable linear program of the form: minimize $\{\langle d,w\rangle: Lw = b,\ -\infty < \alpha^i \leqq w^i \leqq \beta^i < +\infty\}$. (*Hint:* Use "slack" variables and determine artificial, but valid, bounds α^i and β^i where necessary.) □

42 **Exercise.** Transform the linear programming problem defined in exercise (41) into the form: minimize $\{\langle d,w\rangle: Lw = b,\ -\infty < \alpha^i \leqq w^i\}$. □

In view of the above exercises, we may suppose that for a given $z_0 \in \Omega'$, (σ_0,h_0) is an optimal solution to subproblem (36) (with a simple S) obtained, for example, by using the bounded-variable simplex algorithm. Now, if $\sigma_0 = 0$, then, by exercise (37) z_0 solves problem (28). Suppose, therefore, that $\sigma_0 < 0$, that is, that

$$\min_{h\in S}\ \max_{i\in I_0(z_0)} \langle \nabla q^i(z_0),h\rangle < 0.$$

It follows, then, that we have determined a vector $h_0 \in S$ such that $\langle \nabla q^i(z_0),h_0\rangle < 0$ for all $i \in I_0(z_0)$, which in expanded form becomes

43
$$\begin{aligned} &\langle \nabla q^0(z_0),h_0\rangle < 0 \qquad && Rh_0 = 0 \\ &\langle \nabla q^i(z_0),h_0\rangle < 0 && \text{for all } i \in I(z_0). \end{aligned}$$

44 **Exercise.** Consider the parametrized vector $z(\lambda) = z_0 + \lambda h_0$, where $z_0 \in \Omega'$ and h_0 satisfies (43). Show that there exists a scalar $\lambda_0 > 0$ such that $z(\lambda) \in \Omega'$ and $q^0(z(\lambda)) < q^0(z_0)$ for all $0 \leqq \lambda \leqq \lambda_0$. □

Thus for all values of λ sufficiently small $z_0 + \lambda h_0 \in \Omega'$ and $q^0(z_0 + \lambda h_0) < q^0(z_0)$. Put another way, moving in the *feasible direction* h_0, we have reduced the value of the cost function $q^0(\cdot)$. Having gone to all the trouble of calculating this feasible direction h_0, we shall make the most of it. Let

45
$$\gamma_0 = \max\{\gamma: q^i(z_0 + \beta h_0) \leqq 0 \text{ for all } \beta \leqq \gamma,\ i = 1, 2, \ldots, k\};$$

that is, γ_0 (which may be $+\infty$) is the largest value of γ such that $z_0 + \beta h_0 \in \Omega'$ for all $0 \leqq \beta \leqq \gamma$. Next, let $\lambda_0 \in [0,\gamma_0]$ be selected such that

46 $$\lambda_0 = \max \{\lambda: q^0(z_0 + \lambda h_0) \leqq q^0(z_0 + \beta h_0) \text{ for all } 0 \leqq \beta \leqq \lambda,\ 0 \leqq \lambda \leqq \gamma_0\}.$$

47 **Remark.** By exercise (44), $\lambda_0 > 0$ and $q^0(z + \lambda_0 h_0) < q^0(z_0)$. It may turn out, however, that $\lambda_0 = +\infty$, or that $q^0(z_0 + \lambda h_0) \to -\infty$ as $\lambda \to \lambda_0$, or both may occur. In the latter case the nonlinear programming problem (1) does not have a solution. □

Computationally, the determination of γ_0 in (45) is carried out by means of a one-dimensional search over the parameter $\gamma \geqq 0$ for every $i \in \{1,2, \ldots ,k\}$. The same approach is usually used to determine λ_0 in (46). If it turns out that $\lambda_0 < +\infty$, we may set $z_1 = z_0 + \lambda_0 h_0$ and repeat the above procedure, with z_1 replacing z_0.

It would appear, therefore, that a sequence $z_0, z_1, z_2, \ldots$ of vectors in Ω', constructed as shown below, might converge to a solution of (28). Thus, starting at $z_0 \in \Omega'$, with some set S defined as in (20), let

48 $$z_{j+1} = z_j + \lambda_j h_j \qquad j = 0, 1, 2, \ldots ,$$

where $h_j \in S$ satisfies

49 $$\max_{i \in I_0(z_j)} \langle \nabla q^i(z_j), h_j \rangle = \min_{h \in S} \max_{i \in I_0(z_j)} \langle \nabla q^i(z_j), h \rangle,$$

$\lambda_j \in [0,\gamma_j]$ satisfies

50 $$\lambda_j = \max \{\lambda: q^0(z_0 + \lambda h_0) \leqq q^0(z_0 + \beta h_0) \text{ for all } 0 \leqq \beta \leqq \lambda,\ 0 \leqq \lambda \leqq \gamma_j\}$$

and finally, $\gamma_j = \min \{\gamma_j', \gamma_j''\}$, where

51 $$\begin{aligned} \gamma_j' &= \max \{\gamma: q^i(z_j + \beta h_j) \leqq 0 \text{ for all } 0 \leqq \beta \leqq \gamma,\ i \in I(z_j)\} \\ \gamma_j'' &= \max \{\gamma: q^i(z_j + \beta h_j) \leqq 0 \text{ for all } 0 \leqq \beta \leqq \gamma,\ i \in \bar{I}(z_j)\}. \end{aligned}$$

Unfortunately, unless we take certain precautions, a sequence of feasible points $\{z_j\}$ generated as above may not converge to a solution of problem (28), and in addition, none of its subsequences need converge to a solution of (28) either. We shall now show heuristically why this is so.

From exercise (44) we know that if z_j is not a solution of (28), then $q^0(z_j + \lambda_j h_j) = q^0(z_{j+1}) < q^0(z_j)$. Now, the actual numerical difference between these two quantities depends on several factors, and it turns out that the most critical one is the scalar γ_j determined in (51). Clearly, if γ_j is small, then the interval $[0,\gamma_j]$ over which the minimization in (50) is to be performed is small, and hence $q^0(z_{j+1})$ differs only slightly from $q^0(z_j)$. The numerical value of γ_j is, in turn, a function of the two independent scalars γ_j' and γ_j'', as is evident in (51). The first quantity, γ_j', is not particularly critical, since, by (49), $\langle \nabla q^i(z_j), h_j \rangle < 0$ for all $i \in I(z_j)$; that is, to first-order effects h_j is indeed a feasible direction for the $q^i(\cdot)$, with $i \in I(z_j)$. It is the second term in (51), γ_j'', which is the source of difficulty. While, by definition, $q^i(z_j) < 0$ for $i \in \bar{I}(z_j)$, this number can be arbitrarily small, and should the circumstances be such that $\langle \nabla q^i(z_j), h_j \rangle > 0$ for an $i \in \bar{I}(z_j)$, it is intuitively clear that γ_j'' could be arbitrarily small. Hence γ_j, and, a fortiori, $|q^0(z_{j+1}) - q^0(z_j)|$, may be arbitrarily small (certainly smaller than first-order quantities). Examples have been constructed (see [2]) where precisely this set of circumstances occurs for infinitely many vectors z_j for $j \in \{0,1,2, \ldots\}$, the result being that the sequence $\{z_j\}_{j=1}^{\infty}$ converges to a vector $\hat{z}$, but $\hat{z}$ does not solve problem (28). Behavior of this type is called *zigzagging* or *jamming* in the mathematical programming literature.

One way to take into account the fact that some of the inactive constraints $q^i(\cdot)$ for $i \in \bar{I}(z_j)$ are "almost active" is to modify relation (49), which determines h_j, in the following manner. Suppose we agree that for $q^i(\cdot)$, with $i \in \bar{I}(z_j)$, to be "almost active" at z_j means that

52 $$q^i(z_j) + \epsilon \geqq 0,$$

where $\epsilon > 0$ is preassigned and small. Relation (49), which determines h_j, now becomes

53 $$\min_{h \in S} \max_{i \in I_\epsilon(z_j)} \langle \nabla q^i(z_j), h \rangle \triangleq \sigma_j,$$

where, by (17),

$$I_\epsilon(z_j) = \{i\colon q^i(z_j) + \epsilon \geqq 0, i \in \{1,2, \ldots ,k\}\} \cup \{0\}.$$

Clearly, $I_\epsilon(z_j) \supset I(z_j)$ and in addition, $I_\epsilon(z_j)$ contains the indices $i \in \bar{I}(z_j)$ for which $q^i(z_j)$ is within ϵ of being zero. It should be rather obvious that all the remarks pertaining to the solution of relation (49) are applicable to the modified subproblem defined by (53). Suppose, therefore, that (σ_j, h_j) is a solution to (53). If $\sigma_j < 0$, it now follows that h_j has the property that

54 $$\langle \nabla q^i(z_j), h_j \rangle < 0 \qquad \text{for all } i \in I_0(z_j)$$

and, more important, that

55 $$\langle \nabla q^i(z_j), h_j \rangle < 0 \qquad \text{for all } i \in \bar{I}(z_j) \text{ such that } q^i(z_j) + \epsilon \geqq 0.$$

Thus by taking into account inequality constraints which are almost active we have eliminated the cause of jamming.

There is one important matter left to clear up. Suppose that $\sigma_j = 0$ in (53). If $I_\epsilon(z_j) = I_0(z_j)$ (within computational tolerances), we have indeed solved problem (28). Otherwise all that can be said is that there does not exist a vector $h \in S$ with $\langle \nabla q^i(z_j), h\rangle < 0$ for all $i \in I_\epsilon(z_j)$; but this does not imply that the necessary conditions of optimality are satisfied. In this case we can replace ϵ by $\epsilon/2$ and resolve (53), repeating the halving of ϵ either until we obtain $\sigma_j < 0$ in (53) or until $\sigma_j = 0$ and $I_\epsilon(z_j) = I_0(z_j)$ for some value of $\epsilon = \epsilon/m$, with $m \in \{2, 2^2, 2^3, \ldots,\}$, whichever occurs first.† One of these two alternatives must occur after a finite number of steps.

Now that we are acquainted with a few of the subtleties involved, let us proceed with a rigorous treatment of the methods of feasible directions. Incidentally, at this point it should be quite clear that the reason for saying *methods* rather than *method* is that each different choice of the set S defines a different algorithm in this family.

56 **Algorithm: methods of feasible directions.** We are given two sets, Ω' and $S = S' \cap S''$, where

57 $$\Omega' = \{z: Rz = c,\ q^i(z) \leqq 0,\ i = 1, 2, \ldots, k\},$$

58 $$S'' = \{h: Rh = 0\},$$

R, c, and q^i for $i = 1, 2, \ldots, k$ are as in problem (28), and S' is a (any) compact convex set containing the origin in its interior. For any $z \in \Omega'$ and for any $\alpha \geqq 0$ let $\phi_\alpha: E^n \to E^1$ be defined by

59 $$\phi_\alpha(z) = \min_{h \in S} \max_{i \in I_\alpha(z)} \langle \nabla q^i(z), h\rangle.$$

Let $\epsilon > 0$ and $z_0 \in \Omega'$ be given, and suppose that $z_0, z_1, \ldots, z_j$ have been computed and are in Ω'.

Step 1. Using the given $\epsilon > 0$, set $\epsilon_j = \epsilon$.

Step 2. Let h_{ϵ_j} be such that

60 $$\phi_{\epsilon_j}(z_j) = \langle \nabla q^l(z_j), h_{\epsilon_j}\rangle \qquad \text{for some } l \in I_{\epsilon_j}(z_j).$$

If $\phi_{\epsilon_j}(z_j) \leqq -\epsilon_j < 0$, then set $h_j = h_{\epsilon_j}$ and go to step 4. If $\phi_{\epsilon_j}(z_j) > -\epsilon_j$, then go to step 3.

† The repeated halving of ϵ is a device which simplifies our exposition. We could equally well use any other factor $\beta \in (0,1)$ for multiplying ϵ. Computationally, of course, we would choose the largest number $\tilde{\epsilon} = \beta^l\epsilon$, for some integer l, such that $I_{\tilde{\epsilon}}(z_j)$ is a proper subset of $I_\epsilon(z_j)$, for resolving (53), rather than blindly resolve (53) for $\beta\epsilon, \beta^2\epsilon, \ldots, \beta^{l-1}\epsilon$, which all give the same σ_j as ϵ.

Step 3. If $\phi_{\epsilon_j}(z_j) < 0$, or $I_{\epsilon_j}(z_j) \neq I_0(z_j)$, then set $\epsilon_j = \epsilon_j/2$ and return to step 2. Otherwise $\phi_{\epsilon_j}(z_j) = 0$ and $I_{\epsilon_j}(z_j) = I_0(z_j)$, in which case stop, since z_j solves problem (28).

Step 4. Select $\gamma_j > 0$ such that

61 $$\gamma_j = \max \{\gamma: q^i(z_j + \beta h_j) \leqq 0 \text{ for all } 0 \leqq \beta \leqq \gamma, \quad i = 1,2, \ldots ,k\}$$

Step 5. Select $\lambda_j > 0$ to satisfy

62 $$\lambda_j = \max \{\lambda: q^0(z_j + \lambda h_j) \leqq q^0(z_j + \beta h_j) \text{ for all } 0 \leqq \beta \leqq \lambda, \quad 0 \leqq \lambda \leqq \gamma_j\}.$$

If $\lambda_j = +\infty$, then stop. If $q^0(z_j + \lambda h_j) \to -\infty$ as $\lambda \to \lambda_j$, then stop, since in this case $\inf \{q^0(z): z \in \Omega'\} = -\infty$. Otherwise let

63 $$z_{j+1} = z_j + \lambda_j h_j \in \Omega',$$

set $j = j + 1$, and return to step 1. □

64 **Remark.** In order to initialize algorithm (56) it is necessary to know a $z_0 \in \Omega$. Techniques for finding such a point are described in Section 1. □

65 **Remark.** By exercise (44), if z_j does not solve problem (28), then the parameter λ_j determined in step 5 is such that $\lambda_j > 0$, $z_j + \lambda_j h_j \in \Omega'$, and $q^0(z_j + \lambda_j h_j) < q^0(z_j)$. The last property implies that the infinite sequence $\{q^0(z_j)\}_{j=0}^{\infty}$ is strictly monotonically decreasing. □

66 **Exercise.** Show that if z_j does not solve problem (28), then either the halving procedure indicated in step 3 will, after a finite number of halvings, allow the algorithm to proceed to step 4 or, if z_j is a solution of (28), the stop command in step 3 will be reached in a finite number of steps. Thus the algorithm is well defined. □

67 **Theorem.** Let $z_0, z_1, z_2, \ldots$ be any infinite sequence generated by algorithm (56). If $\{z_l\}$ for $l \in L$ is any subsequence converging to a point $\hat{z}$, then $\hat{z} \in \Omega'$ and

$$\phi_0(\hat{z}) = \min_{h \in S} \max_{i \in I_0(\hat{z})} \langle \nabla q^i(\hat{z}), h\rangle = 0;$$

that is, $\hat{z}$ solves problem (28).

Proof. Let $\{z_l\}$ for $l \in L$ be a convergent subsequence generated by (56), with limit point $\hat{z}$. The set $\Omega' = \{z: Rz = c, q^i(z) \leqq 0, i = 1, 2,$

$\ldots, k\}$ is closed because the functions $q^i(\cdot)$ for $i = 1, 2, \ldots, k$ and the function $r(z) = Rz - c$ is continuous. Consequently, since $z_l \in \Omega'$ and $z_l \to \hat{z}$ for $l \in L$, it follows that $\hat{z} \in \Omega'$.

We next prove that $\phi_0(\hat{z}) = 0$. Suppose that $\phi_0(\hat{z}) < 0$. To arrive at the desired contradiction it is sufficient to show that there is an integer $\hat{l} \in L$ and an $\bar{\epsilon} > 0$ such that for all $l \in L$ and $l \geqq \hat{l}$

68 $$q^0(z_{l+1}) - q^0(z_l) \leqq -\bar{\epsilon}.$$

Indeed, suppose that (68) holds. Then for any two successive points z_l and z_{l+j} of the subsequence, with $l, l + j \in L$ and $l \geqq \hat{l}$, we have

69 $$q^0(z_{l+j}) - q^0(z_l) = [q^0(z_{l+j}) - q^0(z_{l+j-1})] + \cdots + [q^0(z_{l+1}) - q^0(z_l)] < -\hat{\epsilon}.$$

But since $z_l \to \hat{z}$ for $l \in L$, $q^0(z_l) \to \alpha > -\infty$, which contradicts (69). We shall now see that if $\phi_0(\hat{z}) < 0$, then (68) is satisfied.

Since $z_l \to \hat{z}$ for $l \in L$ and the functions $q^i(\cdot)$ are continuous, it is easily verified that corresponding to every $\hat{\epsilon} > 0$ and sufficiently small there is an integer $l' \in L$ such that for $l \geqq l'$ and $l \in L$

70 $$I_{\hat{\epsilon}}(z_l) \subset I_0(\hat{z}).$$

Since $\phi_0(\hat{z}) < 0$, we may assume that $\hat{\epsilon}$ is chosen such that (70) holds, and

71 $$\phi_0(\hat{z}) < -\hat{\epsilon},$$

and $\hat{\epsilon} = \epsilon/m$ for some $m \in \{2, 2^2, \ldots, 2^p\}$, where $\epsilon > 0$ is as specified at the beginning of algorithm (56). Let $M: E^n \to E^1$ be defined by

72 $$M(z) = \min_{h \in S} \max_{i \in I_0(\hat{z})} \langle \nabla q^i(z), h \rangle.$$

Then M is continuous, and there is an $l'' \in L$ such that for all $l \geqq l''$ and $l \in L$

73 $$|M(z_l) - \phi_0(\hat{z})| \leqq \frac{\hat{\epsilon}}{2}.$$

Let $\hat{l} = \max(l', l'')$; then, because of (70) to (72), for all $l \geqq \hat{l}$ and $l \in L$

74 $$\phi_{\hat{\epsilon}}(z_l) \leqq M(z_l) \leqq -\frac{\hat{\epsilon}}{2}.$$

But $I_{\hat{\epsilon}/2}(z_l) \subset I_{\hat{\epsilon}}(z_l)$, and hence for all $l \geqq \hat{l}$ and $l \in L$ we have

75 $$\phi_{\hat{\epsilon}/2}(z_l) \leqq \phi_{\hat{\epsilon}}(z_l) \leqq -\frac{\hat{\epsilon}}{2}.$$

We therefore conclude that for all $l \geqq \hat{l}$ and $l \in L$ the algorithm will use a value of $\epsilon_l \geqq \hat{\epsilon}/2$ in computing h_l in step 2;† that is, for all $l \geqq \hat{l}$, $l \in L$, and for all $i \in I_{\epsilon_l}(z_l)$, $\langle \nabla q^i(z_l), h_l \rangle \leqq -\hat{\epsilon}/2$.

Let $\rho > 0$ be such that $z_l + \xi h_l \in B(\hat{z},\rho)$, a closed ball of radius ρ about $\hat{z}$, for all $l \geqq \hat{l}$, $l \in L$, and $0 \leqq \xi \leqq 1$. Now, for every $l \in L$ and $i = 0, 1, \ldots, k$ we have, by the mean-value theorem, that

76 $$q^i(z_l + \beta h_l) = q^i(z_l) + \beta \langle \nabla q^i(z_l + \xi h_l), h_l \rangle,$$

where $\xi \in [0,\beta]$. Since the functions $\langle \nabla q^i(\cdot),\cdot \rangle$ are uniformally continuous on $B(\hat{z},\rho) \times S$, there exist $0 < \beta_i \leqq 1$ such that for $l \geqq \hat{l}$

$$|\langle \nabla q^i(z_l + \xi h_l), h_l \rangle - \langle \nabla q^i(z_l), h_l \rangle| \leqq \frac{\hat{\epsilon}}{4} \qquad \text{for all } \xi \in [0,\beta_i].$$

Similarly, since the functions $q^i(\cdot)$ are uniformally continuous on $B(\hat{z},\rho)$, there exist $0 < \bar{\beta}_i \leqq 1$ such that for $l \geqq \hat{l}$, and $l \in L$,

77 $$|q^i(z_l + \xi h_l) - q^i(z_l)| \leqq \frac{\hat{\epsilon}}{2} \qquad \text{for all } \xi \in [0,\bar{\beta}_i].$$

Now, for all $l \geqq \hat{l}$ and $l \in L$ and for each $i \in I_{\epsilon_l}(z_l)$, $\langle \nabla q^i(z_l), h_l \rangle \leqq -\hat{\epsilon}/2$, and for each $i \in \bar{I}_{\epsilon_l}(z_l)$, $q^i(z_l) \leqq -\hat{\epsilon}/2$. Hence, setting

78 $$\bar{\mu} = \min \{\beta_0, \beta_1, \ldots, \beta_k, \bar{\beta}_0, \bar{\beta}_1, \ldots, \bar{\beta}_k\},$$

we have for all $l \geqq \hat{l}$, $l \in L$, and $\beta \in [0,\bar{u}]$,

79 $$\begin{aligned} q^i(z_l + \beta h_l) - q^i(z_l) &\leqq -\beta \frac{\hat{\epsilon}}{4} \qquad && \text{for all } i \in I_{\epsilon_l}(z_l) \\ q^i(z_l + \beta h_l) &\leqq 0 && \text{for all } i \in \bar{I}_{\epsilon_l}(z_l). \end{aligned}$$

It follows from (79) that $\lambda_l \geqq \bar{\mu}$ (see step 5), so that we are led to the conclusion that for all $l \geqq \hat{l}$ and $l \in L$

$$q^0(z_{l+1}) - q^0(z_l) \leqq -\bar{\mu}\frac{\hat{\epsilon}}{4} \triangleq -\bar{\epsilon};$$

that is, (68) holds. □

80 **Exercise.** Suppose that for the nonlinear programming problem (1) there are no inequality constraint functions, that is, $q^i \equiv 0$ for $i = 1, 2, \ldots, k$, and hence subproblem (59) reduces to

$$\phi(z) = \min_{h \in S} \langle \nabla q^0(z), h \rangle.$$

Show that the antijamming precaution of algorithm (56) can be

† In (56) j is a dummy subscript. Substitute l for j to compute ϵ_l, h_l, and λ_l.

eliminated without changing the result of theorem (67). Thus steps 1 to 3 of algorithm (56) are replaced by the following one:

Step 1′. Let h_j be such that $\phi_0(z_j) = \langle \nabla q^0(z_j), h_j \rangle$. If $\phi_0(z_j) = 0$, then stop, since z_j solves problem (28). Otherwise proceed to step 4. □

The reader is cautioned not to read more into theorem (67) than is actually stated. In particular, it has not been shown that algorithm (56) necessarily generates an infinite sequence (at some point $\lambda_j = +\infty$ may occur), nor is there any guarantee that a convergent subsequence can be extracted. The following exercises are directed to this problem.

81 **Exercise.** Suppose that for every $y \in \Omega'$ the set $\{z: q^0(z) \leqq q^0(y), z \in \Omega'\}$ is bounded. Show that algorithm (56) either determines a solution to problem (28) in a finite number of steps or else generates an infinite sequence $\{z_j\}_{j=0}^{\infty}$ which has a convergent subsequence. □

82 **Exercise.** Suppose that the functions $q^i(\cdot)$ for $i = 0, 1, \ldots, k$ are convex, that $m \triangleq \min \{q^0(z): z \in \Omega'\}$ exists, and that the set $\{z: q^0(z) = m, z \in \Omega'\}$ is bounded. Show that for every $y \in \Omega'$ the set $\{z: q^0(z) \leqq q^0(y), z \in \Omega'\}$ is bounded. □

83 **Exercise.** In addition to the hypotheses in exercise (82), suppose that the function $q^0(z)$ is strictly convex and that assumption (8) is satisfied. Show that the infinite sequence $\{z_j\}_{j=0}^{\infty}$ generated by algorithm (56) converges to a point $\hat{z}$ satisfying $q^0(\hat{z}) = \min \{q^0(z): z \in \Omega'\}$. □

We shall now show how the algorithm (56) can be used for solving discrete optimal control problems. Thus, suppose we wish to solve the following problem:

84 Minimize

$$\sum_{i=0}^{k-1} f_i^0(x_i, u_i) \qquad x_i \in E^n,\ u_i \in E^1$$

subject to

a. $x_{i+1} - x_i = f_i(x_i, u_i) \qquad i = 0, 1, \ldots, k-1,$

b. $x_0 = c_0,\ \bar{q}^j(x_k) \leqq 0 \qquad j = 1, 2, \ldots, m,$

c. $|u_i| \leqq 1 \qquad i = 0, 1, \ldots, k-1,$

where the $f_i^0(\cdot,\cdot)$, $i = 0, 1, \ldots, k-1$, and $\bar{q}^j(\cdot)$, $j = 1, 2, \ldots, m$, are continuously differentiable in all their arguments. □

Setting $z = (u_0, u_1, \ldots, u_{k-1})$, problem (84) assumes the form:

85 Minimize $q^0(z)$ subject to $q^j(z) \leqq 0$, $j = 1, 2, \ldots, m$, $|u_i| \leqq 1$, $i = 0, 1, 2, \ldots, k-1$, where

86
$$q^0(z) = \sum_{i=0}^{k-1} f_i^0(x_i(z), u_i)$$

and

87
$$q^j(z) = \bar{q}^j(x_k(z)) \qquad j = 1, 2, \ldots, m. \quad \square$$

In (86) and (87), the $x_i(z)$ are obtained by solving (84) with $x_0 = c_0$ and the controls $(u_0, u_1, \ldots, u_{k-1}) = z$. In order to apply the algorithm (56) to problem (85), we need to calculate frequently $\nabla q^0(z)$ and $\nabla q^i(z)$, $i \in \{1, 2, \ldots, m\}$. The dynamical structure (84) of this problem can be utilized to simplify this calculation, or to be more precise, to transform it into a sequence of relatively simple calculations. We begin with $\nabla q^0(z)$.

Now, we can break up $\nabla q^0(z)$ into block form as follows:

88
$$(\nabla q^0(z))^T = \frac{\partial q^0(z)}{\partial z} = \left(\frac{\partial q^0(z)}{\partial u_0} \,\vdots\, \frac{\partial q^0(z)}{\partial u_1} \,\vdots\, \cdots \,\vdots\, \frac{\partial q^0(z)}{\partial u_{k-1}} \right)$$

and, by inspection of (84),

89
$$\frac{\partial q^0(z)}{\partial u_i} = \frac{\partial f_i^0(x_i(z), u_i)}{\partial u_i} + \sum_{j=i+1}^{k-1} \frac{\partial f_j^0(x_j(z), u_j)}{\partial x_j} \frac{\partial x_j(z)}{\partial u_i}$$

Referring to Section 2.4, we find that $\partial x_j(z)/\partial u_i$, $j > i$, can be expressed as follows. For $i = 0, 1, 2, \ldots, k$ and $k \geqq j \geqq i$, let $G_{j,i}$ be an $n \times n$ matrix, such that $G_{i,i} = I$, the identity matrix, and

90
$$G_{j+1,i} - G_{j,i} = \frac{\partial f_i(x_i(z), u_i)}{\partial x_i} G_{j,i},\ j = 1, i+1, \ldots, k-1,$$

where $(u_0, u_1, \ldots, u_{k-1}) = z$. Then,

91
$$\frac{\partial x_j(z)}{\partial u_i} = \begin{cases} G_{j,i+1} \dfrac{\partial f_i(x_i(z), u_i)}{\partial u_i} & \text{for } j = i+1, i+2, \ldots, k \\ 0 & \text{for } j = 1, 2, \ldots, i, \end{cases}$$

and hence,

92
$$\frac{\partial q^0(z)}{\partial u_i} = \frac{\partial f_i^0(x_i(z), u_i)}{\partial u_i} + \left(\sum_{j=i+1}^{k-1} \frac{\partial f_j^0(x_j(z), u_j)}{\partial x_j} G_{j,i+1} \right) \frac{\partial f_i(x_i(z), u_i)}{\partial u_i}$$

Now, for $i = 1, 2, \ldots, k$, let p_i be the solution of

93 $$p_i - p_{i+1} = \left(\frac{\partial f_i(x_i(z),u_i)}{\partial x}\right)^T p_{i+1} + \left(\frac{\partial f_i^0(x_i(z),u_i)}{\partial x}\right)^T \qquad i = 0, 1, \ldots, k-1$$

with $p_k = 0$. Then (see Section 2.4),

94 $$p_i = \sum_{j=i}^{k-1} G_{j,i}^T \left(\frac{\partial f_j^0(x_j(z),u_j)}{\partial x_j}\right)^T \qquad i = 1, 2, \ldots, k.$$

Comparing (92) and (94), we find that

95 $$\frac{\partial q^0(z)}{\partial u_i} = \frac{\partial f_i^0(x_i(z))}{\partial u_i} + \left\langle p_{i+1}, \frac{\partial f_i(x_i(z),u_i)}{\partial u_i}\right\rangle.$$

Thus, to calculate $\partial q^0(z)/\partial u_i$, we solve (93) (or even more simply, its transpose) for the p_i, $i = 1, 2, \ldots, k$ and then calculate the scalars $\partial q^0(z)/\partial u_i$ by means of (95).

Next, to calculate $\nabla q^i(z)$, $i \in \{1,2, \ldots ,m\}$, we observe that

96 $$\nabla q^i(z)^T = \frac{\partial q^i(z)}{\partial z} = \frac{\partial \bar{q}^i(x_k(z))}{\partial x_k} \frac{\partial x_k(z)}{\partial z},$$

that is,

97 $$\frac{\partial q^i(z)}{\partial u_j} = \left\langle \frac{\partial x_k(z)}{\partial u_j}, \frac{\partial \bar{q}^i(x_k(z))}{\partial x_k}\right\rangle.$$

Substituting for $\partial x_k(z)/\partial u_j$ from (91), we obtain

98 $$\begin{aligned}\frac{\partial q^i(z)}{\partial u_j} &= \left\langle G_{k,j+1} \frac{\partial f_j(x_j(z),u_j)}{\partial u_j}, \frac{\partial \bar{q}^i(x_k(z))}{\partial x_k}\right\rangle \\ &= \left\langle \frac{\partial f_j(x_j(z),u_j)}{\partial u_j}, G_{k,j+1}^T \nabla \bar{q}^i(x_k(z))\right\rangle\end{aligned}$$

Now, let $p_{1,i}, p_{2,i}, \ldots, p_{k,i}$, $i \in \{1,2, \ldots ,m\}$ be the solution of

99 $$p_{j,i} - p_{j+1,i} = \left(\frac{\partial f_j(x_j,u_j)}{\partial x_j}\right)^T p_{j+1,i} \qquad j = i, i+1, \ldots, k-1,$$

with $p_{k,i} = \nabla \bar{q}^i(x_k(z))$. Then

100 $$p_{j+1,i} = G_{k,j+1}^T \nabla \bar{q}^i(x_k(z))$$

and hence

101 $$\frac{\partial q^i(z)}{\partial u_j} = \left\langle \frac{\partial f_j(x_j(z),u_j)}{\partial u_j}, p_{j+1,i}\right\rangle,$$

which again indicates a method for computing $\nabla q^i(z)$.

Suppose set $S = \{h: |h^i| \leqq 1$ in (56). Then $\phi_\epsilon(z)$ is the solution of

102 Minimize σ subject to

a. $\langle \nabla q^i(z), h \rangle - \sigma \leqq 0$ for $i = 0$ and for all $i \epsilon \{1, \ldots, m\}$ such that $q^i(z) + \epsilon \geqq 0$

b. $h^{i+1} - \sigma \leqq 0$ for all i such that $u_i - 1 + \epsilon \geqq 0$, $i \epsilon \{0, \ldots, k - 1\}$

c. $-h^{i+1} - \sigma \leqq 0$ for all i such that $-u_i - 1 + \epsilon \geqq 0$

d. $|h^i| \leqq 1$, $i = 1, 2, \ldots, k$.

A solution to this problem could conveniently be obtained either by using the bounded-variable simplex algorithm (5.11.23), or preferably, by generalized upper bounding techniques which require the inversion of matrices whose dimension is governed only by the inequalities *a* in (102) [rather than by *b*, *c*, and *d*; see (12)].

103 **Exercise.** Consider again problem (1) and suppose that some of the inequalities in (2) are affine. For every $z \in \Omega'$ [defined in (6)] and every $\epsilon \geqq 0$, let $I_\epsilon^A(z) \subset I_\epsilon(z)$ and $I_\epsilon^N(z) \subset I_\epsilon(z)$ [defined in (17)] be such that $I_\epsilon^A(z) \cap I_\epsilon^N(z) = \phi$, $I_\epsilon^A(z) \cup I_\epsilon^N(z) = I_\epsilon(z)$, $0 \epsilon I_\epsilon^N(z)$, and, in addition, for every $i \in I_\epsilon^A(z)$, $q^i(\cdot)$ is affine. For $\epsilon \geqq 0$, let $\eta_\epsilon: \Omega' \to E^1$ be defined by

104 $$\eta_\epsilon(z) = \min \{\sigma: \sigma - \langle \nabla q^i(z), h \rangle \geqq 0 \text{ for } i \in I_\epsilon^N(z),\; -\langle \nabla q^i(z), h \rangle \geqq 0 \text{ for } i \in I_\epsilon^A(z),\; Rh = 0,\; |h^i| \leqq 1\}.$$

Show that (*a*) for every $z \in \Omega'$ and $\epsilon \geqq 0$, $\eta_\epsilon(z) \leqq \varphi_\epsilon(z)$ (provided $S' = \{h: |h^i| \leqq 1)$; (*b*) for every $\hat{z}$ which is optimal for (1) $\eta_0(\hat{z}) = 0$; and (*c*) if $\eta_\epsilon(\cdot)$ is substituted for $\varphi_\epsilon(\cdot)$ in the algorithm (56), the convergence properties of this algorithm remain unaltered. In addition, show that when algorithm (56), with $\eta_\epsilon(\cdot)$ taking the place of $\varphi_\epsilon(\cdot)$, is applied to the previously discussed optimal control problem, the feasible direction h at z is now determined by solving

105 Minimize σ subject to

a. $\langle \nabla q^i(z), h \rangle - \sigma \leqq 0$ for $i = 0$ and for all $i \epsilon \{1, \ldots, m\}$ such that $q^i(z) + \epsilon \geqq 0$

b. $-h^{i+1} \leqq 0$ for all i such that $u_i - 1 + \epsilon \geqq 0$, $i \epsilon \{0, \ldots, k - 1\}$

c. $h^{i+1} \leqq 0$ for all i such that $-u_i - 1 + \epsilon \geqq 0$, $i \epsilon \{0, \ldots, k - 1\}$

d. $|h^i| \leqq 1$, $i = 1, 2, \ldots, k$.

Note that (105) is a simpler problem than (102). □

The reader should now have no difficulty in obtaining similar derivations for more complex cases of the discrete optimal control problem. When reading the gradient projection methods in the next section, he should have no difficulty in utilizing the above developments for calculating the required gradients in control applications.

7.3 STEEPEST DESCENT AND GRADIENT PROJECTION

The methods of feasible directions [algorithm (2.56)] presented in the preceding section were characterized by the fact that at each iteration we had to solve two subsidiary optimization problems. The first one was solved to find a feasible direction and the second one to obtain the step size. Let us now examine a few algorithms which entail only one subsidiary optimization at each iteration, but which are really effective only when all the constraint functions are affine. We shall see that in these algorithms certain fairly simple calculations take the place of solving a subsidiary optimization problem. In view of the above remarks, we shall restrict ourselves to problems of the following form:

1 **Problem.** Given a real-valued continuously differentiable function $f(\cdot)$ defined on E^n and affine functions $r(z) = Rz - c$ and $q(z) = Qz - b$, where R, Q, c, and b are, respectively, $m \times n$, $k \times n$, $m \times 1$, and $k \times 1$ matrices, find a $\hat{z} \in E^n$ such that

2 $$R\hat{z} = c$$

3 $$Q\hat{z} \leqq b$$

and such that for all vectors $z \in E^n$ satisfying (2) and (3)

4 $$f(\hat{z}) \leqq f(z). \quad \square$$

Obviously, this is a special case of the nonlinear programming problem (2.1).

Throughout this section we shall assume that the following regularity condition holds:

5 **Assumption.** Let r^i for $i = 1, 2, \ldots, m$, q^i for $i = 1, 2, \ldots, k$, and b^i for $i = 1, 2, \ldots, m$ denote the rows of R, Q, and b, respectively. If $z \in E^n$ is any vector satisfying (2) and (3), then the vectors r^i for $i = 1, 2, \ldots, m$, taken together with the vectors q^i, with $i \in I(z) = \{i: \langle q^i, z \rangle - b^i = 0\}$, are linearly independent. $\square$

6 **Remark.** We anticipate the need to invert certain matrices which will be nonsingular because of assumption (5). $\square$

As we noted in Section 2, algorithm (2.56), defining the methods of feasible directions, is in fact a family of algorithms, where each different choice of the compact set S' [see (2.20)] defines a different algorithm. We shall now consider two well-known algorithms which are obtainable from (2.56) by considering specific forms of constraints (2) and (3), as well as of the set S', and which involve only one optimization at each iteration. We begin with the simplest possible case of problem (1), the unconstrained minimization problem.

Unconstrained Minimization Problems

Let us consider the case when all the matrices and vectors appearing in (2) and (3) are identically zero. Thus we wish to find a $\hat{z} \in E^n$ such that $f(\hat{z}) \leqq f(z)$ for all $z \in E^n$, where $f(\cdot)$ is a real-valued continuously differentiable function defined on E^n.

The algorithm we are about to discuss is commonly known as the method of steepest descent [4], and under rather liberal assumptions, it can be used to find a zero of the gradient function $\nabla f(\cdot)$. The condition $\nabla f(\hat{z}) = 0$ is, of course, the first-order necessary condition for $\hat{z}$ to minimize $f(\cdot)$. If $f(\cdot)$ is a convex function, then we may assert that $f(\hat{z}) \leqq f(z)$ for all $z \in E^n$ whenever $\nabla f(\hat{z}) = 0$, that is, that $\hat{z}$ is an optimal solution.

We shall apply algorithm (2.56) to our problem. Referring to equations (2.57) and (2.58), we see that for the unconstrained optimization problem

7
$$\Omega' = \{z: Rz = c, Qz \leqq b\} = E^n \qquad S'' = \{h: Rh = 0\} = E^n$$
$$I_\alpha(z) = \{0\} \qquad \text{for all } \alpha \geqq 0.$$

Therefore subproblem (2.59) becomes:[1]

8 Minimize $\langle \nabla f(z), h \rangle$, with $h \in S'$, where S' is any compact convex subset of E^n containing the origin as an interior point. □

9 If we let $S' = \{h: \|h\| \leqq 1\}$,

then a solution to (8) is given by

10
$$\hat{h} = \begin{cases} 0 & \text{if } \nabla f(z) = 0 \\ \dfrac{-\nabla f(z)}{\|\nabla f(z)\|} & \text{otherwise.} \end{cases}$$

Thus we see that algorithm (2.56) simplifies considerably when it is applied to unconstrained optimization problems. For future reference the resulting algorithm is summarized below.

11 **Algorithm: steepest descent.** Let $z_0 \in E^n$ be arbitrary. Suppose that $z_0, z_1, \ldots, z_j$ have been computed by the algorithm and that $\nabla f(z_j) \neq 0$.

[1] Observe that we now return to our usual convention of denoting the cost function by $f(\cdot)$ rather than by $q^0(\cdot)$, as in Section 2.

Step 1. Set $h_j = -\nabla f(z_j)$.†

Step 2. Select $\lambda_j > 0$ to satisfy

12 $$\lambda_j = \max \{\lambda\colon f(z_j + \lambda h_j) \leqq f(z_j + \beta h_j) \text{ for all } 0 \leqq \beta \leqq \lambda\}$$

[that is, if $f(\cdot)$ is convex, λ_j is the smallest positive real root of the equation

13 $$\frac{d}{d\lambda} f(z_j + \lambda h_j) = \langle \nabla f(z_j + \lambda h_j), h_j \rangle = 0].$$

If $\lambda_j = +\infty$, then stop. If $f(z_j + \lambda h_j) \to -\infty$ as $\lambda \to \lambda_j$, then stop. Otherwise let

14 $$z_{j+1} = z_j + \lambda_j h_j.$$

If $\nabla f(z_{j+1}) = 0$, then stop. Otherwise set $j = j + 1$ and go to step 1. □

15 **Theorem.** Let $z_0, z_1, z_2, \ldots$ be any infinite sequence generated by algorithm (11). If $\{z_l\}$ for $l \in L$ is any subsequence converging to a point $\hat{z}$, then $\nabla f(\hat{z}) = 0$.

Proof. This theorem is an immediate consequence of exercise (2.80) and theorem (2.67). □

It should be noted that a different selection of the set S' in (9) would lead to a different "steepest-descent" algorithm.

16 **Exercise.** For each of the following sets S' find an explicit solution to (8) and modify algorithm (11) accordingly:

$$S' = \{h\colon |h^i| \leqq 1, i = 1, 2, \ldots, n\}$$

$$S' = \left\{h\colon \sum_{i=1}^{n} |h^i| \leqq 1\right\}.$$

Would there be any computational advantages in using the second set? □

Concerning the convergence rate of algorithm (11), consider the following exercise.

17 **Exercise.** Consider the problem of minimizing the quadratic form $f(z) = \frac{1}{2}\langle z,Qz\rangle$, where Q is a symmetric positive-definite $n \times n$

† Actually, to be consistent with (10), we should set $\tilde{h}_j = -\nabla f(x_j)/\|\nabla f(x_j)\|$ and compute $\tilde{\lambda}_j$ in (12) with $\tilde{h}_j$ replacing h_j. But since $1/\|\nabla f(x_j)\|$ is a positive constant, it can be absorbed into λ_j as in (12).

matrix. Let $z_0, z_1, z_2, \ldots$ be any infinite sequence generated when algorithm (11) is applied to $f(\cdot)$. Show that if $\gamma_{\min}$ and $\gamma_{\max}$ are the smallest and largest eigenvalues of the matrix Q, then

$$f(z_{l+1}) \leqq f(z_l)\left(1 - \frac{\gamma_{\min}}{\gamma_{\max}}\right).$$

[*Hint:* Find an explicit expression for λ_j, express $f(z_{j+1})$ in terms of $f(z_j)$, and use the fact that Q is positive definite.] □

18 **Exercise.** Find an explicit solution for (8) when $S' = \{h: \langle h,Qh\rangle \leqq 1\}$, where Q is a symmetric positive-definite $n \times n$ matrix, and modify algorithm (11) accordingly. [Note that whenever $\partial^2 f(z)/\partial z^2$ is positive definite for all $z \in E^n$ and is used in place of Q above, then algorithm (11) becomes *Newton's method* with a variable step size.] □

Gradient Projection: A Special Case

Next we shall consider the problem of minimizing $f(z)$ subject to the constraint $Rz = c$, where f, R, and c are as defined in (1). We shall again apply algorithm (2.56). Referring to equations (2.57) and (2.58), we see that in this particular case

$$\Omega' = \{z: Rz = c\} \qquad S'' = \{h: Rh = 0\}$$
$$I_\alpha(z) = \{0\} \qquad \text{for all } \alpha \geqq 0,$$

so that subproblem (2.59) becomes:

19 Minimize $\langle \nabla f(z),h\rangle$ subject to the constraints

20 $Rh = 0 \qquad h \in S'$. □

Again we shall take

$$S' = \{h: \langle h,h\rangle \leqq 1\},$$

and hence (19) becomes a convex programming problem. By theorem (3.6.1), a sufficient condition for $\hat{h}$ to be an optimal solution to problem (19) is that there exist multipliers $\lambda \in E^m$ and $\mu \leqq 0$, real, such that

21
$$-\nabla f(z) + R^T\lambda + 2\mu\hat{h} = 0 \qquad R\hat{h} = 0$$
$$\langle \hat{h},\hat{h}\rangle - 1 \leqq 0 \qquad \mu(\langle \hat{h},\hat{h}\rangle - 1) = 0$$

From (21) we have

22 $$2\mu\hat{h} = \nabla f(z) - R^T\lambda,$$

and $R\hat{h} = 0$ implies that

23 $$RR^T\lambda = R\,\nabla f(z).$$

Since R has full row rank, by assumption (5), the $m \times m$ matrix RR^T is nonsingular. Consequently, we obtain

24 $$\lambda = (RR^T)^{-1}R\,\nabla f(z),$$

which, when substituted into (22), yields

25 $$2\mu\hat{h} = [I - R^T(RR^T)^{-1}R]\,\nabla f(z) \triangleq w.$$

To determine the scalar $\mu \leqq 0$ we proceed as follows. If $w = 0$, let $\hat{h} = 0$ and $\mu = 0$. If $w \neq 0$, let $\mu = -\frac{1}{2}\|w\|$; then, by (25), $\hat{h} = -w/\|w\|$, that is, $\|\hat{h}\|^2 = 1$, and again $(\|\hat{h}\|^2 - 1)\mu = 0$. Thus, an optimal solution to problem (19) is given by

26 $$\hat{h} = \begin{cases} 0 & \text{if } [I - R^T(RR^T)^{-1}R]\,\nabla f(z) = 0 \\ \dfrac{-[I - R^T(RR^T)^{-1}R]\,\nabla f(z)}{\|[I - R^T(RR^T)^{-1}R]\,\nabla f(z)\|} & \text{otherwise.} \end{cases}$$

27 **Exercise.** Consider the linear subspace $\mathcal{L}$ of E^n defined by $\mathcal{L} = \{h\colon Rh = 0\}$. Show that the orthogonal projection of $\nabla f(z) \in E^n$ onto $\mathcal{L}$ is given by

$$h = [I - R^T(RR^T)^{-1}R]\,\nabla f(z). \quad \square$$

Note that if $\hat{h} = 0$ in (26), then, by theorem (2.23), z satisfies the first-order necessary conditions of optimality for the problem under consideration. Indeed, if $\hat{h} = 0$, then we have

28 $$\nabla f(z) = R^T(RR^T)^{-1}R\,\nabla f(z),$$

and so if we define $\lambda = (RR^T)^{-1}R\,\nabla f(z)$, we obtain

29 $$-\nabla f(z) + R^T\lambda = 0;$$

that is, z satisfies the Lagrange multiplier rule of theorem (3.2.6).

Let us now summarize the algorithm sketched out above.

30 **Algorithm.** Set $z_0 = R^T(RR^T)^{-1}c$. Then $Rz_0 = c$; that is, z_0 is a feasible solution. Suppose that the points $z_0, z_1, \ldots, z_j$ have been generated by the algorithm, starting with z_0 defined as above, that $Rz_i = c$ for $i = 0, 1, \ldots, j$, and that $[I - R^T(RR^T)^{-1}R]\,\nabla f(z_j) \neq 0$.

Step 1. Set $h_j = -[I - R^T(RR^T)^{-1}R]\,\nabla f(z_j)$.† Note that $Rh_j = 0$.

† Here again the constant $1/\|[I - R^T(RR^T)^{-1}R]\,\nabla f(z)\|$ has been absorbed into λ_j.

Step 2. Select $\lambda_j > 0$ to satisfy

31 $$\lambda_j = \max \{\lambda : f(z_j + \lambda h_j) \leqq f(z_j + \beta h_j) \text{ for all } 0 \leqq \beta \leqq \lambda\}.$$

If $\lambda_j = +\infty$, then stop. If $f(z_j + \lambda h_j) \to -\infty$ as $\lambda \to \lambda_j$, then stop. Otherwise set $z_{j+1} = z_j + \lambda_j h_j$ and go to step 3.

Step 3. If $[I - R^T(RR^T)^{-1}R] \nabla f(z_{j+1}) = 0$, then stop. Otherwise set $j = j + 1$ and go to step 1. □

32 **Remark.** It follows from exercise (2.80) and theorem (2.67) that if $\{z_l\}$ for $l \in L$ is any convergent subsequence generated by algorithm (30) and converging to a point $\hat{z}$, then $R\hat{z} = c$ and there is a multiplier $\lambda \in E^m$ such that $-\nabla f(\hat{z}) + R^T\lambda = 0$. Obviously, when $f(\cdot)$ is convex this implies that $-\hat{z}$ is an optimal solution. □

Gradient Projection: The General Case

We now turn our attention to the most general case of problem (1), the minimization of $f(z)$ subject to the constraints

33 $$z \in \Omega' \triangleq \{z: Rz = c,\ Qz \leqq b\},$$

defined as in (1). The rows of R, Q, and b will be denoted by r^i, q^i, and b^i, respectively, and as usual, $I(z)$ will be the index set identifying the active inequality constraints, that is, for $z \in \Omega'$,

34 $$I(z) = \{i: \langle q^i,z\rangle - b^i = 0\}.$$

The algorithm described below is due to Rosen [2] and is called the *gradient-projection algorithm*. It is very much akin to algorithm (30) in that at every iteration a feasible direction h is computed by projecting the gradient vector $-\nabla f(z)$ onto a subspace defined by the equations $Rh = 0$ and $\langle q^i,h\rangle = 0$ for $i \in K(z)$, where $K(z)$ is a subset of $I(z)$, which differs from $I(z)$ by at most one index.

To ensure convergence, we must incorporate in the gradient-projection algorithm certain very cumbersome features which prevent jamming, or zigzagging, a phenomenon discussed in some detail in the previous section. Fortunately, it has been found that in practice jamming occurs rather rarely and that a partial antijamming precaution is usually adequate. We shall therefore consider here a version of the gradient-projection algorithm which is reasonably simple and performs very well in practice, but which cannot be proved to converge, since it uses only a partial antijamming procedure.

We begin by developing the necessary projection operators.

35 **Definition.** Let $z \in \Omega'$, and let $L(z) = \{i_1, i_2, \ldots, i_\alpha\}$ be a subset of $I(z)$. We define the $(m + \alpha) \times n$ matrix $S_{L(z)}$ to be the matrix whose first m rows are the rows of R (r^i for $i = 1, 2, \ldots, m$) and whose remaining rows are the q^{i_j} for $j = 1, 2, \ldots, \alpha$, with $i_j \in L(z)$. □

36 **Remark.** It follows from assumption (5) that $S_L(z)$ has full row rank for every $z \in \Omega'$ and for every $L(z) \subset I(z)$.† Hence the $(m + \alpha) \times (m + \alpha)$ matrix $S_{L(z)}S^T_{L(z)}$ is nonsingular. □

37 **Definition.** Let $z \in \Omega'$ and let $L(z) \subset I(z)$. We define the $n \times n$ *projection matrix* $P_{L(z)}$ to be

$$P_{L(z)} = I - S^T_{L(z)}(S_{L(z)}S^T_{L(z)})^{-1}S_{L(z)}. \quad \square$$

38 **Remark.** The matrix $P_{L(z)}$ has the following properties: (*a*) It is symmetric and $P_{L(z)}S^T_{L(z)} = S_{L(z)}P_{L(z)} = 0$. (*b*) If $l \in L(z)$, then $P_{L(z)/\{l\}}P_{L(z)} = P_{L(z)}P_{L(z)/\{l\}} = P_{L(z)}$, where $L(z)/\{l\} = \{i \in L(z): i \neq l\}$. □

Now, let $z_0 \in \Omega'$ be arbitrary and let

$$h_0 = -P_{I(z)}\ \nabla f(z_0).$$

Then, by exercise (27), h_0 is the projection of $-\nabla f(z_0)$ onto the linear subspace $\{h: S_{I(z_0)}h = 0\}$. Since $S_{I(z_0)}h_0 = 0$, it follows that for all real $\gamma \geqq 0$

39
$$\begin{aligned} R(z_0 + \gamma h_0) &= c \\ \langle q^i, z_0 + \gamma h_0\rangle - b^i &= 0 \qquad \text{for all } i \in I(z_0). \end{aligned}$$

Now, if $i \in \bar{I}(z_0)$, the complement of $I(z_0)$ in $\{1,2, \ldots, k\}$, then $q^i(z_0) - b^i < 0$, so that for all $\gamma > 0$ sufficiently small

40
$$\langle q^i, z_0 + \gamma h_0\rangle - b^i \leqq 0 \qquad \text{for all } i \in \bar{I}(z_0),$$

and therefore h_0 is a feasible direction. Furthermore, since h_0 is the projection of $-\nabla f(z_0)$ onto a linear subspace, we have

41
$$\langle \nabla f(z_0), h_0\rangle \leqq 0,$$

with equality holding if and only if $h_0 = 0$. Thus when $h_0 \neq 0$ a displacement in the feasible direction h_0 will reduce the value of $f(\cdot)$.

Now let us consider (in anticipation that we shall need it in a partial antijamming procedure) what happens when we increase the dimension of the subspace on which $-\nabla f(z_0)$ is being projected.

† To avoid having to continually consider special cases, we shall assume that $m > 0$, that is, that R is not identically zero.

Resolving $\nabla f(z_0)$ into orthogonal components, we obtain

42 $$\nabla f(z_0) = P_{I(z_0)} \nabla f(z_0) + S^T_{I(z_0)}\pi$$

for some vector π. Making use of the definition of $S_{I(z_0)}$, we obtain

43 $$\nabla f(z_0) = P_{I(z_0)} \nabla f(z_0) + \sum_{i=1}^{m} \psi^i r^i + \sum_{i\in I(z_0)} \mu^i q^i,$$

where the q^i are now used as column vectors, the components of the vector π are denoted by ψ^i and μ^i, and the μ^i are assumed to be numbered with indices in $I(z_0)$. Let $l \in I(z_0)$, and let $L(z_0) = I(z_0)/\{l\}$. Then from (43) and (38) we obtain

44 $$\begin{aligned} P_{L(z_0)} \nabla f(z_0) &= P_{L(z_0)}P_{I(z_0)} \nabla f(z_0) + \mu^l P_{L(z_0)}q^l \\ &= P_{I(z_0)} \nabla f(z_0) + \mu^l P_{L(z_0)}q^l. \end{aligned}$$

Note that

45 $$\langle P_{I(z_0)} \nabla f(z_0), P_{L(z_0)}q^l\rangle = \langle P_{I(z_0)} \nabla f(z_0), q^l\rangle = 0,$$

and hence that

46 $$\begin{aligned} \|P_{L(z_0)} \nabla f(z_0)\|^2 &= \|P_{I(z_0)} \nabla f(z_0)\|^2 + (\mu^l)^2 \|P_{L(z_0)} q^l\|^2 \\ &> \|P_{I(z_0)} \nabla f(z_0)\|^2 \geqq 0. \end{aligned}$$

The strict inequality in (47) is due to the fact that

47 $$P_{L(z_0)}q^l \neq 0$$

[otherwise q^l would be a linear combination of the q^i for $i \neq l$, with $i \in I(z_0)$, and r^i for $i = 1, 2, \ldots, m$, contradicting assumption (5)].

Now suppose that $\mu^l > 0$; then, from (45) to (47),

48 $$\langle P_{L(z_0)} \nabla f(z_0), q^l\rangle > 0$$

49 $$\langle P_{L(z_0)} \nabla f(z_0), q^i\rangle = 0 \qquad \text{for all } i \in L(z_0).$$

Thus $-P_{L(z_0)} \nabla f(z_0)$ is also a feasible direction, and the value of $f(\cdot)$, to first-order terms, is reduced along it.

Hence when $P_{I(z_0)} \nabla f(z_0) = 0$, we can find a new feasible direction, $-P_{L(z_0)} \nabla f(z_0)$, along which the value of $f(\cdot)$ will again be reduced, provided, of course, that there is a $\mu^l > 0$ in (43).

50 **Remark.** Suppose that all the μ^i in (43) are nonpositive; then the point z_0, which is feasible, satisfies the necessary conditions of optimality (3.4.22). If $f(\cdot)$ is convex, then the sufficiency conditions (3.6.1) are also satisfied, and z_0 is an optimal solution to the (convex) programming problem (1). □

51 **Remark.** A procedure which chooses as its feasible direction, at $z_i \in \Omega'$, the vector $-P_{I(z_i)} \nabla f(z_i)$, as long as this vector is not zero, can often be shown to take an infinite number of iterations to converge to a point z^* such that $-P_{I(z^*)} \nabla f(z^*) = 0$, but z^* does not satisfy the necessary conditions of optimality. Thus this procedure jams. A *partial* remedy to jamming, which works very well in practice, is to choose an $\epsilon > 0$ and then proceed as follows. Given $z_i \in \Omega'$, we compute the vector π_i, from (42), to be

52 $$\pi_i = (S_{I(z_i)} S^T_{I(z_i)})^{-1} S_{I(z_i)} \nabla f(z_0)$$

and label its components as ψ^j for $j = 1, 2, \ldots, m$ and μ^j for $j \in I(z_i)$, as was done in (43). If

53 $$\|P_{I(z_i)} \nabla f(z_i)\| \geqq \{\max \epsilon \mu^j \|P_{I(z_i)/\{j\}} q^j\| : \mu^j > 0, j \in I(z_i)\},$$

we choose the feasible direction $h_i = P_{I(z_i)} \nabla f(z_i)$. Otherwise we let $l \in I(z_i)$ be the index for which the minimum in (53) takes place and let $L(z_i) = I(z_i)/\{l\}$. Then we choose the feasible direction $h_i = -P_{L(z_i)} \nabla f(z_i)$. The effect of this is to increase the dimension of the subspace on which $\nabla f(z_i)$ is projected *before* its projection becomes arbitrarily small. □

It must be emphasized once again that although the precaution indicated above has been found to be quite adequate in practice, it is still not sufficient to guarantee convergence in all possible cases.

We now summarize the preceding discussion.

54 **Algorithm: gradient projection.** We are given an $\epsilon > 0$. Let $z_0 \in \Omega'$ be given, and suppose that $z_1, z_2, \ldots, z_j$ in Ω' have been computed by the algorithm.

Step 1. Compute the vectors

55 $$P_{I(z_j)} \nabla f(z_j)$$

56 $$\pi_j = (S_{I(z_j)} S^T_{I(z_j)})^{-1} S_{I(z_j)} \nabla f(z_j).$$

Then

57 $$\nabla f(z_j) = P_{I(z_j)} \nabla f(z_j) + S^T_{I(z_j)} \pi_j.$$

Step 2. If $P_{I(z_j)} \nabla f(z_j) = 0$ and all the components $\mu_j{}^i$ associated with the columns q^i of $S^T_{I(z_j)}$, with $i \in I(z_j)$, are nonpositive, then stop, since z_j satisfies the necessary conditions of optimality. If there is at least one $\mu_j{}^i > 0$, $i \in I(z_j)$, and

58 $$\|P_{I(z_j)} \nabla f(z_j)\| \geqq \max \{\epsilon \mu_j{}^i \|P_{I(z_j)/\{i\}} q^i\| : \mu_j{}^i > 0, i \in I(z_j)\},$$

or if $P_{I(z_j)}\, \nabla f(z_j) \neq 0$ and $\mu_j^i \leqq 0$ for all $i \in I(z_j)$, then set

59 $$h_j = -P_{I(z_j)}\, \nabla f(z_j)$$

and go to step 3. If there is at least one $\mu_j^i > 0$ and (58) does not hold, then set

60 $$h_j = -P_{L(z_j)}\, \nabla f(z_j)$$

and go to step 3. In (60), $L(z_j) = I(z_j)/\{l\}$, where l is any index for which the maximum in (58) is achieved.

Step 3. Choose $\gamma_j > 0$ such that

61 $$\gamma_j = \max\,\{\gamma\colon Q(z_j + \beta h_j) \leqq b \text{ for all } 0 \leqq \beta \leqq \gamma\},$$

and choose λ_j to satisfy

62 $$\lambda_j = \max\,\{\lambda\colon f(z_j + \lambda h_j) \leqq f(z_j + \beta h_j) \text{ for all } 0 \leqq \beta \leqq \lambda \leqq \gamma_j\}.$$

If $\lambda_j = +\infty$, then stop. If $f(z_j + \lambda h_j) \to -\infty$ as $\lambda \to \lambda_j$, then stop. Otherwise set

63 $$z_{j+1} = z_j + \lambda_j\, h_j;$$

then $z_{j+1} \in \Omega'$ and $f(z_{j+1}) < f(z_j)$. Set $j = j + 1$ and return to step 1. □

64 **Remark.** One of the reasons that we do not encounter difficulties with this algorithm in practice is that we never establish with infinite precision whether a quantity is zero. This tends to make us consider as active at z_j constraints which are only "almost" active, and as we recall from the preceding section, the mechanism to avoid jamming consists to a great extent in considering as active all constraints which satisfy a condition of the form $\langle q^i, z_j\rangle - b^i + \epsilon_j \geqq 0$ for initially chosen values of $\epsilon_j > 0$. □

This concludes our discussion of gradient methods. In the next section we shall discuss two procedures for combining the cost function with the constraint functions in order to produce a new family of unconstrained minimization problems whose solutions converge to a solution of the original problem.

7.4 PENALTY FUNCTIONS

Some years ago Courant [6] proposed a method for solving constrained minimization problems which has recently been revived and considerably generalized. The gist of this method consists of solving, instead of the given constrained optimization problem, a sequence of derived unconstrained optimization problems.

For an intuitive understanding of the method, suppose that we wish to minimize $f(z)$ subject to $r(z) = 0$, with $f: E^n \to E^1$ and $r: E^n \to E^m$, both continuously differentiable. If we form the sequence of auxiliary cost functions

1 $$f_i(z) = f(z) + \lambda_i \|r(z)\|^2 \qquad i = 1, 2, \ldots,$$

with $\lambda_i > 0$, $\lambda_{i+1} > \lambda_i$, and $\lambda_i \to \infty$ as $i \to \infty$, then when we minimize $f_i(z)$ at some point z_i the term $\lambda_i \|r(z_i)\|^2 > 0$ penalizes us for choosing a z_i not in the set $\{z: r(z) = 0\}$. Intuition now leads us to believe that since the penalty for z_i, the point minimizing $f_i(z)$ and not belonging to $\{z: r(z) = 0\}$, goes to infinity with i, the z_i should converge to a z^* satisfying $r(z^*) = 0$, which is an optimal solution to the original problem.

An important aspect of the method (or rather, methods) we are about to discuss is that their success depends greatly on the particular unconstrained optimization algorithm eventually chosen for solving the sequence of problems that are generated. Unfortunately, the most successful unconstrained optimization algorithms are rather complex and are mostly based on heuristic considerations. Unconstrained minimization is rather a large subject and lies somewhat outside of the scope of this book. The interested reader is encouraged to consult references [9,10,11] at the end of the chapter.

We shall now examine two representative methods for choosing penalty functions.

Exterior Penalty Functions

Suppose that we wish to solve the following problem:

2 **Problem.** Let $f: E^n \to E^1$ be a continuous function, and let Ω' be a nonempty closed subset of E^n. Find a vector $\hat{z} \in \Omega'$ such that $f(\hat{z}) \leq f(z)$ for all $z \in \Omega'$. □

3 **Definition.** A sequence $\{p_i(\cdot)\}_{i=1}^{\infty}$ of real-valued functions defined on E^n is called a *sequence of penalty functions for the set* Ω' if for every $i = 1, 2, \ldots$ the following properties hold:

4 $p_i(\cdot)$ is continuous on E^n.

5 $p_i(z) = 0$ if and only if $z \in \Omega'$.

6 $p_i(z) > 0$ for every $z \notin \Omega'$.

7 $p_{i+1}(z) > p_i(z)$ for every $z \notin \Omega'$.

8 $p_i(z) \to +\infty$ as $i \to +\infty$, for every fixed $z \notin \Omega'$. □

We now construct our derived problem:

9 **Derived problem.** Let $i \in \{1,2, \ldots\}$ be fixed. Find a vector $z_i \in E^n$ such that $f(z_i) + p_i(z_i) \leqq f(z) + p_i(z)$ for all $z \in E^n$. □

Now let

10 $$b = \inf \{f(z): z \in \Omega'\}$$

11 $$b_i = \inf \{f(z) + p_i(z): z \in E^n\} \qquad i = 1, 2, \ldots .$$

We shall assume that b_1 is finite.

12 **Lemma.** The sequence $\{b_i\}_{i=1}^{\infty}$ satisfies the ordering relation

$$b_1 \leqq b_2 \leqq \cdots \leqq b_i \leqq \cdots \leqq b.$$

Proof. By definition of b_i in (11),

13 $$b_i \leqq f(z) + p_i(z) \qquad \text{for all } z \in E^n.$$

Using (7), we obtain

$$b_i \leqq f(z) + p_i(z) \leqq f(z) + p_{i+1}(z) \qquad \text{for all } z \in E^n,$$

and hence

$$b_i \leqq \inf \{f(z) + p_{i+1}(z): z \in E^n\} = b_{i+1}.$$

Now, using (5) and (13), we get

$$b_i \leqq f(z) + p_i(z) = f(z) \qquad \text{for all } z \in \Omega',$$

that is,

$$b_i \leqq \inf \{f(z): z \in \Omega'\} = b,$$

and the proof is complete. □

The next lemma is the key to the main theorem.

14 **Lemma.** Let $\{p_i(\cdot)\}_{i=1}^{\infty}$ be a sequence of penalty functions for the constraint set Ω', and let $\{z_i\}_{i=1}^{\infty}$ be a sequence in E^n. If

15 $\{z_i\}_{i=1}^{\infty}$ converges to a point z^*,

16 $z_i \notin \Omega'$ for $i = 1, 2, \ldots,$

17 the sequence $\{p_i(z_i)\}_{i=1}^{\infty}$ is bounded,

then $z^* \in \Omega'$.

Proof. We shall prove this lemma by contradiction. Suppose that z^* is not in Ω', and let $M > 0$ be the bound on $p_i(z_i)$; that is, let $0 < p_i(z_i) \leqq M$ for $i = 1, 2, \ldots$. Since $z^* \notin \Omega'$, and, by (8), $p_i(z^*) \to$

$+\infty$, there exists an integer N such that $p_N(z^*) > 2M$. Now, since $p_N(\cdot)$ is continuous, there exists a ball B with center z^* such that for all $z \in B$

18 $$p_N(z) \geqq \frac{3M}{2}.$$

Note that $p_N(z) = 0$ for all $z \in \Omega'$, so that $B \cap \Omega' = \phi$, the empty set. Now, $z_i \to z^*$, and hence there is an integer N' such that $z_i \in B$ for all $i \geqq N'$. Let $N'' = \max\{N, N'\}$; then for all $i \geqq N''$, $z_i \in B$ and, by (7) and (18),

19 $$p_i(z_i) \geqq p_N(z_i) \geqq \frac{3M}{2},$$

which is a contradiction, since $p_i(z_i) \leqq M$. Hence $z^* \in \Omega'$. □

20 **Theorem.** Suppose that the derived problem (9) has an optimal solution z_i for every $i = 1, 2, \ldots$. Then any cluster point of the sequence $\{z_i\}_{i=1}^{\infty}$ is an optimal solution to problem (2).

Proof. For notational simplicity, and with no loss in generality, assume that $z_i \to z^*$. First, if for any integer i_0, $p_{i_0}(z_{i_0}) = 0$, then $z_{i_0} \in \Omega'$, and z_{i_0} also solves problem (2) [since $f(z) \equiv f(z) + p_{i_0}(z)$ for $z \in \Omega'$]. Consequently, by lemma (12), $b_i = b$ for every $i \geqq i_0$, and hence $p_i(z_i) = 0$ for all $i \geqq i_0$, since $p_i(z) > 0$ for all $z \notin \Omega'$. Hence $z_i \in \Omega'$ for all $i \geqq i_0$, and z_i is also an optimal solution to problem (2) for every $i \geqq i_0$. Since Ω' is closed, $z^* \in \Omega'$, and since $f(\cdot)$ is continuous, $f(z^*) = b$; that is, z^* is an optimal solution to problem (2).

Now suppose that $z_i \notin \Omega'$ for $i = 1, 2, \ldots$. Then, by lemma (12),

21 $$f(z_i) + p_i(z_i) \leqq b = \inf\{f(z) : z \in \Omega'\}.$$

Since $z_i \notin \Omega'$, $p_i(z_i) > 0$, and hence

$$f(z_i) < b \qquad i = 1, 2, \ldots.$$

Since $f(\cdot)$ is continuous and $z_i \to z^*$,

22 $$f(z^*) \leqq b.$$

Now, $f(z_i) - f(z^*) \to 0$, so that there exists a positive integer L such that

23 $$f(z^*) - f(z_i) < 1 \qquad \text{for every } i \geqq L.$$

Combining (21) and (23), we obtain

24 $$p_i(z_i) \leqq b - f(z_i) \leqq b + 1 - f(z^*) < +\infty \quad \text{for every } i \geqq L.$$

Therefore the sequence $\{p_i(z_i)\}_{i=1}^{\infty}$ is bounded. By lemma (14), $z^* \in \Omega'$, and so, by the definition of b,

25 $$b \leqq f(z^*).$$

But $b \geqq f(z^*)$, by (22), and therefore $b = f(z^*)$. Since $z^* \in \Omega'$ and $f(z^*) = b$, z^* is an optimal solution to problem (2). □

We shall now consider some examples of penalty functions which satisfy the properties stipulated in definition (3).

26 **Lemma.** Let $q^i: E^n \to E^1$ for $i = 1, 2, \ldots, k$ be continuous functions, and let

27 $$\Omega' \triangleq \{z: q^i(z) \leqq 0, i = 1, 2, \ldots, k\}.$$

For each $i = 1, 2, \ldots$ let the map $p_i: E^n \to E^1$ be defined as

28 $$p_i(z) = \lambda_i \sum_{i=1}^{k} [\max \{q^i(z),0\}]^\alpha,$$

where λ_i and α are scalars satisfying $\lambda_i > 0$ and $\alpha \geqq 1$. If $\lambda_{i+1} > \lambda_i$ for $i = 1, 2, \ldots$ and $\lambda_i \to +\infty$, then $\{p_i(\cdot)\}_{i=1}^{\infty}$ is a sequence of penalty functions for the set Ω'.

Proof. First note that Ω' is closed, since the functions $q^i(\cdot)$ for $i = 1, 2, \ldots, k$ are continuous. We next show that $p_i(\cdot)$ is continuous on E^n for every $i = 1, 2, \ldots$. Since the finite sum of continuous functions is itself a continuous function and the function

29 $$[\max \{q^i(z),0\}]^\alpha \triangleq h^i(z)$$

is continuous, $p_i(\cdot)$ is continuous.

By (29), $h^i(z) = 0$ if and only if $q^i(z) \leqq 0$ and $h^i(z) > 0$ if $q^i(z) > 0$. Hence, since $\lambda_i > 0$, $p_i(z) = 0$ if and only if $z \in \Omega'$ and $p_i(z) > 0$ for all $z \notin \Omega'$. Since $\lambda_{i+1} > \lambda_i$ for $i = 1, 2, \ldots$, $p_{i+1}(z) > p_i(z)$ for every $z \notin \Omega'$, and since $\lambda_i \to +\infty$, $p_i(z) \to +\infty$ for every $z \notin \Omega'$. Therefore, by definition (3), $\{p_i(\cdot)\}_{i=1}^{\infty}$ is a sequence of penalty functions for Ω'. □

30 **Exercise.** Show that for every $i = 1, 2, \ldots$ the function $p_i(\cdot)$ defined in (28) is continuously differentiable on E^n if the functions $q^i(\cdot)$ for $i = 1, 2, \ldots, k$ are continuously differentiable on E^n and $\alpha \geqq 2$. □

31 **Exercise.** Let $r: E^n \to E^m$ be a continuous function on E^n, and let

$$\Omega' = \{z: r(z) = 0\}.$$

For each $i = 1, 2, \ldots$ let the map $p_i: E^n \to E^1$ be defined as

32 $$p_i(z) = \lambda_i \|r(z)\|^\alpha,$$

where λ_i and α are scalars, with $\lambda_i > 0$ and $\alpha \geqq 1$. Show that if $\lambda_{i+1} > \lambda_i$ for $i = 1, 2, \ldots$ and $\lambda_i \to +\infty$, then $\{p_i(\cdot)\}_{i=1}^\infty$ is a sequence of penalty functions for Ω'. Show that $p_i(\cdot)$ is continuously differentiable on E^n if $r(\cdot)$ is continuously differentiable on E^n and $\alpha \geqq 2$. □

33 **Exercise.** Suppose that the functions $q^i(\cdot)$ introduced in lemma (26) are convex and that the function $r(\cdot)$ defined in exercise (31) is affine. Show that for $i = 1, 2, \ldots$ the function $p_i(\cdot)$ defined in (28) and the function $p_i(\cdot)$ defined in (32) are convex. □

34 **Exercise.** Show that if $\{p_i^1(\cdot)\}_{i=1}^\infty$ is a sequence of penalty functions for the set Ω_1 and $\{p_i^2(\cdot)\}_{i=1}^\infty$ is a sequence of penalty functions for the set Ω_2, then $\{p_i^1(\cdot) + p_i^2(\cdot)\}_{i=1}^\infty$ is a sequence of penalty functions for $\Omega_1 \cap \Omega_2$. Also show that $\{\min\{p_i^1(\cdot), p_i^2(\cdot)\}\}_{i=1}^\infty$ is a sequence of penalty functions for $\Omega_1 \cup \Omega_2$. □

35 **Remark.** Penalty functions can be used to transform a constrained optimization problem not only into a sequence of unconstrained minimization problems, but also into a sequence of constrained minimization problems more amenable to solution. For example, suppose we wish to minimize $f(z)$ subject to $r(z) = 0$ and $q(z) \leqq 0$, and the the function $r(\cdot)$ is not affine. Then we cannot use any of the methods of feasible directions. If $\{p_i(\cdot)\}_{i=1}^\infty$ is a sequence of penalty functions for the set $\{z: r(z) = 0\}$, then, under suitable assumptions, we can obtain a solution of the original problem by using a feasible-directions method to solve the sequence of problems: minimize $f(z) + p_i(z)$ subject to $q(z) \leqq 0$, with $i = 1, 2, \ldots$. □

36 **Exercise.** Consider the problem: minimize $f(z)$ subject to $r(z) = 0$ and $q(z) \leqq 0$, where $f: E^n \to E^1$, $r: E^n \to E^m$, and $q: E^n \to E^k$ are continuously differentiable. Let $\{p_i(\cdot)\}_{i=1}^\infty$ be any sequence of penalty functions for the set $\{z: r(z) = 0\}$ satisfying definition (3), and let z_i be an optimal solution to the problem: minimize $f(z) + p_i(z)$ subject to $q(z) \leqq 0$. Show that any cluster point z^* of $\{z_i\}_{i=1}^\infty$ is an optimal solution of the original problem. □

Interior Penalty Functions

We shall now consider a different type of penalty function which is particularly useful when all the functions in question are convex. However, rather than consider a problem as general as (2), let us restrict ourselves to the following special case.

37 **Problem.** Let $f(\cdot)$ and $q^i(\cdot)$ for $i = 1, 2, \ldots, k$ be strictly convex functions from E^n into E^1. Minimize $f(z)$ subject to $q^i(z) \leqq 0$ for $i = 1, 2, \ldots, k$. [Note that the $q^i(\cdot)$ and $f(\cdot)$ are continuous.] □

We shall make the following assumptions.

38 **Assumption.** The interior of the set $\Omega' = \{z\colon q^i(z) \leqq 0,\ i = 1, 2, \ldots, k\}$ is not empty. □

39 **Assumption.** For every real α $\{z\colon f(z) \leqq \alpha\}$ is a bounded set. □

We now define a sequence of penalty functions for Ω'.

40 **Definition.** Let $\{\lambda_i\}_{i=0}^{\infty}$ be a strictly monotonically decreasing sequence of positive numbers which converges to zero. We define the penalty functions $\tilde{p}_i(\cdot)$ for $i = 0, 1, 2, \ldots$ from $\dot{\Omega}'$, the interior of $\dot{\Omega}'$, into E^1 by

41
$$\tilde{p}_i(z) = -\lambda_i \sum_{j=1}^{k} \frac{1}{q^j(z)}.$$

[Note that for every $z \in \dot{\Omega}'$, $\tilde{p}_i(z) \to 0$ as $i \to \infty$.]

We can now formulate the derived problem:

42 **Derived problem.** Find a $z_i \in \dot{\Omega}'$ such that

$$f(z_i) + \tilde{p}_i(z_i) \leqq f(z) + \tilde{p}_i(z) \qquad \text{for all } z \in \dot{\Omega}'. \quad \square$$

43 **Exercise.** Show that there exists an optimal solution to problem (37), and to problem (42) for every i. [*Hint:* Let z_0 be any point in $\dot{\Omega}'$. Then the set $\{z \in \dot{\Omega}'\colon f(z) + p_i(z) \leqq f(z_0) + p_0(z_0)\}$ is compact.] □

44 **Exercise.** Show that problem (37) has a unique optimal solution. □

45 **Theorem.** Let z_i for $i = 0, 1, 2, \ldots$ be a solution to problem (42). Then the sequence $\{z_i\}_{i=0}^{\infty}$ converges to the optimal solution $\hat{z}$ of problem (37).

Proof. First we note that for all $z \in \dot{\Omega}'$, the interior of Ω',

46 $$\tilde{p}_i(z) > \tilde{p}_{i+1}(z) > 0.$$

Therefore, if we let

47 $$b_i = \min_{z \in \dot{\Omega}'} f(z) + \tilde{p}_i(z) \qquad i = 0, 1, 2, \ldots,$$

then $b_i \geqq b_{i+1}$ for $i = 0, 1, 2, \ldots$. Now we let

48 $$b = \min_{z \in \Omega'} f(z),$$

which gives us

49 $$b_0 \geqq b_1 \geqq \cdots \geqq b_i \geqq b_{i+1} \cdots \geqq b.$$

Since the b_i form a bounded, monotonically decreasing sequence, they must converge; that is, $b_i \to b^*$. Suppose that $b^* \neq b$; then, from (49), $b^* > b$. Since $f(\cdot)$ is continuous, there exists a ball B with center $\hat{z}$, the optimal solution to problem (37), such that for all $z \in B \cap \dot{\Omega}'$

50 $$f(z) < b^* - \tfrac{1}{2}(b^* - b).$$

Now take any $z' \in B \cap \dot{\Omega}'$; then for i sufficiently large, since $\tilde{p}_i(z') \to 0$ as $i \to \infty$,

51 $$\tilde{p}_i(z') < \tfrac{1}{4}(b^* - b),$$

and hence for all i sufficiently large

52 $$f(z') + \tilde{p}_i(z') < b^* - \tfrac{1}{4}(b^* - b) < b^*,$$

which is a contradiction. Thus

53 $$b^* = b.$$

Since $b_i = f(z_i) + \tilde{p}_i(z_i) \leqq f(z_0) + \tilde{p}_0(z_0)$, we must have that

54 $$f(z_i) \leqq f(z_0) + \tilde{p}(z_0) \qquad \text{for all } i = 1, 2, \ldots,$$

and hence, by assumptions (38) and (39), $\{z_i\}$ is a bounded sequence. Let $\{z_j\}$, with $j \in L \subset \{0,1,2, \ldots\}$, be any convergent subsequence of $\{z_i\}_{i=0}^{\infty}$, with limit point $z^* \in \Omega'$, and suppose that $z^* \neq \hat{z}$, the optimal solution to (37). Then $f(z^*) > f(\hat{z})$, since $\hat{z}$ is the unique optimal solution of (37), and the sequence

55 $$\{[f(z_j) - f(\hat{z})] + \tilde{p}_j(z_j)\} \qquad j \in L$$

cannot converge to zero, which contradicts the fact that $b_i - b$ converges to zero. Hence we must have $z^* = \hat{z}$. Thus all convergent subsequences of $\{z_i\}$ converge to $\hat{z}$, and hence z_i converges to $\hat{z}$. [Note also that $\tilde{p}_j(z_j) \to 0$, since $f(z_j) - f(\hat{z}) + \tilde{p}_j(z_j) \to 0$ and $z_j \to \hat{z}$.] □

To utilize penalty functions of the above type we must have an initial feasible solution in the interior of Ω' as a starting point for the unconstrained optimization algorithm used for the solution of (42). Since $f_i(z) + p_i(z) \rightarrow +\infty$ as z approaches the boundary of Ω', the unconstrained optimization algorithm will then generate a sequence of points z_{ij} for $j = 1, 2, \ldots$ which will all be in the interior of Ω'. For a detailed and comprehensive description of this method and recommended unconstrained-optimization procedures see reference [7].

This concludes our introductory discussion of algorithms for nonlinear programming problems. Bear in mind that the literature of nonlinear programming is rather vast; for a study in depth the reader is referred to any of the number of texts which deal exclusively with this subject.

REFERENCES

1. G. Zoutendijk: "Methods of Feasible Directions," Elsevier Publishing Company, Amsterdam, 1960.
2. P. Wolfe: On the Convergence of Gradient Methods Under Constraints, *IBM Res. Rept.* RC 1752, Yorktown Heights, N.Y., Jan. 24, 1967.
3. E. Polak: On the Convergence of Optimization Algorithms, *Revue Française d'Informatique et de Recherche Opérationnelle Série Rouge,* **16** (1969).
4. H. B. Curry: The Method of Steepest Descent for Non-linear Minimization Problems, *Quart. Appl. Math.,* **2**:258–261 (1944).
5. J. B. Rosen: The Gradient Projection Method for Nonlinear Programming, part I. Linear Constraints, *SIAM J. Appl. Math.,* **8**:181–217 (1960).
6. R. Courant: "Calculus of Variations and Supplementary Notes and Exercises" (mimeographed notes), Supplementary Notes by Martin Kruskal and Hanah Rubin, rev. and amended by J. Moser, New York University, New York, 1956–1957.
7. A. V. Fiacco and G. P. McCormic: The Sequential Unconstrained Minimization Technique for Nonlinear Programming: A Primal Dual Method, *Management Science,* **10**:360–364 (1964).
8. W. Zangwill: Nonlinear Programming Via Penalty Functions, *Management Science,* **13**:344–358 (1967).
9. W. C. Davidon: Variable Metric Method for Minimization, *Argonne Natl. Lab.* ANL-5990 (rev.), November, 1959.
10. R. Fletcher and M. J. D. Powell: A Rapidly Convergent Descent Method for Minimization, *Computer J.*, **6**:163–168 (1963).
11. R. Fletcher and C. M. Reeves: Function Minimization by Conjugate Gradients, *Computer J.*, **7**:149–154 (1964).
12. R. M. Van Slyke: Generalized Upper Bounding Techniques, *J. of Computer and Systems Science,* **1** (3):213–226 (1967).

8

Free-end-time optimal control problems

8.1 DESCRIPTION OF THE FREE-END-TIME PROBLEM

So far we have dealt with optimal control problems in which the initial and final times were specified. However, it is clear that there are optimal control problems for which the final time cannot be fixed in advance. The best-known class of such problems is the class of minimum-time problems, in which it is required to go from some initial state or manifold to some terminal state or manifold in a minimum time. Of course, there are many other types of problems in which the final time cannot be fixed beforehand, and we shall classify all such problems as *free-time problems.*

The free-time problem has already been stated [see (1.2.14)], but it is repeated here for the sake of completeness.

1 **The free-time optimal control problem.** Given a dynamical system described by the difference equation

2 $$x_{i+1} - x_i = f_i(x_i,u_i) \qquad i = 0, 1, 2, \ldots,$$

together with subsets $X_i \subset E^n$ for $i = 0, 1, 2, \ldots$, subsets $U_i \subset$

E^m for $i = 0, 1, 2, \ldots$, subsets $D_k \subset E^s$ for $k = 0, 1, 2, \ldots$, a sequence of constraint functions $h_{(k)}(\cdot,\cdot)$ mapping $E^{n(k+1)} \times E^{mk}$ into E^s for $k = 0, 1, 2, \ldots$, and a sequence of real-valued cost functions $f_{(k)}(\cdot,\cdot)$ defined on $E^{n(k+1)} \times E^{mk}$ for $k = 0, 1, 2, \ldots$, find an integer $\hat{k}$, a control sequence $\hat{\mathcal{U}}_k = (\hat{u}_0, \hat{u}_1, \ldots, \hat{u}_{k-1})$, and a corresponding trajectory $\hat{\mathcal{X}}_k = (\hat{x}_0, \hat{x}_1, \ldots, \hat{x}_k)$ satisfying (2), with

3 $$\hat{u}_i \in U_i \qquad i = 0, 1, \ldots, \hat{k} - 1$$

4 $$\hat{x}_i \in X_i \qquad i = 0, 1, \ldots, \hat{k}$$

5 $$h_{(\hat{k})}(\hat{\mathcal{X}}_{\hat{k}}, \hat{\mathcal{U}}_{\hat{k}}) \in D_{(\hat{k})},$$

such that for every $k = 0, 1, 2, \ldots$, every control sequence $\mathcal{U}_k = (u_0, u_1, \ldots, u_{k-1})$, and every corresponding trajectory $\mathcal{X}_k = (x_0, x_1, \ldots, x_k)$ satisfying (2) to (5), with k taking the place of $\hat{k}$,

6 $$f_{(\hat{k})}(\hat{\mathcal{X}}_{\hat{k}}, \hat{\mathcal{U}}_{\hat{k}}) \leqq f_{(k)}(\mathcal{X}_k, \mathcal{U}_k). \quad \square$$

7 **Remark.** Note that the statement of problem (1) implies that the optimal time must be finite. Optimal control problems in which the optimal terminal time is infinite are optimization problems in infinite-dimensional spaces and hence are beyond the scope of this book. □

8.2 THE FREE-END-TIME PROBLEM AS A SEQUENCE OF FIXED-TIME PROBLEMS

Since the number of variables in the free-end-time problem is itself a variable, we recognize these problems as being of the mixed-integer programming type. Although there does not appear to be any direct way for handling such problems, they can often be solved by the simple expedient of solving a sequence of fixed-time problems. Of course, in principle every free-time problem can be solved in this manner, since, by assumption, the optimal solution corresponds to some fixed final time. The difficulty, of course, is in knowing when to stop. Generally, there is no way of establishing the optimal final time. There are, however, a wide variety of problems for which we can establish an upper bound on the optimal time. It is to this type of problem that we now direct our attention.

1 **The free-time problem with a penalty on time.** Given the free-time problem (1.1), let the cost function $f_{(k)}(\mathcal{X}_k, \mathcal{U}_k)$ take the form

2 $$f_{(k)}(\mathcal{X}_k, \mathcal{U}_k) = \phi_{(k)}(\mathcal{X}_k, \mathcal{U}_k) + \alpha k \qquad k = 0, 1, 2, \ldots,$$

where

3 $$\phi_{(k)}(\mathcal{X}_k, \mathcal{U}_k) \geqq 0 \qquad \text{for all } \mathcal{X}_k, \mathcal{U}_k$$

and $\alpha > 0$ is a constant which may be thought of as a penalty on time. □

Consider solving a problem of this type as a sequence of fixed-time problems. Let k_1 be the first value of k for which problem (1) has a feasible solution. Let us assume, for simplicity, that an optimal solution exists for all the fixed-time problems defined by (1) with final time $k \geqq k_1$. For every $k \geqq k_1$ let $c(k)$ be the optimal cost for the fixed-time version of this problem, with final time given by k, that is, $c(k) = f_k(\hat{\mathfrak{X}}_k, \hat{\mathfrak{U}}_{d,k})$, where $\hat{\mathfrak{X}}_k$ and $\hat{\mathfrak{U}}_k$ are the optimal trajectory and control sequence for the corresponding fixed-time problem. In particular, $c(k_1)$ is the optimal cost corresponding to the fixed end time k_1, the first time at which there is a feasible solution.

From (2) and (3) it is clear that for every k

4 $$c(k) \geqq \alpha k.$$

Hence if

5 $$k > \frac{c(k_1)}{\alpha},$$

then, from (4),

6 $$c(k) > c(k_1).$$

It follows that the right-hand side of (5) is an upper bound on any optimal final time $\hat{k}$; that is,

7 $$\hat{k} < \frac{c(k_1)}{\alpha}.$$

8 **Remark.** We must say *any* optimal final time here, since it is quite possible that the minimum cost may be attained for more than one final time. However, the strict inequality of (7) guarantees that *all* optimal final times satisfy (7). □

The implications of inequality (7) are clear in terms of our stated objective of solving the free-time problem by solving a finite sequence of fixed-time problems. We begin by finding the first final time, k_1, for which there is a feasible solution. We then solve the optimal control problem with the final time fixed at k_1 (assuming that an optimal solution exists for this time). Finally, we obtain from (7) an upper bound on the optimal final time $\hat{k}$. Consequently, we need only solve a finite number of fixed-time problems, corresponding to all final times from k_1 to the bound in (7),† in order to obtain an optimal solution by finding the least cost in this range.

† The reader should recognize the fact that it is possible to update the bound in (7) (with $k_1 + 1$, $k_1 + 2$, . . . taking the place of k_1) as successive fixed-time problems are solved.

There are many simple examples of cost functions of the type specified in (2).

9 **Example.** $f_{(k)}(\mathfrak{X}_k,\mathfrak{U}_k) = \sum_{i=0}^{k-1} |u_i| + \alpha k$. This is the so-called *fuel-plus-time cost function*. In the case of linear constraints, we may solve a finite set of linear programming problems to obtain an optimal solution (see Chapter 5). □

10 **Example.** $f_{(k)}(\mathfrak{X}_k,\mathfrak{U}_k) = \sum_{i=0}^{k-1} u_i^2 + \alpha k$. This is the *energy-plus-time cost function*. In the case of linear constraints, we may solve a finite set of quadratic programming problems to obtain an optimal solution (see Chapter 6). □

11 **Remark.** In general, the existence of a feasible solution for any final time k will not guarantee the existence of an optimal solution for that final time, even if there is an optimal solution for the free-time problem. Hence the definition of k_1 given above should be modified to make k_1 the first time for which there is an optimal solution. Similarly, inequality (7) should be interpreted as holding for all times $k > c_0(k_1)/\alpha$ for which optimal solutions exist. □

12 **Remark.** The essence of form (2) of the cost function is that it can be bounded from below by $c(k_1)$ for all k; hence the optimal cost for any fixed k must also be so bounded. Clearly, the property which is really essential for establishing a bound on $c(k)$ is that the cost be bounded from below by some strictly monotone-increasing function of k. Thus we can also consider nonlinear penalties on time, provided they have the required growth properties. □

The discussion of problems with penalties on time brings us to the following group of optimal control problems, which, while not fitting the definition of the free-time problem (1), can nevertheless be handled in the same way.

13 **The bounded-final-time optimal control problem.** Given the free-time optimal control problem (1.1), make the additional assumption that we are given a positive integer k_2 such that the optimal time $\hat{k}$ must satisfy $\hat{k} \leq k_2$. □

Clearly, this problem can be solved by solving a finite set of fixed-time problems for all final times less than or equal to k_2, and hence it may be grouped with the free-time problems with a penalty on time for the purpose of discussing methods of solution.

8.3 THE FIRST TIME FOR WHICH A FREE-END-TIME PROBLEM HAS A FEASIBLE SOLUTION: THE MINIMUM-TIME PROBLEM

It is clear from the discussion in Section 2 that in solving free-time problems it may be necessary to find the first time k_1 for which there is a feasible solution, that is, a control-sequence trajectory pair $(\mathcal{U}_{k_1},\mathcal{X}_{k_1})$ satisfying all the constraints of the problem. This subproblem is known as the *minimum-time problem*. It may also arise independently of any other problem, and there has probably been as much written on this one problem as on all other discrete optimal control problems combined. Before proceeding with a discussion, let us formally introduce the problem.

1 **The minimum-time problem.** Given the free-time optimal control problem (1.1), let the cost function take the form

2 $$f_{(k)}(\mathcal{X}_k,\mathcal{U}_k) = k. \quad \square$$

As has been already noted, minimizing (2) is equivalent to finding the first k for which problem (1.1) has a feasible solution.

Let us now concentrate our attention on the relevant fixed-time problem. In keeping with the philosophy of this book, we first convert this fixed-time problem into the Basic Problem form (1.4.1). The details of this task are left to the reader. The resulting problem has the following form:

3 With k a given positive integer, determine a vector $\hat{z} \in E^{n_k}$ which minimizes $f_{(k)}(z) = k$ subject to the constraints $r_{(k)}(z) = 0$ and $z \in \Omega_k$, where $r_{(k)}$ is a continuously differentiable function from E^{n_k} into E^{m_k} and Ω_k is a subset of E^{n_k}.† $\square$

Note that if we are to obtain a solution to the minimum-time problem (1) by solving a sequence of fixed-time problems of form (3), we must be able to solve (3), for each $k = 0, 1, 2, \ldots$, in a finite number of steps. Hence we must consider the following problem:

4 Given the constraints $r_{(k)}(z) = 0$ and $z \in \Omega_k$, defined as in problem (3), determine *in a finite number of steps* either (*a*) a point $\hat{z}$ satisfying $r_{(k)}(\hat{z}) = 0$ and $\hat{z} \in \Omega_k$ or (*b*) that no such $\hat{z}$ exists. $\square$

Note that part (*b*) of this problem is as important as part (*a*), since for all k smaller than the optimal time $\hat{k}$ no feasible solution to problem (3) will exist.

Problem (4) is far too difficult to yield to any general computational technique. In order to give specific procedures it is neces-

† Clearly, any feasible solution to problem (3) is an optimal solution.

sary to make some simplifying assumptions on $r_{(k)}$ and Ω_k. The more restrictive the assumptions we make, the more effective are the procedures we can bring to bear. Let us consider a few specific cases.

Case 1. $\Omega_k = \{z: q_k(z) \leqq 0\}$. Here $q_k(z)$ is assumed to be a *continuously differentiable* function, and hence problem (4) becomes a special case of the nonlinear programming problem. The techniques of Chapter 7 may now be used to attempt a solution to the equations $r_{(k)}(z) = 0$ and the inequalities $q_k(z) \leqq 0$. However, since no assumptions have been made about the linearity or convexity of r and q, convergence to a feasible solution can be expected only if a starting point sufficiently close to a feasible solution is chosen. Similarly, it is not possible to establish with certainty that a feasible solution does not exist. Hence for case 1 problem (4) must still be classified as essentially unsolvable. □

Case 2. $\Omega_k = \{z: q_k(z) \leqq 0\}$, $q_k: E^{n_k} \to E^{l_k}$ *is continuously differentiable and convex, and* $r_k(z) = R_k z - c_k$, *where* R_k *is an* $m_k \times n_k$ *matrix and* c_k *is an m-dimensional vector.* The constraints here are the same as those of the convex programming problem (7.2.1), and hence in this case problem (4) can be solved by the methods of feasible directions, described in Section 7.2. □

Case 3. $\Omega_k = \{z: Q_k z - d_k \leqq 0\}$, *where* Q_k *is an* $l_k \times n_k$ *matrix,* d_k *is an* l_k *vector, and* $r_{(k)}(z) = R_k z - c_k$, *where* R_k *is an* $m_k \times n_k$ *matrix and* c_k *is an* m_k *vector.* It is clear from inspection that this case can be solved by the linear-programming techniques for finding an initial feasible solution described in Section 5.7 (see this section for details). □

5 **Remark.** The problem of finding a vector z satisfying $R_k z = c_k$ and $Q_k z \leqq d_k$ in case 3 does not, in general, have a unique solution, and this presents us with the opportunity of finding a vector z which not only satisfies the above constraints, but also minimizes some auxiliary cost criterion.

For such a scheme to make sense, the auxiliary cost criterion selected must have certain features. First, the auxiliary cost criterion $f_{(k)}(\cdot)$ must be such that the following *auxiliary minimization problem*

6 Minimize $f_{(k)}(z)$ subject to $R_k z = c_k$ and $Q_k z \leqq d_k$.

has an optimal solution whenever it has a feasible solution.

In addition, the cost criterion must be such that problem (6) can be treated by means of a standard finite-step algorithm either to obtain an optimal solution or to determine that an optimal solution does not exist. Note that this second property of $f_{(k)}(\cdot)$ is really needed only at the nonoptimal times $k < \hat{k}$. Thus, once we have computed the optimal time $\hat{k}$, we may change the form of the cost function, so that $f_{(\hat{k})}$ does not necessarily give rise to a problem, of form (6), which can be solved by finite-step algorithms.

In this book we have discussed only two classes of problems solvable by finite-step algorithms, linear programming problems and quadratic programming problems. Of these two, linear programming problems may not always satisfy the first of the previously stated conditions. However, if we choose an absolute-value type of cost function which is, a priori, bounded from below, then the *resultant* linear programming problem will have the required properties. □

7 **Example.** One cost criterion which could be used in problem (6) is

$$f_{(k)}(z) = \sum_{i=1}^{n} \alpha_k{}^i |z^i|,$$

where the $\alpha_k{}^i$ are nonnegative constants. If the $\alpha_k{}^i$ were chosen to be unity for those z^i which correspond to components of the controls u_j and zero for all other z^i, then the cost criterion here would correspond to the *minimum-fuel* criterion and the auxiliary minimization problem would select that minimum-time control sequence which used the least amount of *fuel.*

It should be pointed out that the addition of this auxiliary cost does not significantly deteriorate the efficiency of the linear-programming approach to solving the minimum-time problem compared with its use only to find a feasible solution. □

In many ways a quadratic cost criterion seems ideally suited as a choice in forming an auxiliary minimization problem. We saw in Section 6.2 that with a minimum of assumptions we can guarantee that the quadratic programming problem will have a solution whenever a feasible solution exists. Since the algorithm given in Section 6.10 is a finite-step procedure which will either find a solution or determine that no feasible solution exists, all our conditions are met. In addition, since the quadratic programming algorithm presented in Section 6.10 does not require that we begin with a feasible solution, it is possible to use this algorithm in direct competition with algorithms which find only feasible solutions.

The reader can doubtless form many quadratic cost criteria which have practical significance. Below are a number of examples of control problem–oriented criteria which, when translated into Basic Problem format, are acceptable for use in an auxiliary minimization problem.

8 **Example.** If we choose as a criterion in problem (6)

$$\sum_{i=0}^{k-1} \langle u_i, u_i \rangle,$$

we are minimizing the *control energy.* □

9 **Example.** A criterion sometimes proposed for problem (6) in the case where the controls u_i are scalars, restricted to satisfy $|u_i| \leqq 1$, and the system is completely controllable, is

10 $$\sum_{i=k-n}^{k-1} u_i^2,$$

where n is the dimension of the state vector. For a completely controllable system, the last n control variables can be manipulated so as to take the system to all points in a neighborhood of the terminal state which can be reached when these control variables are set to zero. Thus the differences between the values which these controls take in a computed optimal control sequence and the maximum and minimum values that they can assume can be considered as a reserve, available at time $k - n$ for correcting minor errors or disturbances which have caused x_{k-n} to differ from its precomputed value. Minimizing (10) corresponds, in a crude way, to maximizing this reserve. □

This concludes our general discussion of how minimum-time problems can be solved by conventional methods. In the next two sections we shall consider a linear minimum-time problem for which there is a special algorithm.

8.4 A LINEAR MINIMUM–TIME PROBLEM

Of all the minimum-time problems, the following one has received the most attention in the literature:

1 **Problem.** Given a dynamical system described by

$$x_{i+1} - x_i = Ax_i + bu_i \qquad i = 0, 1, 2, \ldots,$$

with $x_i \in E^n$ and $u_i \in E^1$† for $i = 0, 1, 2, \ldots$ and A and b constant matrices[1] of appropriate dimensions, find a control sequence $\hat{u}_0$, $\hat{u}_1$,

† We could assume $u_i \in E^r$, written $r > 1$, but this would only complicate the notation without shedding additional light on the methods we are to describe.

[1] Again, for the sake of simplicity, we keep the matrices A and b constant. There is no intrinsic difficulty encountered when these matrices are actually functions of the time index i.

$\hat{u}_2, \ldots$ which takes the system from the given initial state $x_0 = \xi_0$ to the desired terminal state ξ_T in a minimum number of steps, subject to the constraint $|\hat{u}_i| \leqq 1$ for $i = 0, 1, 2, \ldots$.

We assume that the matrix $I + A$ is nonsingular, and that the system is completely controllable. □

We saw in Section 5.6 that such problems (with k fixed) are best transformed into the form of the Basic Problem (1.4.1) by means of the alternative procedure. Specifically, if we solve for x_k, we obtain

2 $$x_k = (I + A)^k x_0 + \sum_{i=0}^{k-1} (I + A)^{k-1-i} b u_i.$$

Substituting ξ_0 for x_0 and setting $x_k = \xi_T$, we have

3 $$\xi_T - (I + A)^k \xi_0 = \sum_{i=0}^{k-1} (I + A)^{k-1-i} b u_i.$$

Because of the assumption that the matrix $I + A$ is nonsingular, we can rewrite (3) as

4 $$(I + A)^{-k} \xi_T - \xi_0 = \sum_{i=0}^{k-1} (I + A)^{-1-i} b u_i.$$

Now, if for $k = 0, 1, \ldots$ we define

5 $$z^i = u_{i-1} \qquad i = 1, 2, \ldots, k$$

6 $$c_k = (I + A)^{-k} \xi_T - \xi_0$$

7 $$r_j = (I + A)^{-j} b \qquad j = 1, 2, \ldots, \dagger$$

then (4) becomes

8 $$c_k = \sum_{j=1}^{k} z^j r_j,$$

and the constraints on the vector $z = (z^1, z^2, \ldots, z^k)$ are seen to be

9 $$|z^j| \leqq 1 \qquad j = 1, 2, \ldots, k.$$

Obviously, problem (1) can be solved by linear-programming techniques. In addition, if we wish, we may take advantage of the nature of the sets $\Omega_k = \{z \in E^k : |z^i| \leqq 1\}$ by using the bounded-variable linear programming algorithm described in Section 5.11.

We shall now consider a somewhat less direct, but rather useful

† Note that $r_1, \ldots, r_n$ are linearly independent because of the controllability assumption.

method for using linear-programming techniques to solve the minimum-time problem (1). We begin by defining an error vector.

10 $$e \triangleq \xi_T - x_k.$$

Substituting for x_k from (2), we obtain

11 $$e = \xi_T - (I + A)^k \xi_0 + \sum_{i=0}^{k-1} (I + A)^{k-1-i} b u_i.$$

Next, for fixed k, we attempt to minimize

12 $$\max_{i=1,\ldots,n} |e^i|$$

As already pointed out in (5.3.7), this term may be reduced to a linear criterion by introducing a new variable y subject to the constraints

13 $$\begin{matrix} y + e^i \geqq 0 \\ y - e^i \geqq 0 \end{matrix} \qquad i = 1, 2, \ldots, n.$$

Thus the problem of minimizing (12) subject to (11) and $|u_i| \leqq 1$ for $i = 0, 1, \ldots, k - 1$ is found to be equivalent to:

14 Minimize y subject to (11), (13), and $|u_i| \leqq 1$ for $i = 0, 1, \ldots, k - 1$. □

Obviously, (14) is a linear programming problem.

Clearly, if k is less than the minimum time $\hat{k}$, then $\hat{y}$, the minimum value of y for (14), will be positive, and for the minimum time it will be zero. Hence, as before, we may solve the linear minimum-time problem by solving (14) and increasing the values of k until the minimum cost $\hat{y}$ is driven to zero.

The extra benefits derived from this approach become apparent when we note that (12) defines a norm in n-space. Hence for values of k less than the minimum time the solution obtained for (14) yields a control sequence which minimizes a distance between the final state x_k and the desired state ξ_T, the distance in this case being defined by (12). In certain applications it could be quite useful to know how close the system can get to the desired final state for those times for which the final state is not actually reachable.

15 **Remark.** Another useful error criterion is

16 $$\sum_{i=1}^{n} |e^i|.$$

We saw in Section 5.3 that problems with this criterion can be reduced to linear-programming form. Criterion (16) has the advantage over criterion (12) that in reducing the problem to linear-programming form there is no need for additional constraints such as (13). It does require the addition of n more variables, but the number of variables is not as important as the number of constraints in linear programming. □

Obviously, as was pointed out in the preceding section, we may use

17 $$\sum_{i=0}^{k-1} u_i^2$$

as our auxiliary cost criterion, in which case the conversion to Basic Problem form is especially simple.

Alternatively, we may choose to minimize

18 $$\sum_{i=1}^{n} (e^i)^2$$

at each step k. In this case the error criterion is recognized to be the squared euclidean norm, so that we are finding the reachable point closest to the desired terminal state. This results in a simple quadratic programming problem which is easily handled by the algorithm of Section 6.10, but the dimensions of the resultant problem are larger than in the case of criterion (16), which was proposed for use with the simplex method. For this reason it may be preferable to use (16).

19 **Remark.** Clearly, we could use any other positive-definite or positive-semidefinite quadratic form in e in place of (18). □

20 **Exercise.** Show that the quadratic programming problem obtained with (18) will not, in general, have a unique solution. □

8.5 A GEOMETRIC APPROACH TO THE LINEAR MINIMUM–TIME PROBLEM

In the preceding section we considered various methods for solving the linear minimum-time problem. All these methods depended upon increasing the value of the terminal time k by 1 at each iteration. In this section we shall obtain a rule, based on geometric considerations, for eliminating certain values of k as not being possible optimal times. Clearly, such a rule helps to reduce the total amount of calculation necessary to solve the minimum-time problem.

1 **Definition.** Let r_i for $i = 1, 2, \ldots$ be a sequence of n-dimensional vectors, with $r_1, r_2, \ldots, r_n$ linearly independent. For each integer $k \geqq 1$ we define the compact convex set $A_k \subset E^n$ by

2 $$A_k = \left\{c \colon c = \sum_{i=1}^{k} \alpha^i r_i,\ |\alpha^i| \leqq 1\right\}. \quad \square$$

Using (2), we may state the linear minimum-time problem, defined in the preceding section, in the following way:

3 **Problem.** Given the sequence of vectors $r_i \in E^n$ for $i = 1, 2, \ldots,$ satisfying the conditions given in (1), and a sequence of vectors $c_k \in E^n$ for $k = 1, 2, \ldots,$ find the smallest positive integer $\hat{k}$ such that $c_{\hat{k}} \in A_{\hat{k}}$. $\square$

4 **Assumption.** There is an integer $k \geqq 1$ such that $c_k \in A_k$. $\square$

5 **Remark.** For the linear minimum-time problem, with ξ_T taken as the origin, the set A_k consists of all the initial states ξ_0 from which the origin can be reached in time k or less. $\square$

In principle, the following two theorems give a test for determining whether or not $c_k \in A_k$.

6 **Separation theorem.** Suppose that A_k is a closed convex set; then a vector c_k is not an element of A_k if and only if there exists a nonzero vector η such that

7 $$\langle \eta, c_k \rangle > \langle \eta, a \rangle \qquad \text{for all } a \in A_k. \quad \square$$

[The proof of this theorem can be found in (A.5.28).]

Since A_k is compact, (7) is equivalent to

8 $$\langle \eta, c_k \rangle - \max_{a \in A_k} \langle \eta, a \rangle > 0.$$

From definition (1) of the set A_k it is easy to see that

9 $$\max_{a \in A_k} \langle \eta, a \rangle = \max_{\substack{|\alpha_i| \leqq 1 \\ 1 \leqq i \leqq k}} \sum_{i=1}^{k} \langle \eta, r_i \rangle \alpha_i = \sum_{i=1}^{k} |\langle \eta, r_i \rangle|.$$

10 **Definition.** Let the function $f_{(k)} \colon E^n \times E^n \to E^1$ be defined by

11 $$f_{(k)}(x,y) = \langle x,y \rangle - \sum_{i=1}^{k} |\langle x, r_i \rangle|. \quad \square$$

Making use of (8) and (9), we arrive at the following result.

12 **Theorem.** The vector c_k is not an element of A_k if and only if there exists a vector η such that

13 $$f_{(k)}(\eta,c_k) > 0. \quad \square$$

The computational significance of theorem (12) is best illustrated by an example.

14 **Example.** Consider problem (3). Suppose $n = 2$,

$$r_1 = \begin{bmatrix} 3 \\ 1 \end{bmatrix} \quad r_2 = \begin{bmatrix} -1 \\ 0 \end{bmatrix} \quad r_3 = \begin{bmatrix} 1 \\ -1 \end{bmatrix} \quad r_4 = \begin{bmatrix} -2 \\ 1 \end{bmatrix} \quad r_5 = \begin{bmatrix} -2 \\ -2 \end{bmatrix},$$

and

$$c_k = c = \begin{bmatrix} 5 \\ 4 \end{bmatrix} \qquad k = 1, 2, \ldots, 5.$$

To show that $c \notin A_1$, it is sufficient to find a vector η such that $f_{(1)}(\eta,c) > 0$. When c is quite far from A_1, as in this case, it is not unreasonable to try $\eta = c$. To test this choice, let us evaluate $f_{(1)}(c,c)$. We find that

15 $$f_{(1)}(c,c) = \langle c,c \rangle - |\langle c,r_1 \rangle| = 22;$$

therefore $c \notin A_1$. We next try $k = 2$. Note that

16 $$f_{(k+1)}(\eta,c) = f_{(k)}(\eta,c) - |\langle \eta,r_{k+1} \rangle|.$$

Thus we see that $f_{(2)}(\eta,c)$ can be obtained from $f_{(1)}(\eta,c)$ by evaluating one additional scalar product, and we also find that since $f_{(1)}(c,c)$ was large, it is reasonable to ask if $\eta = c$ will also work with $f_{(2)}$. In fact, from (16), we have

17 $$f_{(2)}(c,c) = 22 - |\langle c,r_2 \rangle| = 22 - 5 = 17.$$

Continuing in this manner, we find that

18 $$\begin{aligned} f_{(3)}(c,c) &= f_{(2)}(c,c) - |\langle c,r_3 \rangle| = 17 - 1 = 16 \\ f_{(4)}(c,c) &= 16 - 6 = 10 \\ f_{(5)}(c,c) &= 10 - 18 = -8. \end{aligned}$$

Thus by evaluating only six scalar products we have determined that c does not belong to A_1, A_2, A_3, or A_4. Note that the fact that $f_{(5)}(c,c) < 0$ does not necessarily mean that $c \in A_5$. The only implication is that the hyperplane through c with outward normal c is no longer a separating hyperplane. $\square$

We now propose that the first step in an algorithm for solving problem (3) is to find the smallest integer k such that $f_{(k)}(c_k,c_k) \leq 0$. If M is the integer so obtained, then $c_k \notin A_k$ for $k = 1, 2, \ldots, M - 1$.

19 **Remark.** To summarize the above considerations, we note that the choice of $\eta = c_k$ is natural in trying to establish that $c_k \notin A_k$ by showing that $f_{(k)}(\eta, c_k) > 0$. □

Suppose that we have an integer M such that $c_k \notin A_k$ for all $k < M$ and $f_{(M)}(c_M, c_M) \leqq 0$. Then c_M may belong to A_M, and we must determine whether or not the equations and inequalities

20
$$\sum_{i=1}^{M} \alpha^i r_i = c_M$$
$$|\alpha_i^i| \leqq 1 \qquad i = 1, 2, \ldots, M$$

have a solution. One method for solving this problem was discussed in Section 5.11, and we shall now use a minor modification of that procedure. Thus to solve (20) we solve the following linear programming problem:

21 **Auxiliary problem.** Minimize $\langle \tilde{c}_M, \xi \rangle = \sum_{i=1}^{n} \tilde{c}_M{}^i \xi^i$ subject to the constraints

22
$$\sum_{i=1}^{M} \alpha^i r_i + \xi = c_M$$

23
$$-1 \leqq \alpha^i \leqq 1 \qquad i = 1, 2, \ldots, M$$

24
$$\tilde{c}_M{}^i \xi^i \geqq 0 \qquad i = 1, 2, \ldots, n,$$

where $\tilde{c}_M{}^i = c_M{}^i$ if $c_M{}^i \neq 0$ and $\tilde{c}_M{}^i = 1$ if $c_M{}^i = 0$. □

Note that $\alpha_0 = 0$ and $\xi_0 = c_M$ are a basic solution for (22) to (24). If we solve the problem (21) by means of the bounded-variable simplex algorithm (5.11.23), then an optimal solution $(\hat{\xi}, \hat{\alpha})$ will always be obtained in a finite number of steps [observe that with ξ_0 as defined above, a valid upper bound for $\tilde{c}_M{}^i \xi^i$ would be $(c_M{}^i)^2$]. If $\langle \tilde{c}_M, \hat{\xi} \rangle = 0$, then $c_M \in A_M$ and $\hat{\alpha}^i$ for $i = 1, 2, \ldots, M$ constitute a solution to problem (3). If $\langle c_M, \hat{\xi} \rangle > 0$, then $c_M \notin A_M$, and we must increase the final time k.

At this point we can observe an additional advantage in solving problem (21) by means of the simplex algorithm. Suppose $\langle \tilde{c}_M, \hat{\xi} \rangle > 0$. Since $(\hat{\xi}, \hat{\alpha})$ is an optimal solution to the linear programming problem (21), the bounded-variable simplex algorithm yields a set of Lagrange multipliers $\psi^1, \psi^2, \ldots, \psi^m$ satisfying the necessary and sufficient conditions for optimality, theorems (3.3.5) and (3.6.1), for this problem. For problem (21) these conditions assume the following form:

25
$$\sum_{i=1}^{M} \hat{\alpha}^i r_i + \hat{\xi} = c_M.$$

26 $-1 \leqq \hat{\alpha}^i \leqq +1$ for $i = 1, 2, \ldots, M$ and $\tilde{c}_M{}^i \hat{\xi}^i \geqq 0$ for $i = 1, 2, \ldots, n$.

27 For $i = 1, 2, \ldots, M$

$$\begin{aligned} \langle \psi, r_i \rangle &\leqq 0 \qquad \text{if } \hat{\alpha}^i = -1 \\ \langle \psi, r_i \rangle &\geqq 0 \qquad \text{if } \hat{\alpha}^i = +1 \\ \langle \psi, r_i \rangle &= 0 \qquad \text{if } |\hat{\alpha}^i| < 1. \end{aligned}$$

28 For $i = 1, 2, \ldots, n$

$$\begin{aligned} -\tilde{c}_M{}^i + \psi^i &\leqq 0 \qquad \text{if } \tilde{c}_M{}^i \hat{\xi}^i = 0 \\ -\tilde{c}_M{}^i + \psi^i &= 0 \qquad \text{if } \tilde{c}_M{}^i \hat{\xi}^i > 0. \end{aligned}$$

Using conditions (25) to (28), we can now prove the following theorem.

29 **Theorem.** Let $(\hat{\xi},\hat{\alpha})$ be an optimal solution to problem (21), and let ψ be a vector satisfying the necessary and sufficient conditions for optimality, (25) to (28). If $\langle \tilde{c}_M, \hat{\xi} \rangle > 0$, then

$$f_{(M)}(\psi, c_M) > 0.$$

Proof. We take the scalar product of both sides of (25) with ψ to obtain

30 $$\sum_{i=1}^{M} \langle \psi, r_i \rangle \hat{\alpha}^i + \langle \psi, \hat{\xi} \rangle = \langle \psi, c_M \rangle.$$

From (27) it follows that

31 $$\langle \psi, r_i \rangle \alpha^i = |\langle r_i, \psi \rangle| \qquad i = 1, 2, \ldots, M,$$

and from (28), since $\hat{\xi}^i = 0$ whenever $\tilde{c}_M{}^i \hat{\xi}^i = 0$ it follows that for $i = 1, 2, \ldots, n$

32 $$\begin{aligned} \psi^i \hat{\xi}^i &> 0 \qquad \text{if } \tilde{c}_M{}^i \hat{\xi}^i > 0 \\ \psi^i \hat{\xi}^i &= 0 \qquad \text{if } \tilde{c}_M{}^i \hat{\xi}^i = 0; \end{aligned}$$

that is

33 $$\langle \psi, \hat{\xi} \rangle \geqq 0.$$

Since $\langle \tilde{c}_M, \hat{\xi} \rangle > 0$ implies that $\tilde{c}_M{}^i \hat{\xi}^i > 0$ for at least one $i \in \{1, 2, \ldots, n\}$, it follows that

34 $$\langle \psi, \hat{\xi} \rangle > 0.$$

Combining (30), (31), and (34), we obtain

35 $$f_{(M)}(\psi, c_M) = \langle c_M, \psi \rangle - \sum_{i=1}^{M} |\langle r_i, \psi \rangle| = \langle \psi, \hat{\xi} \rangle > 0. \qquad \square$$

In other words, theorem (29) states that if the solution to (21) is such that $\langle \tilde{c}_M, \hat{\xi} \rangle > 0$, then any vector ψ satisfying the necessary and sufficient conditions for optimality defines a hyperplane through c_M with the property that A_M lies strictly on one side of this hyperplane.

We now combine the procedures suggested by theorems (12) and (29) into an algorithm for solving problem (3) under assumption (4), which guarantees the existence of a solution.

36 **Algorithm.** Let j be an index which is used to denote the iteration number.

Step 1. Find the smallest integer $M_1 \geqq 1$ such that $f_{(M_1)}(c_{M_1}, c_{M_1}) \leqq 0$, and set $j = 1$.

Step 2. Use the bounded-variable simplex algorithm to find a vector $\hat{\xi}_j \in E^n$ and a vector $\hat{\alpha}_j \in E^{M_j}$ which minimize $\langle \tilde{c}_{M_j}, \xi \rangle$ subject to the constraints

$$\sum_{i=1}^{M_j} \alpha^i r_i + \xi = c_{M_j}$$
$$-1 \leqq \alpha^i \leqq 1 \qquad i = 1, 2, \ldots, M_j$$
$$\tilde{c}_{M_j}{}^i \xi^i \geqq 0 \qquad i = 1, 2, \ldots, n,$$

where $\tilde{c}_{M_j}{}^i = c_{M_j}{}^i$ if $c_{M_j}{}^i \neq 0$ and $\tilde{c}_{M_j}{}^i = 1$ if $c_{M_j}{}^i = 0$. If $\langle \tilde{c}_{M_j}, \hat{\xi}_j \rangle = 0$, then $\hat{k} = M_j$ is the (minimum-time) solution to problem (3) and $\hat{u}_0 = \hat{\alpha}_j{}^1$, $\hat{u}_1 = \hat{\alpha}_j{}^2$, $\ldots$, $\hat{u}_{M_{j-1}} = \hat{\alpha}_j{}^{M_j}$ is an optimal control sequence. If $\langle \tilde{c}_{M_j}, \hat{\xi}_j \rangle > 0$, then go to step 3.

Step 3. Let ψ_j be the multiplier vector determined by the simplex algorithm according to (5.11.24). Find the smallest integer $M_{j+1} > M_j$ such that $f_{(M_{j+1})}(\psi_j, c_{M_{j+1}}) \leqq 0$. Set $j = j + 1$ and go to step 2. □

37 **Remark.** In carrying out step 3 considerable computation time can be saved by noting that the terms $\langle r_i, \psi \rangle$ are common to all the $f_{(k)}$ for $k \leqq i$. Therefore, if we define

38 $$g_{(k)}(\psi) = \sum_{i=1}^{k} |\langle r_i, \psi \rangle|$$

and store the value of $g_{(k)}$ at each step, we may obtain $f_{(k+1)}(\psi, c_{k+1})$ by the operations

39 $$g_{(k+1)}(\psi) = g_{(k)}(\psi) - |\langle r_{k+1}, \psi \rangle|$$

40 $$f_{(k+1)}(\psi, c_{k+1}) = \langle \psi, c_{k+1} \rangle - g_{(k+1)}(\psi).$$

Hence it is necessary to evaluate only two scalar products for each value of k. □

It should be clear that is is not possible to predict in advance how many values of k will be skipped in steps 1 and 3. This will depend in general on the nature of the vectors r_i and c_k in a particular problem. However, if the minimum-time solution corresponds to a large value of k, it is to be expected that in most cases step 1 will eliminate a large number of nonoptimal integers. In example problems it has been found that step 3 sometimes allows many values of k to be skipped, while at other times it is of no value at all. This depends very much on the initial state. Clearly, however, even in the worst case, where no steps at all can be skipped, this algorithm will not be very much slower than the ordinary linear programming procedure, since it will differ only in the fact that the functions $f_{(k)}$ must be evaluated at every step. For those cases where many steps are skipped, it could be significantly faster.

REFERENCES

1. R. E. Kalman: Optimal Nonlinear Control of Saturating Systems by Intermittent Actions, *IRE Wescon Conv. Rec.*, part IV, 1957, pp. 130–135.
2. C. A. Desoer and J. Wing: A Minimal Time Discrete System, *IRE Trans. Automatic Control,* May, 1961, pp. 111–125.
3. L. A. Zadeh and B. H. Whalen: On Optimal Control and Linear Programming, *IRE Trans. Automatic Control,* **AC-7**:45–46 (1962).
4. H. C. Torng: Optimization of Discrete Control Systems through Linear Programming, *J. Franklin Inst.,* **278**(1):28–44 (1964).

appendix **A**

Convexity

A.1 INTRODUCTION

The purpose of this appendix is to develop, as rapidly as possible, the minimal background in the theory of convex sets and convex functions which the authors deem necessary for an understanding of the material in this book. The development given here is not intended to be complete. Accordingly, a certain number of results will be presented without proof, and the task of either constructing proofs or looking them up in the references is left to the reader.

The presentation which follows assumes an elementary working knowledge of finite-dimensional vector spaces and linear transformations. In addition, familiarity with elementary real analysis, including continuity, the ideas of open, closed, and compact sets, and the interior and closure of sets in finite-dimensional euclidean space is assumed. *Throughout this book, E^n denotes an n-dimensional, real euclidean space.*

A.2 LINES AND HYPERPLANES

1 **Definition.** If $x_1, x_2 \in E^n$, then the *line through x_1 and x_2* is defined to be the set of points

$$\{x: x = x_1 + \lambda(x_2 - x_1), \lambda \text{ real}\}. \quad \square$$

2 **Definition.** The (closed) *line segment joining x_1 and x_2* is defined to be the set of points

$$\{x: x = x_1 + \lambda(x_2 - x_1), 0 \leqq \lambda \leqq 1\}.$$

We shall sometimes denote this line segment by x_1x_2. □

3 **Definition.** If $x = (x^1, \ldots, x^n)$ and $y = (y^1, \ldots, y^n)$ are two vectors in E^n, the *scalar product of x and y*, denoted by $\langle x,y\rangle$, is defined to be

$$\langle x,y\rangle = \sum_{i=1}^{n} x^i y^i. \quad \square$$

4 **Definition.** The *euclidean norm* of a vector $x = (x^1, \ldots, x^n) \in E^n$, denoted by $\|x\|$, is defined to be

$$\|x\| = \sqrt{\langle x,x\rangle}. \quad \square$$

It is assumed that the reader is already familiar with this definition and with the properties of this norm.

5 **Definition.** If a is any nonzero vector in E^n and b is any real number, then the set of points

$$\{x: \langle a,x\rangle = b\}$$

is called an *$(n - 1)$-dimensional hyperplane* in E^n (also a *linear manifold* or a *linear variety*). In the case where $b = 0$ the hyperplane is called an *$(n - 1)$-dimensional subspace* of E^n. The vector a is called the *normal to the hyperplane.* □

6 **Exercise.** Show that an $(n - 1)$-dimensional hyperplane in E^n contains exactly $(n - 1)$ linearly independent vectors. □

In general, we define a k-dimensional linear manifold in the following manner.

7 **Definition.** Let $a_1, \ldots, a_k \in E^n$ be linearly independent vectors, and let $b \in E^n$ be arbitrary. The set

$$X = \{x: x = b + \sum_{i=1}^{k} \alpha^i a_i, \alpha^i \text{ real for } i = 1, \ldots, k\}$$

is called a *k-dimensional linear manifold.* If $b = 0$ (or if $b = \sum_{i=1}^{k} \alpha^i a_i$ for some α^i), then X is called a *k-dimensional subspace.* □

8 **Definition.** Given any hyperplane $X = \{x\colon \langle a,x\rangle = b\}$, the two sets given by $\{x = \langle a,x\rangle < b\}$ and $\{x\colon \langle a,x\rangle > b\}$ are called *open half spaces* bounded by X. The sets $\{x\colon \langle a,x\rangle \leqq b\}$ and $\{x\colon \langle a,x\rangle \geqq b\}$ are called *closed half spaces* bounded by X. □

A.3 CONVEX SETS

1 **Definition.** A nonempty set X in E^n is said to be *convex* if for any two points $x_1, x_2 \in X$ the line segment joining x_1 and x_2 is contained in X, that is, if

$$\lambda x_1 + (1 - \lambda)x_2 \in X \text{ for every } \lambda \in [0,1]. \quad \square$$

Examples of convex sets are balls (open or closed), open or closed half spaces, and hyperplanes. The whole space is convex, and a set consisting of a single point is convex.

2 **Remark.** To avoid having to examine continually special cases, the *empty set*, denoted by ϕ in this book, is not considered to be a convex set. □

3 **Theorem.** Let C be a family of convex sets in E^n, that is $C = \{X_w\colon w \in \Omega\}$. If

$$X = \bigcap_{w\in\Omega} X_w \neq \phi,$$

then X is also convex.

Proof. Let x_1 and x_2 be arbitrary points in the (nonempty) intersection X. Then $x_1, x_2 \in X_w$ for every $w \in \Omega$. Since each X_w is convex, the line segment x_1x_2 joining x_1 and x_2 belongs to X_w for every $w \in \Omega$. This implies that x_1x_2 belongs to X, and thus that X is convex. □

4 **Definition.** If X_1 and X_2 are two subsets of E^n and α and β are real numbers, then the *linear combination of the sets,* denoted by $X = \alpha X_1 + \beta X_2$, is the set

$$X = \{x\colon x = \alpha x_1 + \beta x_2,\ x_1 \in X_1,\ x_2 \in X_2\}. \quad \square$$

5 **Theorem.** If X_1 and X_2 are convex sets, then $\alpha X_1 + \beta X_2$ is a convex set. □

6 **Exercise.** Prove theorem (5). □

7 **Definition.** If $X_1 \subset E^n$ and $X_2 \subset E^m$, then the *direct product* of X_1 and X_2 is denoted by $X_1 \times X_2 \subset E^{n+m}$ and is the set defined by

$$X_1 \times X_2 = \{x \in E^{n+m}: x = (x^1, \ldots, x^n, x^{n+1}, \ldots, x^{n+m}), \\ (x^1, \ldots, x^n) \in X_1, (x^{n+1}, \ldots, x^{n+m}) \in X_2\}. \quad \square$$

8 **Theorem.** The direct product of convex sets is a convex set. $\square$

9 **Exercise.** Prove theorem (8). $\square$

On many occasions we shall need to map convex subsets from one space into another. The following material bears on this matter.

10 **Definition.** A function $f: X \to E^m$, with $X \subset E^n$, is said to be *linear* if for all $x_1, x_2 \in X$ and for all real scalars α_1 and α_2

$$f(\alpha_1 x_1 + \alpha_2 x_2) = \alpha_1 f(x_1) + \alpha_2 f(x_2). \quad \square$$

11 **Definition.** Let $\mathfrak{L} \subset E^n$ be an $(n - 1)$-dimensional subspace, and let η be a normal to this subspace. If X is any subset of E^n, the *projection of X onto $\mathfrak{L}$* is defined to be the set

$$X' = \{z: z \in \mathfrak{L}, z + \alpha\eta \in X \text{ for some real } \alpha\}. \quad \square$$

12 **Exercise.** Show that X' as defined above is the image of X under the linear transformation

$$f(x) = x - \frac{\langle \eta, x \rangle}{\langle \eta, \eta \rangle} \eta. \quad \square$$

13 **Theorem.** If $X \subset E^n$ is a convex set and $f: X \to E^m$ is a linear function, then $f(X) \triangleq \{y: y = f(x), x \in X\}$ is a convex set.

Proof. Let y_1 and y_2 be elements of $f(X)$. Then there exist points x_1 and x_2 in X such that $y_1 = f(x_1)$ and $y_2 = f(x_2)$. Since X is convex,

$$\lambda x_1 + (1 - \lambda)x_2 \in X \qquad \text{for every } \lambda \in [0,1].$$

Since f is linear,

$$f(\lambda x_1 + (1 - \lambda)x_2) = \lambda f(x_1) + (1 - \lambda) f(x_2) \\ = \lambda y_1 + (1 - \lambda) y_2 \in f(X).$$

Thus $f(X)$ is convex. $\square$

14 **Corollary.** The projection of a convex set onto a subspace is a convex set.

Proof. This is an immediate consequence of theorem (13) and exercise (12). □

15 **Definition.** A *convex combination* of a finite number of points $x_1, \ldots, x_k \in E^n$ is defined to be a point $x \in E^n$ satisfying

$$x = \sum_{i=1}^{k} \mu^i x_i,$$

where the μ^i for $i = 1, \ldots, k$ are real scalars such that

$$\mu^i \geqq 0 \qquad i = 1, \ldots, k$$

and

$$\sum_{i=1}^{k} \mu^i = 1. \quad \square$$

With this definition it is now possible to give alternative characterization of a convex set.

16 **Theorem.** A set X in E^n is convex if and only if every convex combination of any finite number of arbitrary points of X belongs to X.

Proof. $\Rightarrow$. If every convex combination of any finite number of arbitrary points of X belongs to X, then, in particular, every convex combination of any two points x_1 and x_2 in X belongs to X; that is,

17 $$\mu^1 x_1 + \mu^2 x_2 \in X$$

for all $\mu^1 \geqq 0$ and $\mu^2 \geqq 0$ such that $\mu^1 + \mu^2 = 1$. Solving for μ^2, we find that

$$\mu^2 = 1 - \mu^1,$$

and $\mu^2 \geqq 0$ implies that $0 \leqq \mu^1 \leqq 1$. Thus we may rewrite (17) as

$$\mu^1 x_1 + (1 - \mu^1) x_2 \in X \qquad \text{for all } 0 \leqq \mu^1 \leqq 1.$$

Hence X is convex.

$\Leftarrow$. The proof in this direction proceeds by induction. The convex combination of any two points in X is in X, by the definition of convexity. Now, suppose that the statement is correct for convex combinations of k points in X. Let $x_1, \ldots, x_k, x_{k+1}$ be arbitrary points in X. Form

18 $$x = \mu^1 x_1 + \cdots + \mu^k x_k + \mu^{k+1} x_{k+1},$$

with $\mu^i \geqq 0$ for $i = 1, \ldots, k+1$ and $\sum_{i=1}^{k+1} \mu^i = 1$. If $\mu^{k+1} = 1$, then

$x = x_{k+1} \in X$, and we are done. Therefore suppose that $\mu^{k+1} < 1$. Then

$$\sum_{i=1}^{k} \mu^k = 1 - \mu^{k+1} > 0.$$

We may rewrite (18) as

19 $$x = \sum_{i=1}^{k} \mu^i \left(\frac{\mu^1}{\sum_{i=1}^{k} \mu^i} x_1 + \cdots + \frac{\mu^k}{\sum_{i=1}^{k} \mu^i} x_k \right) + \mu^{k+1} x_{k+1}.$$

Let $\lambda^j = \mu^j / \sum_{i=1}^{k} \mu^i$ and $\lambda = \sum_{i=1}^{k} \mu^i \geqq 0$. Note that $\lambda^j \geqq 0$ and that $\sum_{j=1}^{k} \lambda^j = 1$. Substituting in (19), we obtain

$$x = \lambda \left(\sum_{j=1}^{k} \lambda^j x_j \right) + (1 - \lambda) x_{k+1}.$$

By the induction hypothesis,

$$\sum_{j=1}^{k} \lambda^j x_j = y \in X,$$

and hence

$$x = \lambda y + (1 - \lambda) x_{k+1}.$$

By definition, $0 \leqq \lambda \leqq 1$, so $x \in X$. □

There are certain points in a convex set which cannot be expressed as a convex combination of other points in the set. These points are given a special name.

20 **Definition.** A point x belonging to a convex set $X \subset E^n$ is said to be an *extreme point* of X if it cannot be expressed as a convex combination of other points of X. □

The set consisting of all the convex combinations of a given finite set of points is of special interest and is given a special name.

21 **Definition.** The *convex hull* of a finite number of points $x_1, \ldots, x_k$ in E^n is defined to be the set

$$\{x: x = \sum_{i=1}^{k} \mu^i x_i, \mu^i \geqq 0, \sum_{i=1}^{k} \mu^i = 1\}$$

and will be denoted by co $\{x_1, \ldots, x_k\}$. Such a set is called a *convex polyhedron* or a *convex polytope*. The extreme points of a convex polytope are called *vertices* and are a subset of the points $x_1, \ldots, x_k$. □

22 **Definition.** In the particular case where $k = n + 1$ and the vectors $x_2 - x_1, x_3 - x_1, \ldots, x_{n+1} - x_1$ are linearly independent, the convex hull of $x_1, x_2, \ldots, x_{n+1}$ is called a *simplex*. [The extreme points of a simplex are the defining vectors $x_1, \ldots, x_n$.] □

The condition that the vectors $x_2 - x_1, \ldots, x_{n+1} - x_1$, with $x_1, \ldots, x_n$ vertices of a simplex, be linearly independent is equivalent to requiring that any scalars $\mu^2, \mu^3, \ldots, \mu^{n+1}$ satisfying

23 $$\mu^2(x_2 - x_1) + \mu^3(x_3 - x_1) + \cdots + \mu^{n+1}(x_{n+1} - x_1) = 0$$

satisfy

$$\mu^2 = \mu^3 = \cdots = \mu^{n+1} = 0.$$

If we rewrite (23) as

24 $$-\left(\sum_{i=2}^{n+1} \mu^i\right) x_1 + \mu^2 x_2 + \cdots + \mu^{n+1} x_{n+1} = 0$$

and define

$$\mu^1 \triangleq - \sum_{i=2}^{n+1} \mu^i,$$

it becomes clear that we obtain the following condition for the linear independence of a set of vectors $x_2 - x_1, x_3 - x_1, \ldots, x_{n+1} - x_1$.

25 **Theorem.** The vectors $x_2 - x_1, \ldots, x_{n+1} - x_1$ are linearly independent if and only if, whenever $\mu^1, \ldots, \mu^{n+1}$ are real numbers such that

26 $$\begin{aligned} &\mu^1 x_1 + \mu^2 x_2 + \cdots + \mu^{n+1} x_{n+1} = 0 \\ &\mu^1 + \mu^2 + \cdots + \mu^{n+1} = 0, \end{aligned}$$

then

$$\mu^1 = \mu^2 = \cdots = \mu^{n+1} = 0. \quad \square$$

27 **Exercise.** Prove theorem (25). □

The following theorem and its corollary are used in proving the Fundamental Theorem (2.3.12).

28 **Theorem.** If S is a simplex in E^n with vertices $x_1, \ldots, x_{n+1}$, then any point in E^n can be written uniquely in the form

$$x = \sum_{i=1}^{n+1} \mu^i x_i,$$

with

$$\sum_{i=1}^{n+1} \mu^i = 1.$$

Proof. It is clear from the statement of the theorem that we wish to determine if the set of simultaneous equations in $\mu^1, \ldots, \mu^{n+1}$,

29
$$\begin{aligned} \mu^1 x_1 + \cdots + \mu^{n+1} x_{n+1} &= x \\ \mu^1 + \cdots + \mu^{n+1} &= 1, \end{aligned}$$

has a unique solution for all x in E^n. That a solution exists and is unique follows immediately from theorem (25), since the matrices on the left-hand sides of (26) and (29) are identical. □

30 **Corollary.** If x belongs to the simplex S, then the μ^i in theorem (28) also satisfy $\mu^i \geqq 0$ for $i = 1, \ldots, n$.

Proof. This follows from the uniqueness of the μ^i and the fact that every point in S can be written as some convex combination of its vertices. □

31 **Definition.** The scalars $\mu^1, \mu^2, \ldots, \mu^n$ in theorem (38) are known as the *barycentric coordinates* of x relative to $x_1, \ldots, x_{n+1}$. □

So far we have defined the *convex hull* of a finite number of points. It is also possible to define the convex hull of an arbitrary subset of E^n.

32 **Definition.** The *convex hull* (*convex closure*) of a subset A of E^n is the intersection of all convex sets containing A. We shall denote the convex hull of A by co A. □

33 **Remark.** Note that co A is a convex set, by theorem (3), since co $A \neq \phi$. □

34 **Exercise.** Show that when A consists of a finite number of points, definitions (21) and (32) are consistent. □

Exercise (34) may be generalized, leading to an alternative characterization of the convex hull of an arbitrary subset of E^n.

35 **Theorem.** The convex hull of A consists of all the convex combinations of finite subsets of A; that is,

$$\text{co } A = \{x: x = \sum_{i=1}^{k} \mu^i a_i, \sum_{i=1}^{k} \mu^i = 1, \mu^i \geqq 0, k \text{ a positive integer}, a_i \in A\}. \quad \square$$

36 **Exercise.** Prove theorem (35). $\square$

We next take up the topic of the dimension of a convex set.

37 **Definition.** The *(linear) dimension* of a convex set $X \subset E^n$ is the largest integer $k \leqq n$ such that there exist $k + 1$ vectors x_1, . . . l $x_{k+1} \in X$ with the property that $x_2 - x_1, \ldots, x_{k+1} - x_1$ are lin, early independent. A convex set in E^n will be called *full dimensiona-* if its dimension is n. $\square$

It is consistent with this definition to consider the dimension of a convex set consisting of a single point to be zero. Using the same convention, we consider a single point to be a zero-dimensional linear manifold. The following theorem should be interpreted in the light of these conventions.

38 **Theorem.** A k-dimensional convex set can be contained in a k-dimensional linear manifold. This manifold is uniquely determined. $\square$

39 **Exercise.** Prove theorem (38). $\square$

We conclude this section with certain topological properties of convex sets.

40 **Definition.** The *closure* of a set $A \subset E^n$, denoted by $\bar{A}$, is the intersection of all closed sets containing A. $\square$

41 **Definition.** The *interior* of a set $A \subset E^n$, denoted by $\dot{A}$, is the union of all open sets contained in A. $\square$

42 **Remark.** Definition (40) is equivalent to saying that $\bar{A}$ consists of A and all limit points of A. Definition (41) is equivalent to saying that $\dot{A}$ consists of all the points of A about which it is possible to construct a ball of some positive radius which is entirely contained in A. $\square$

43 **Definition.** The boundary of a set $A \subset E^n$, denoted by ∂A, is defined to be the set

$$\partial A = \{x: x \in \bar{A}, x \notin \dot{A}\}. \quad \square$$

44 **Theorem.** The closure of a convex set is a convex set.

Proof. Let $A \subset E^n$ be a convex set, and let $\bar{A}$ be its closure. Let $x, y \in \bar{A}$ be arbitrary points. Then, by remark (42), there exist sequences $\{x_i\}$ and $\{y_i\}$ with $x_i, y_i \in A$ for each i and with

$$x_i \to x \qquad y_i \to y.$$

Let $z = \lambda x + (1 - \lambda)y$, with $0 \leqq \lambda \leqq 1$. Form $z_i \triangleq x_i + (1 - \lambda)y_i$ for $i = 1, 2, \ldots$. Clearly, $z_i \in A$ for each i and $z_i \to z$; hence $z \in \bar{A}$. □

45 **Theorem.** The interior of a convex set is either empty or convex. □

46 **Exercise.** Prove theorem (45). □

47 **Theorem.** If X is a convex set and $\dot{X}$ is nonempty, then

$$\bar{\dot{X}} = \bar{X} \qquad \text{and} \qquad \dot{\bar{X}} = \dot{X}. \quad \square$$

48 **Exercise.** Prove theorem (47). □

49 **Definition.** Let X be a k-dimensional convex subset of E^n. The *relative interior* of X is defined to be the interior of X relative to the k-dimensional linear manifold $\mathcal{L}(X)$ containing it; that is, x belongs to the relative interior of X if there exists an open ball $B(x)$ about x such that $\mathcal{L}(X) \cap B(x) \subset X$. □

50 **Remark.** The relative interior of any convex set is always nonempty and hence convex. □

A.4 CONVEX CONES

In the development of necessary conditions for optimality in Chapter 2, convex cones play a crucial role. In this section we shall develop some of their more important properties.

1 **Definition.** A *cone* C in E^n is a set of points such that if $x \in C$, then $\alpha x \in C$ for every $\alpha \geqq 0$. □

2 **Remark.** It is obvious from definition (1) that the origin is always a member of every cone. The origin is called the *vertex* of the cone. □

The definition of a cone given above requires that the cone contain the origin. However, it is often convenient to talk about sets which are *translates* of a cone.

3 **Definition.** A *cone C with vertex x_0* is defined to be a set of points C such that

$$C - \{x_0\} = \{z: z + x_0 \in C\}$$

is a cone. □

It is clear that such a cone need not contain the origin.

4 **Definition.** A *ray*, or *half-line*, is a cone of the form $\{x: x = \alpha c$, where c is a fixed vector, $\alpha \geqq 0\}$. □

We may on occasion translate a ray in the same manner as we did a cone, and in such a case we refer to it as a *ray emanating from x_0*.

5 **Definition.** A cone C is called a *convex cone* if C is a convex set. □

6 **Theorem.** A cone C is a convex cone if and only if $x_1 + x_2 \in C$ whenever $x_1, x_2 \in C$.

Proof. $\Rightarrow$. Suppose that C is convex. Let $x_1, x_2 \in C$ be arbitrary. Then

$$\tfrac{1}{2}x_1 + \tfrac{1}{2}x_2 \in C,$$

by convexity, and

$$x_1 + x_2 = 2(\tfrac{1}{2}x_1 + \tfrac{1}{2}x_2) \in C$$

because C is a cone.

$\Leftarrow$. Let $y_1, y_2 \in C$ be arbitrary. Let $\lambda \in [0,1]$ also be arbitrary, and let

$$y = \lambda y_1 + (1 - \lambda)y_2.$$

Since $\lambda \in [0,1]$, $\lambda \geqq 0$, and $(1 - \lambda) \geqq 0$, $\lambda y_1 \in C$ and $(1 - \lambda)y_2 \in C$. Therefore

$$y = [\lambda y_1 + (1 - \lambda)y_2] \in C,$$

by hypothesis, and C is convex. □

7 **Definition.** The cone C *generated* by a set X is defined to be the set of points

$$C = \{y: y = \lambda x,\ x \in X,\ \lambda \geqq 0\}. \quad □$$

If the set X is convex, then the following theorem holds.

8 **Theorem.** The cone C generated by a convex set X is a convex cone. □

9 **Exercise.** Prove theorem (8). □

In the particular case where the set X is a convex polyhedron, we make the following definition.

10 **Definition.** The cone generated by a convex polyhedron is called a *convex polyhedral cone.* □

11 **Theorem.** If $C_1, C_2 \subset E^n$ are convex cones, then the linear combination $\alpha C_1 + \beta C_2$ is also a convex cone for all real α and β.

Proof. $\alpha C_1 + \beta C_2$ is a convex set, by theorem (2.6). Therefore we need only prove that $\alpha C_1 + \beta C_2$ is a cone. Let $x \in \alpha C_1 + \beta C_2$ be arbitrary; then $x = \alpha x_1 + \beta x_2$ for some $x_1 \in C_1$ and $x_2 \in C_2$. Let $\lambda \geqq 0$ be arbitrary; then

$$\lambda x = \lambda(\alpha x_1 + \beta x_2) = \alpha(\lambda x_1) + \beta(\lambda x_2).$$

Since C_1 and C_2 are cones, $\lambda x_1 \in C_1$ and $\lambda x_2 \in C_2$. Hence $\lambda x \in \alpha C_1 + \beta C_2$. □

12 **Definition.** A ray contained in a cone is called a *boundary ray* of the cone if every point on the ray is a boundary point of the cone. □

13 **Exercise.** Suppose that $\tilde{x} \neq 0$ is a boundary point in a cone C with vertex x_0. Show that every point on the ray $\{x : x = \lambda(\tilde{x} - x_0), \lambda \geqq 0\}$ is a boundary point of C. □

14 **Remark.** It is clear that in E^2 a convex cone which is neither the whole space nor the singleton $\{0\}$ has exactly two boundary rays, and, except for the case where the cone is a line, the cone consists of the sector bounded by these rays.[1] It is also clear that this sector must subtend an angle less than or equal to 180° for the cone to be convex. □

15 **Definition.** A ray of a cone is called an *interior ray* of the cone if every point on the ray other than the vertex is an interior point of the cone. □

16 **Exercise.** Show that if one point on a ray, distinct from the origin, is an interior point of a cone, then every point on this ray other than the origin is an interior point of the cone. □

[1] We consider a cone consisting of a single ray to be the degenerate case where the two boundary rays coincide.

The following theorem is an essential tool in the examination of convex sets.

17 **Theorem.** If $K \subset E^n$ is a convex cone and $K \neq E^n$, then there exists a nonzero vector $a \in E^n$ such that $\langle a,x \rangle \leqq 0$ for every $x \in K$; that is, K can be contained in a closed half space.

Proof. The proof will be by induction on the dimension of the space. The proof is trivial for $n = 1$, and the case of $n = 2$ follows immediately from remark (14).

Suppose the theorem is true in E^{n-1}, with $n - 1 \geqq 2$. We shall show that it must also be true in E^n. We do this by supposing the contrary to be true. An immediate consequence of this supposition and the induction hypothesis is that the projection of K onto any $(n - 1)$-dimensional subspace $\mathfrak{L}$ must be the whole subspace. This follows because if there exists an $(n - 1)$-dimensional subspace $\hat{\mathfrak{L}}$ with normal $\hat{\eta}$ such that the projection $\hat{K}$ of K is not all of $\hat{\mathfrak{L}}$, then, by the induction hypothesis, there exists a vector $a \in \hat{\mathfrak{L}}$ such that

$$\langle a,x \rangle \leqq 0 \qquad \text{for every } x \in \hat{K}.$$

Now, by the definition of a projection, every $y \in K$ is of the form

$$y = x + \alpha\hat{\eta},$$

where $x \in \hat{K}$ and α is some real scalar. Furthermore,

$$\langle a,\hat{\eta} \rangle = 0,$$

because $a \in \mathfrak{L}$ and $\hat{\eta}$ is a normal to $\mathfrak{L}$. Hence

$$\langle a,y \rangle = \langle a,x \rangle + \alpha\langle z,\hat{\eta} \rangle = \langle a,x \rangle \leqq 0,$$

which contradicts our supposition of the nonexistence of a containing half space.

We now show that if K cannot be contained in a half space in E^n, then the intersection of K with every two-dimensional plane cannot be contained in a half plane. To see this, suppose that there exists some two-dimensional subspace $\mathfrak{M}$ such that $K' = K \cap \mathfrak{M}$ could be contained in a half plane. Let $b \in \mathfrak{M}$ be an outward normal vector to the boundary line of the half plane, and let c be a vector in the boundary line, that is, $\langle b,c \rangle = 0$, as shown in Figure 1. If $\mathfrak{L}$ is the $(n - 1)$-dimensional subspace with normal c, then b must lie in $\mathfrak{L}$, and the points in E^n which project onto b come entirely from $\mathfrak{M}$. Clearly, no point of K can project onto b, and hence $\mathfrak{L}$ is not covered by the projection of K. This contradicts the observation of the preceding paragraph.

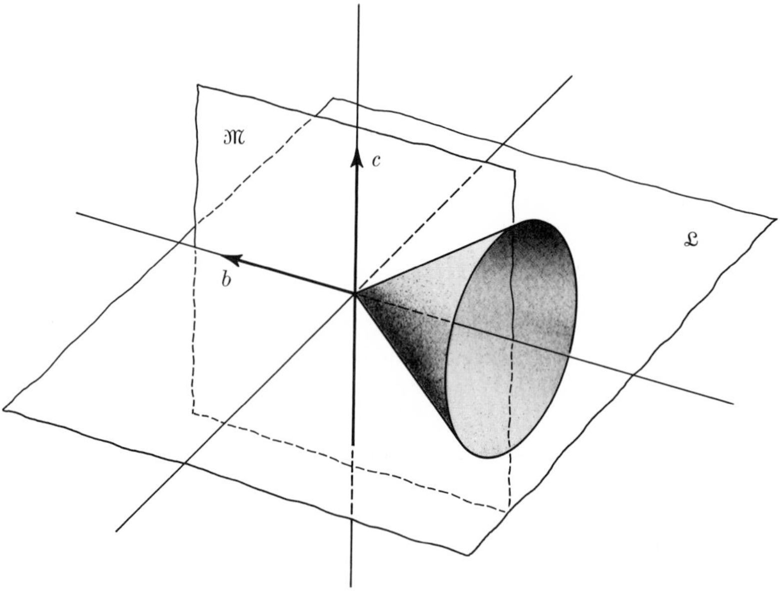

Figure 1

Now, since the theorem is true for $n = 2$, and the intersection of K with every two-dimensional plane is incapable of being contained in a half plane, it follows that the intersection of K with every two-dimensional subspace must be the whole subspace. This, of course, means that $K = E^n$, a contradiction of the original hypothesis. □

Now that we have shown the existence of at least one vector, a, with the property stated in theorem (17), it makes sense to talk about the set of all vectors having this property.

18 **Definition.** Let $K \subset E^n$ be a convex cone. The *polar of* K is defined to be the set

$$P(K) \triangleq \{a\colon \langle a,x\rangle \leqq 0 \text{ for all } x \in K\}. \quad \square$$

Clearly, $0 \in P(K)$ for any convex cone K. If $K = E^n$, then $P(K) = \{0\}$. However, if $K \neq E^n$, then, by theorem (17), $P(K)$ contains at least one point other than the origin, and clearly, it also contains the ray through that point. This suggests that $P(K)$ itself may be a convex cone, which is true.

19 **Theorem.** The polar of a convex cone is a convex cone.

Proof. Clearly, $P(K)$ is a cone, since if $a \in P(K)$, then for any $\alpha \geqq 0$

$$\langle \alpha a, x \rangle = \alpha \langle a, x \rangle \leqq 0 \qquad \text{for all } x \in K.$$

Now let a_1 and a_2 be arbitrary elements of $P(K)$. Then

$$\langle a_1 + a_2, x \rangle = \langle a_1, x \rangle + \langle a_2, x \rangle \leqq 0 \qquad \text{for all } x \in K.$$

Therefore $(a_1 + a_2) \in P(K)$, and $P(K)$ is a convex cone, by theorem (6). □

A.5 SEPARATION OF SETS: SUPPORTING HYPERPLANES

The preceding sections of this appendix have introduced the fundamentals of convex sets. In this section these fundamentals are used to derive certain far-reaching properties of convex sets. The theorems which follow form the basis for many of the results contained in the body of this book. Indeed, the necessary conditions for optimality, to which approximately one-half the book is devoted, are restatements of the separation theorems of this section. The reader who has not encountered this material previously should be careful to obtain a firm grasp of the material in this section.

1 **Definition.** Two sets $X_1, X_2 \in E^n$ are said to be *separated* if there exists a hyperplane $\mathcal{L} = \{x: \langle a, x \rangle = b\}$ in E^n such that

$$X_1 \subset \{x: \langle a, x \rangle \leqq b\}$$
$$X_2 \subset \{x: \langle a, x \rangle \geqq b\}.$$

In this case the hyperplane $\mathcal{L}$ is called a *separating hyperplane.* □

Note that it is possible, as shown in Figure 1, to have two sets separated in the sense of the above definition even though their intersection is nonempty.

2 **Definition.** Two sets $X_1, X_2 \subset E^n$ are said to be *strictly separated* if there exists a hyperplane $\mathcal{L} = \{x: \langle a, x \rangle = b\rangle$ in E^n such that

$$X_1 \subset \{x: \langle a, x\} < b\}$$
$$X_2 \subset \{x: \langle a, x \rangle > b\}. \quad □$$

Clearly, a necessary condition for two sets to be strictly separated is that they have an empty intersection.

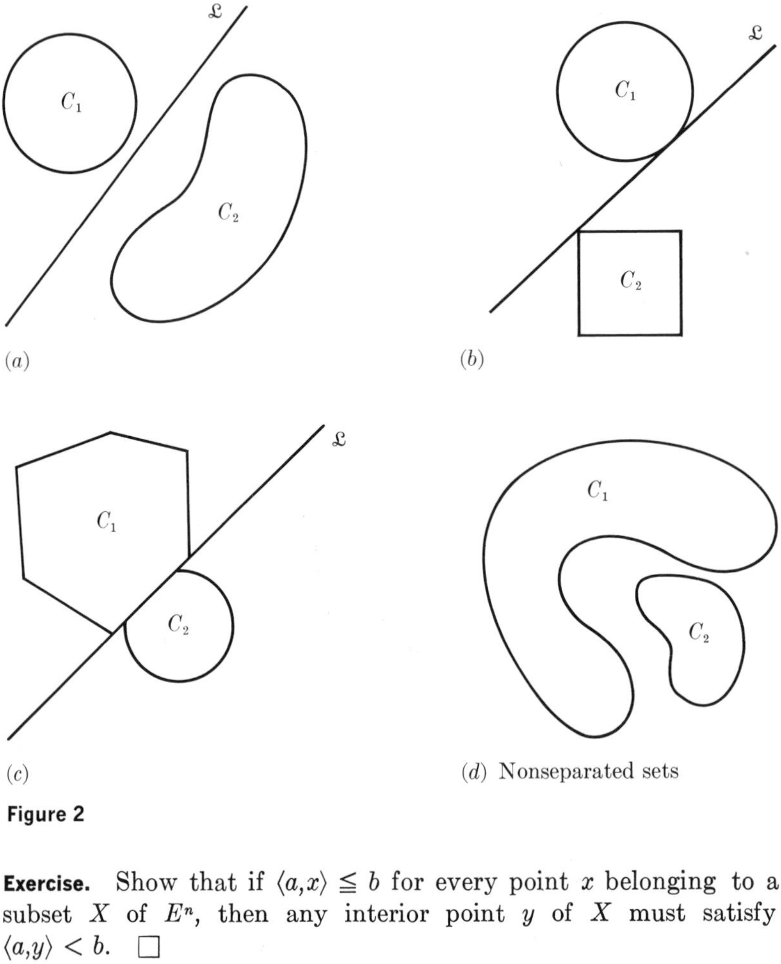

(d) Nonseparated sets

Figure 2

3 **Exercise.** Show that if $\langle a,x \rangle \leqq b$ for every point x belonging to a subset X of E^n, then any interior point y of X must satisfy $\langle a,y \rangle < b$. □

A consequence of the above result is that if two sets $X_1, X_2 \subset E^n$ are separated, and these sets have nonempty interiors $\dot{X}_1$ and $\dot{X}_2$, then $\dot{X}_1$ and $\dot{X}_2$ are strictly separated.

4 **Exercise.** Show that if the relative interiors of two convex sets are separated, then the sets themselves are separated. □

The first condition we shall consider concerning the separation of sets deals with convex cones. It is this theorem which forms the basis for the necessary conditions for optimality given in theorem (2.3.12).

5 **Theorem.** Consider two convex cones $K_1, K_2 \subset E^n$. If either

a. $K_1 \cup K_2$ can be contained in an $(n - 1)$-dimensional hyperplane, or

b. rel int $K_1 \cap$ rel int $K_2 = \phi$, where rel int K_i stands for the relative interior of K_i,

then K_1 and K_2 can be separated.

Proof. If condition (*a*) is satisfied, then the theorem is obviously true. Therefore, consider the case where (*b*) [but not necessarily (*a*)] holds. As observed in (3.50), rel int $K_i \neq \phi$ for $i = 1, 2$. Furthermore, it must be true that for at least one of the sets rel int K_i for $i = 1, 2$ there exists a nonzero $x \in$ rel int K_i such that $-x \notin$ rel int K_i. Otherwise we would have $0 \in$ rel int K_i for $i = 1, 2$, which would contradict (*b*).

Next let

$$C_i \triangleq \text{rel int } K_i \cup \{0\} \qquad i = 1, 2.$$

It is left to the reader to verify that remark (4.16) and theorem (4.6) imply that C_1 and C_2 are convex cones.

Let x be the point whose existence was shown above, and, with no loss of generality, suppose that $x \in C_1$, with $-x \notin C_1$ (clearly $x \in$ rel int K_1 and $-x \notin$ rel int K_1 imply $x \in C_1$ and $-x \notin C_1$).

Now consider the convex cone

6 $$C \triangleq C_1 - C_2.$$

That C is a convex cone follows from theorem (4.11). Suppose that $C = E^n$. Then clearly $-x \in C$, and hence

7 $$-x = x_1 - x_2 \qquad \text{for some } x_1 \in C_1,\ x_2 \in C_2.$$

Rearranging, we have

8 $$x_2 = x_1 + x \in C_1.$$

Since $-x \notin C_1$, we must have $x_2 \neq 0$. This implies that

9 $$x_2 \in \text{rel int } K_1 \cap \text{rel int } K_2,$$

a contradiction of (*b*). Therefore $C \neq E^n$. From theorem (4.17), there exists a vector $a \in E^n$ such that

10 $$\langle a,z \rangle \leqq 0 \qquad \text{for all } z \in C.$$

In particular, since the origin 0 belongs to both C_1 and C_2, there are points in C of the form

$$x_1 = x_1 - 0 \qquad \text{for each } x_1 \in C_1$$

and also points of the form

11 $$-x_2 = 0 - x_2 \qquad \text{for each } x_2 \in C_2.$$

Substituting into (10), we have

12 $$\langle a,x_1\rangle \leqq 0 \qquad \text{for all } x_1 \in C_1$$
13 $$\langle a,x_2\rangle \geqq 0 \qquad \text{for all } x_2 \in C_2.$$

Finally, applying exercise (4), we have

14 $$\langle a,x_1\rangle \leqq 0 \qquad \text{for all } x_1 \in K_1$$
15 $$\langle a,x_2\rangle \geqq 0 \qquad \text{for all } x_2 \in K_2. \quad \square$$

In the remainder of this section we consider some of the fundamental theorems regarding separation of sets and supporting hyperplanes to sets.

16 **Theorem.** If $C \subset E^n$ is a convex set and $x \notin C$, then there exists a hyperplane $\mathfrak{L} = \{z: \langle a,z\rangle = b\}$ such that $x \in \mathfrak{L}$ and $\langle a,z\rangle \leqq b$ for all $z \in C$.

Proof. The set $C_1 = C - \{x\}$ is convex, since C and $\{x\}$ are convex. The origin does not belong to C_1, since $0 \in C_1$ would imply that $x \in C$. Let K be the cone generated by C_1 [see (4.7)]. K is a convex cone, by theorem (4.8). If $K = E^n$, then for any $y \neq 0$, $y \in K$ and $-y \in K$. However, by the definition of K, there must exist positive scalars α_1 snd α_2 such that $\alpha_1 y \in C_1$ and $\alpha_2(-y) \in C_1$. This, however, would mean that $0 \in C_1$, which we have already observed to be false. Hence $K \neq E^n$.

Applying theorem (4.17), we find that there exists a vector $a \in E^n$ such that

17 $$\langle a,z\rangle \leqq 0 \qquad \text{for every } z \in K.$$

By the definition of K, $C_1 \subset K$, and hence

18 $$z = c - x \in K \qquad \text{for every } c \in C.$$

Thus

19 $$\langle a,z\rangle = \langle a,c\rangle - \langle a,x\rangle \leqq 0 \qquad \text{for every } c \in C.$$

Clearly, the hyperplane

20 $$\mathfrak{L} = \{y: \langle a,y\rangle = \langle a,x\rangle\}$$

is the required hyperplane. $\square$

Using theorem (16), we can prove the following theorem on the separation of convex sets.

21 **Theorem.** If $C_1, C_2 \subset E^n$ are disjoint convex sets, that is, $C_1 \cap C_2 = \phi$, then C_1 and C_2 are separated.

Proof. Let $C = C_1 - C_2$. Clearly, $0 \notin C$, since $0 \in C$ would imply that $x_1 = x_2$ for some $x_1 \in C_1$ and $x_2 \in C_2$, which is a contradiction. Therefore, by theorem (16), there exists a hyperplane

$$\mathfrak{L} = \{z: \langle a,z \rangle = \langle a,0 \rangle = 0\}$$

such that $\langle a,x \rangle \leqq 0$ for every $x \in C$. Fix $\tilde{x}_2 \in C_2$. Clearly, $\langle a,x_1 \rangle \leqq \langle a,\tilde{x}_2 \rangle$ for every $x_1 \in C_1$, and therefore

22 $$b \triangleq \sup_{x_1 \in C_1} \langle a,x_1 \rangle$$

must be finite. Obviously, then,

23 $$\langle a,x_1 \rangle \leqq b \qquad \text{for every } x_1 \in C_1.$$

We shall show by contradiction that $\langle a,x_2 \rangle \geqq b$ for every $x_2 \in C_2$. Suppose that for some $x_2 \in C_2$

24 $$\langle a,x_2 \rangle < b.$$

Then there exists an $x_1 \in C_1$ such that

25 $$\langle a,x_2 \rangle < \langle a,x_1 \rangle,$$

or

26 $$\langle a, x_1 - x_2 \rangle > 0.$$

But this contradicts the fact that $\langle a,x \rangle \leqq 0$ for every $x \in C$, and therefore $\mathfrak{L}_1 = \{z: \langle a,z \rangle = b\}$ is the required hyperplane. □

27 **Exercise.** Show that if C_1 is a convex cone in theorem (21), then we may always choose $b = 0$. □

28 **Corollary.** If $C \subset E^n$ is a closed convex set and $\tilde{x} \notin C$, then there exists a hyperplane $\{x: \langle a,x \rangle = b\}$ such that

$$\langle a,\tilde{x} \rangle > b$$
$$\langle a,y \rangle \leqq b \qquad \text{for all } y \in C.$$

Proof. Since $\tilde{x}$ belongs to the open complement of C, there exists a ball S of radius $r > 0$ about $\tilde{x}$ such that $S \cap C = \phi$. Since a ball is convex, theorem (21) may be applied to obtain a hyperplane $\{z: \langle a,z \rangle = b\}$ such that

$$\langle a,z \rangle \geqq b \qquad \text{for every } z \in S$$
$$\langle a,z \rangle \leqq b \qquad \text{for every } z \in C.$$

However, $\tilde{x}$ is an interior point of S, and hence by exercise (3), we must have $\langle a,\tilde{x}\rangle > b$. □

29 **Remark.** Clearly, corollary (28) states that $\tilde{x}$ and C are strictly separated, since we could consider instead the hyperplane $\{x: \langle a,x\rangle = \frac{1}{2}[b + \langle a,\tilde{x}\rangle]\}$. □

In (4.18) the concept of the *polar* of a convex cone was introduced. In the following theorem and corollary we prove a very interesting and useful property of polars.

30 **Theorem.** If $C \subset E^n$ is a closed convex cone, then the polar of $P(C)$ is C itself; that is, $P(P(C)) = C$.

Proof. Since $P(C)$ is itself a convex cone, as was demonstrated in (4.19), $P(P(C))$ is well defined. Clearly, $C \subset P(P(C))$, so we need only show that $P(P(C)) \subset C$. Let $a \in P(P(C))$ be arbitrary, and suppose that $a \notin C$. Then, by corollary (28) and exercise (27), there exists an $\eta \in E^n$ such that

31 $$\langle \eta,a\rangle > 0$$

32 $$\langle \eta,x\rangle \leqq 0 \qquad \text{for all } x \in C.$$

By (32) and the definition of $P(C)$, $\eta \in P(C)$. Therefore, by the definition of $P(P(C))$ and the fact that $a \in P(P(C))$, we must have

33 $$\langle a,\eta\rangle \leqq 0,$$

which contradicts (31). Therefore $a \in C$ and $C = P(P(C))$. □

The following corollary, commonly known as *Farkas' lemma,* is one of the basic tools in deriving necessary conditions for optimality for nonlinear programming problems.

34 **Corollary: Farkas' lemma.** If $a_1, \ldots, a_k$ and b are a finite set of vectors in E^n, then

35 $$\langle b,x\rangle \leqq 0$$

for all $x \in E^n$ satisfying

36 $$\langle a_i,x\rangle \leqq 0 \qquad i = 1, \ldots, k$$

if and only if

$$b = \sum_{i=1}^{k} \mu^i a_i,$$

with $\mu^i \geqq 0$ for $i = 1, \ldots, k$.

Proof. $\Leftarrow$. The proof in this direction is trivial.

$\Rightarrow$. The theorem is also trivial if $a_i = 0$ for $i = 1, \ldots, k$, if $b = 0$, or if $k = 0$, and so we may consider the case where none of these occur. Let K be the convex polyhedral cone generated by $a_1, \ldots, a_k$, that is, the cone generated by the convex hull of $a_1, \ldots, a_k$. Clearly, K is closed. It is easily verified that the polar of K is given by

37 $$P(K) = \{x: \langle a_i,x\rangle \leqq 0, i = 1, \ldots, k\}.$$

The hypothesis implies that $b \in P(P(K))$. Therefore, by theorem (30),

38 $$b \in K,$$

which is the desired result, since every element of K may be written in the form $\sum_{i=1}^{k} \mu^i a_i$ for some $\mu^i \geqq 0$, with $i = 1, \ldots, k$. □

39 **Remark.** If we change (36) in the statement of corollary (34) to include $\langle a_i,x\rangle = 0$ for some $i \in \{1, \ldots, k\}$, then in the construction of b the corresponding μ^i have no specified sign. This is immediately apparent if the equality $\langle a_i,x\rangle = 0$ is rewritten as the two inequalities $\langle a_i,x\rangle \leqq 0$ and $\langle -a_i,x\rangle \leqq 0$. □

40 **Exercise.** Show that if $C \subset E^n$ is a closed convex cone with the property that for all nonzero vectors $x \in C$, $-x \notin C$, then there exists a vector $a \in E^n$ such that $\langle a,x\rangle < 0$ for all nonzero $x \in C$. [*Hint:* It is easy to show that any vector a in the *interior* of the polar of C must have the above property. Therefore, show that $P(C)$ has a nonempty interior by deducing that otherwise $P(P(C)) \neq C$. The interested reader may attempt to prove this result without resorting to the material in this section.] □

We conclude this introduction to convex sets with the following results on supporting hyperplanes.

41 **Definition.** A *supporting hyperplane* to a set $X \subset E^n$ at a point $\hat{x} \in \bar{X}$, the closure of X, is a hyperplane $\mathcal{L} = \{x: \langle a,x\rangle = b\}$ such that $\hat{x} \in \mathcal{L}$ and $\langle a,x\rangle \leqq b$ for all $x \in X$. □

42 **Theorem.** If $C \subset E^n$ is a convex set, then there exists a supporting hyperplane to C at every boundary point of C.

Proof. If the dimension of C is less than n, then the theorem follows immediately. Therefore we suppose that C is of dimension n. It follows that C has a nonempty interior $\dot{C}$. By theorem (3.45), $\dot{C}$ is also convex. Let x be any boundary point of C. Then, since $x \notin \dot{C}$, we may use theorem (16) to obtain a hyperplane $\mathcal{L} = \{z: \langle a,x \rangle = b\}$, with the property that $\langle a,x \rangle = b$ and $\langle a,z \rangle \leqq b$ for all $z \in \dot{C}$. By theorem (3.47) and exercise (4), we have that $\langle a,x \rangle \leqq b$ for all $z \in C$. □

A.6 CONVEX FUNCTIONS

It is natural to study convex and concave functions in conjunction with convex sets. In our case they are of additional importance because many of the necessary conditions for optimality, developed in Chapter 3, become sufficient conditions, and because, in optimization, simplifications always result when some of the relevant functions are convex or concave.

1 **Definition.** A function $f: X \to E^1$, with X a convex subset of E^n, is said to be *convex* if for any two points x_1 and x_2 in X and any real λ, $0 \leqq \lambda \leqq 1$, we have

2 $$f(\lambda x_1 + (1 - \lambda)x_2) \leqq \lambda f(x_1) + (1 - \lambda)f(x_2).$$

If strict inequality holds in (2) for all $x_1 \neq x_2$ in X and for all $0 < \lambda < 1$, then $f(\cdot)$ is said to be *strictly convex.* □

3 **Definition.** A function $f: X \to E^1$, with X a convex subset of E^n, is called *concave* (*strictly concave*) if $-f(\cdot)$ is convex (strictly convex). □

4 **Theorem.** A function $f(\cdot)$ from a convex set X into E^1 is convex if and only if for every finite number of points $x_1, \ldots, x_k$ in X

$$f\left(\sum_{i=1}^{k} \mu^i x_i\right) \leqq \sum_{i=1}^{k} \mu^i f(x_i)$$

whenever $\sum_{i=1}^{k} \mu^i = 1$, with $\mu^i \geqq 0$ and $i = 1, \ldots, k$. □

5 **Exercise.** Prove theorem (4). [*Hint:* Proceed as in the proof of Theorem (3.16).] □

6 **Theorem.** Let $X \subset E^n$ be a convex set. If the functions $f^i: X \to E^1$ for $i = 1, \ldots, k$ are convex and if α^i for $i = 1, \ldots, k$ are real scalars satisfying $\alpha^i \geqq 0$, then the function

$$f(x) \triangleq \sum_{i=1}^{k} \alpha^i f^i(x)$$

is convex.

Proof. Let $x_1, x_2 \in X$ be arbitrary and let $\lambda \in [0,1]$ also be arbitrary. Since each $f^i(\cdot)$ is convex and $\alpha^i \geqq 0$,

7 $$f(\lambda x_1 + (1-\lambda)x_2) = \sum_{i=1}^{k} \alpha^i f^i(\lambda x_1 + (1-\lambda)x_2) \leqq \sum_{i=1}^{k} \alpha^i[\lambda f^i(x_1) + (1-\lambda)f^i(x_2)].$$

This inequality may be rewritten in the form

8 $$f(\lambda x_1 + (1-\lambda)x_2) \leqq \lambda \sum_{i=1}^{k} \alpha^i f^i(x_1) + (1-\lambda) \sum_{i=1}^{k} \alpha^i f^i(x_2) = \lambda f(x_1) + (1-\lambda)f(x_2).$$

Hence f is convex. □

9 **Theorem.** Let $f(\cdot)$ be a convex function from a convex set $X \subset E^n$ into E^1; then for all real α the set $\{x: f(x) \leqq \alpha\}$ is either empty or convex. □

10 **Exercise.** Prove theorem (9). □

Functions which have the property stipulated in theorem (9) are given a special name.

11 **Definition.** A function $f: X \subset E^n \to E^1$, with X convex, is said to be *quasi-convex on X* if for any real α the set $\{x: f(x) \leqq \alpha\}$ is either empty or convex. □

12 **Remark.** The function $f(x) \triangleq -(1 - e^{-|x|})$ mapping E^1 into E^1 is quasi-convex on E^1, but it is not convex. □

As we shall see, if a function is twice continuously differentiable, there is a relatively simple test to determine if it is convex. Before imposing any differentiability conditions, however, we prove an important property of convex functions.

13 **Theorem.** Let $f(\cdot)$ be a convex function from an *open* convex set $X \subset E^n$ into E^1; then f is continuous on X.

Proof. Let $x_0 \in X$ be arbitrary. Since X is open, we can construct a simplex [see (3.22)] $S \subset X$ with vertices $x_1, \ldots, x_{n+1}$ in X such that x_0 is an interior point of S. By corollary (3.30), every point in S can be written uniquely in the form

14 $$x = \sum_{i=1}^{n+1} \mu^i x_i,$$

where $\mu^i \geqq 0$ and $\sum_{i=1}^{n+1} \mu^i = 1$. Let α be any real scalar satisfying

15 $\alpha > \max \{f(x_1), \ldots, f(x_{n+1})\}.$

Since f is convex, it follows from theorem (4) that for every $x \in S \subset X$

$$f(x) = f\Big(\sum_{i=1}^{n+1} \mu^i x_i\Big) \leqq \sum_{i=1}^{n+1} \mu^i f(x_i) < \alpha \sum_{i=1}^{n+1} \mu^i = \alpha.$$

Therefore f is bounded from above on S.

Let $B_\delta(x_0)$ be a ball centered at x_0 with radius $\delta > 0$ such that $B_\delta(x_0) \subset S$. It is possible to construct such a ball because x_0 is an interior point of S. Let $x \in B_\delta(x_0)$ be such that $0 < \|x - x_0\| < \delta$, and define the vector w to be

$$w = \frac{\delta(x - x_0)}{\|x - x_0\|}.$$

Clearly, the points $x_0 \pm w$ belong to the boundary of the ball $B_\delta(x_0)$, while the points x and x_0 lie on the line segment $(x_0 - w)(x_0 + w)$. Indeed, it is easily verified that

16 $x = \lambda(x_0 + w) + (1 - \lambda)x_0$

17 $x_0 = \dfrac{x}{1 + \lambda} + \dfrac{\lambda}{1 + \lambda}(x_0 - w),$

where

18 $\lambda \triangleq \dfrac{\|x - x_0\|}{\delta} \leqq 1.$

Since $f(\cdot)$ is convex on X and $B_\delta(x_0) \subset S$, we have

19 $f(x) \leqq \lambda f(x_0 + w) + (1 - \lambda) f(x_0) \leqq \lambda\alpha + (1 - \lambda) f(x_0),$

20 $f(x_0) \leqq \dfrac{1}{1 + \lambda} f(x) + \dfrac{\lambda}{1 + \lambda} f(x_0 - w) \leqq \dfrac{1}{1 + \lambda} f(x) + \dfrac{\lambda\alpha}{1 + \lambda},$

where α is as defined in (15). Rearranging these inequalities, we obtain

21 $f(x) - f(x_0) \leqq \lambda(\alpha - f(x_0))$

22 $f(x) - f(x_0) \geqq -\lambda(\alpha - f(x_0)),$

which, because of the definition of λ in (18), is equivalent to

23 $|f(x) - f(x_0)| \leqq \dfrac{\alpha - f(x_0)}{\delta} \|x - x_0\|.$

Hence if $\epsilon > 0$ is given and $\|x - x_0\| \leqq \min \{\delta, \delta\epsilon/[\alpha - f(x_0)]\}$, then

$|f(x) - f(x_0)| \leqq \epsilon$. Therefore $f(\cdot)$ is continuous at x_0. Since x_0 was arbitrary, $f(\cdot)$ is continuous on X. □

24 **Example.** Let $X = \{x: 0 \leqq x \leqq 1\} \subset E^1$, let $f(x) = x$ if $0 \leqq x < 1$, and let $f(1) = 2$. Then $f(\cdot)$ is convex on the closed convex set X, but $f(\cdot)$ is not continuous at 1. □

We now turn to properties of differentiable convex functions.

25 **Theorem.** Let $f(\cdot)$ be a continuously differentiable function from an open convex set $X \subset E^n$ into E^1. Then $f(\cdot)$ is convex if and only if

26 $$f(x) \geqq f(x_0) + \langle \nabla f(x_0), x - x_0 \rangle,$$

where

$$\nabla f(x_0) = \left[\frac{\partial f(x_0)}{\partial x^1}, \ldots, \frac{\partial f(x_0)}{\partial x^n} \right]^T,$$

for every $x, x_0 \in X$.

Proof. $\Rightarrow$. Let $x_0, x \in X$ be arbitrary, let $\lambda \in (0,1)$, and let $h = (x - x_0)$. Then $x_0 + \lambda h \in X$, since X is convex, and since $f(\cdot)$ is convex on X,

27 $$f(x_0 + \lambda h) \leqq \lambda f(x) + (1 - \lambda) f(x_0).$$

Subtracting $\langle \nabla f(x_0), h \rangle$ from both sides of (27) and rewriting the inequality, we obtain

28 $$\frac{f(x_0 + \lambda h) - f(x_0) - \lambda \langle \nabla f(x_0), h \rangle}{\lambda} \leqq f(x) - f(x_0) - \langle \nabla f(x_0), h \rangle.$$

Since $f(\cdot)$ is differentiable at x_0, the left-hand side of (28) converges to zero as $\lambda \to 0^+$. Thus the right-hand side is nonnegative, which is equivalent to (26).

$\Leftarrow$. Suppose that (26) holds for all $x_0, x \in X$. Let $x_1, x_2 \in X$, with $x_1 \neq x_2$, and let $0 < \lambda < 1$. Set

29 $$x_0 = \lambda x_1 + (1 - \lambda) x_2 \qquad h = (x_1 - x_0).$$

It is easily verified that

30 $$x_2 = x_0 - \frac{\lambda}{1 - \lambda} h.$$

By (26),

31 $$f(x_1) \geqq f(x_0) + \langle \nabla f(x_0), h \rangle$$

32 $$f(x_2) \geqq f(x_0) + \langle \nabla f(x_0), h \rangle \frac{-\lambda}{1 - \lambda}.$$

Multiplying (31) by $\lambda/(1-\lambda)$ and adding it to (32), we obtain

$$\frac{\lambda}{1-\lambda} f(x_1) + f(x_2) \geqq \left(\frac{\lambda}{1-\lambda} + 1\right) f(x_0),$$

or

33 $$\lambda f(x_1) + (1-\lambda) f(x_2) \geqq f(x_0).$$

Thus we have shown that

34 $$f(\lambda x_1 + (1-\lambda)x_2) \leqq \lambda f(x_1) + (1-\lambda) f(x_2) \quad \text{for all } 0 < \lambda < 1.$$

If $\lambda = 0$ or $\lambda = 1$, the inequality holds trivially. Therefore $f(\cdot)$ is convex. □

35 **Theorem.** Let $f(\cdot)$ be a continuously differentiable function from an open convex set $X \subset E^n$ into E^1. Then $f(\cdot)$ is strictly convex if and only if

$$f(x) > f(x_0) + \langle \nabla f(x_0), x - x_0 \rangle$$

for every $x, x_0 \in X$, with $x \neq x_0$.

36 **Exercise.** Prove theorem (35). □

The following results are useful in Chapters 3 and 7.

37 **Theorem.** Let $f(\cdot)$ be a convex differentiable function from an open convex set $X \subset E^n$ into E^1, and let x_0 be any point in X. Then $f(x_0) \leqq f(x)$ for every $x \in X$ if and only if $\nabla f(x_0) = 0$.

Proof. $\Rightarrow$. This part of the proof follows directly from elementary calculus.

$\Leftarrow$. Suppose that $\nabla f(x_0) = 0$. Since $x_0 \in X$, $f(x) \geqq f(x_0)$ for all $x \in X$, by theorem (25). □

38 **Theorem.** If $f(\cdot)$ is a strictly convex function from a convex set $X \subset E^n$ into E^1, then there is at most one point $x_0 \in X$ such that $f(x_0) \leqq f(x)$ for every $x \in X$.

Proof. Suppose that $x_0 \neq x_1$ in X satisfy $f(x_i) \leqq f(x)$ for every $x \in X$ and for $i = 0, 1$. Then, obviously, $f(x_0) = f(x_1)$. Since X is convex, $x_0 + \lambda(x_1 - x_0) \in X$ for every $0 < \lambda < 1$. Since f is strictly convex on X,

39 $$f(x_0 + \lambda(x_1 - x_0)) < \lambda f(x_1) + (1-\lambda) f(x_0) = f(x_0),$$

which is in contradiction to the original hypothesis. □

We conclude this section with a relatively simple test for determining whether or not a function is convex.

40 **Definition.** An $n \times n$ matrix Q is called *positive semidefinite* if $\langle x,Qx\rangle \geqq 0$ for every $x \in E^n$. If $\langle x,Qx\rangle > 0$ for every nonzero $x \in E^n$, then Q is called *positive definite.* □

41 **Exercise.** Show that if Q is an $n \times n$ positive-semidefinite matrix, then Q^T and $Q + Q^T$ are positive-semidefinite matrices. □

42 **Theorem.** Let $f(\cdot)$ be a twice continuously differentiable function from an open convex set $X \subset E^n$ into E^1. Then $f(\cdot)$ is convex on X if and only if the $n \times n$ hessian matrix

43
$$H(x) = \begin{bmatrix} \frac{\partial^2 f(x)}{\partial x^1\, \partial x^1} & \frac{\partial^2 f(x)}{\partial x^1\, \partial x^2} & \cdots & \frac{\partial^2 f(x)}{\partial x^1\, \partial x^n} \\ \frac{\partial^2 f(x)}{\partial x^2\, \partial x^1} & \frac{\partial^2 f(x)}{\partial x^2\, \partial x^2} & \cdots & \frac{\partial^2 f(x)}{\partial x^2\, \partial x^n} \\ \cdots & \cdots & \cdots & \cdots \\ \frac{\partial^2 f(x)}{\partial x^n\, \partial x^1} & \frac{\partial^2 f(x)}{\partial x^n\, \partial x^2} & \cdots & \frac{\partial^2 f(x)}{\partial x^n\, \partial x^n} \end{bmatrix}$$

is positive semidefinite for every $x \in X$.

Proof. $\Leftarrow$. Let x_0, $x \in X$ be arbitrary, and let $h = x - x_0$. Then $(x_0 + \lambda h) \in X$ for every $\lambda \in [0,1]$, since X is convex. By Taylor's theorem,

44
$$f(x) = f(x_0) + \langle \nabla f(x_0),h\rangle + \tfrac{1}{2}\langle h,\ H(x_0 + \lambda h)h\rangle \quad \text{for some } \lambda \in [0,1].$$

Since $H(y)$ is positive semidefinite for every $y \in X$, the third term in (43) is nonnegative. Hence

45
$$f(x) \geqq f(x_0) + \langle \nabla f(x_0),h\rangle = f(x_0) + \langle \nabla f(x_0),\ x - x_0\rangle \quad \text{for every } x,\ x_0 \in X.$$

Therefore $f(\cdot)$ is convex, by theorem (25).

$\Rightarrow$. The proof in this direction is by contraposition. Suppose there is an $x_0 \in X$ and an $h \in E^n$ such that $\langle h,H(x_0)h\rangle < 0$. By assumption, the real-valued function $\langle h,H(y)h\rangle$ is continuous at every point $y \in X$. Hence there is a ball $B_\delta(x_0) \subset X$ about x_0 of radius $\delta > 0$ such that $\langle h,H(y)h\rangle < 0$ for every $y \in B_\delta(x_0)$. Let $\epsilon > 0$ be chosen such that $x \triangleq (x_0 + \epsilon h) \in B_\delta(x_0)$, and set $h' = \epsilon h$. Using (44), with $h = h'$, we obtain

46
$$f(x) = f(x_0) + \langle \nabla f(x_0),h'\rangle + \tfrac{1}{2}\langle h',\ H(x_0 + \lambda h')h'\rangle \quad \text{for some } \lambda \in [0,1].$$

Now, $\|\lambda h'\| = \|\lambda \epsilon h\| = |\lambda| \, \|\epsilon h\| \leqq \delta$, so that $x_0 + \lambda h' \in B_\delta(x_0)$, which implies that $\frac{1}{2}\langle h', H(x_0 + \lambda h')h'\rangle = \frac{1}{2}\epsilon^2 \langle h, H(x_0 + \lambda h')h\rangle < 0$. Thus

$$f(x) < f(x_0) + \langle \nabla f(x_0), h'\rangle = f(x_0) + \langle \nabla f(x_0), x - x_0\rangle$$

for two points $x, x_0 \in X$, and therefore f is not convex, by theorem (25). We conclude from this that if $f(\cdot)$ is convex, then $H(x)$ is positive semidefinite for every $x \in X$. □

47 **Corollary.** Let $f: E^n \to E^1$ be defined by

$$f(x) = \langle x, Qx\rangle + \langle x, d\rangle,$$

where Q is an $n \times n$ positive-semidefinite matrix and $d \in E^n$ is a constant vector. Then $f(\cdot)$ is convex.

Proof. We observe that $\nabla f(x) = (Q + Q^T)x + d$, and so $H(x) = Q + Q^T$. By exercise (41) and theorem (42), f is convex. □

We also have a test for strictly convex functions.

48 **Theorem.** Let $f(\cdot)$ be a twice continuously differentiable function from an open convex set $X \subset E^n$ into E^1. If the $n \times n$ hessian matrix $H(x)$ [see (43)] is positive definite for every $x \in X$, then f is strictly convex on X. □

49 **Corollary.** Let $f(\cdot)$ be as defined in corollary (47). If the $n \times n$ matrix Q is positive definite, then f is strictly convex. □

50 **Exercise.** Prove theorem (48) and corollary (49). □

51 **Remark.** The converse of theorem (48) is false. Let $X = E^1$, and take $f(x) = x^4$. Then $f(\cdot)$ is strictly convex on X and twice continuously differentiable. But $H(0) = d^2f(0)/dx^2 = 0$. □

This concludes our discussion of convex sets and convex functions. For further detail, the reader is referred to standard texts on convexity.

REFERENCES

1. H. G. Eggleston: "Convexity," Cambridge Tracts in Mathematics and Mathematical Physics, Cambridge University Press, Cambridge, 1955.
2. C. Berge: "Topological Spaces," Oliver & Boyd, Ltd., Edinburgh and London, 1963.

appendix **B**

Constrained minimization problems in infinite-dimensional spaces

B.1 AN EXTENSION OF THE FUNDAMENTAL THEOREM (2.3.12)

The purpose of this appendix is to extend the Fundamental Theorem (2.3.12) to problems in linear topological spaces. As an application of the extended theorem, we shall derive the *Pontryagin maximum principle* [1] for fixed-time optimal control problems with continuous dynamics.

First let us formulate the equivalent of the Basic Problem (1.4.1) in an infinite-dimensional space.

1 **The Basic Problem.** Let $\mathcal{L}$ be a linear topological space. Given a continuous function $f(\cdot)$ from $\mathcal{L}$ into the reals, a continuous function $r(\cdot)$ from $\mathcal{L}$ into E^m, and a subset Ω of $\mathcal{L}$, find a vector $\hat{z} \in \Omega$, satisfying $r(\hat{z}) = 0$, such that for all $z \in \Omega$ which satisfy $r(z) = 0$

2 $$f(\hat{z}) \leqq f(z). \quad \square$$

As before, we shall call any $\hat{z}$ with the above properties an optimal solution.

Observe that in formulation (1.4.1) we specified that the functions $f(\cdot)$ and $r(\cdot)$ are continuously differentiable. However, we could not do this in problem (1) because differentiability is not a well-defined concept in a linear topological space. Consequently, to make a straightforward extension of theorem (2.3.12) possible, we shall need to *stipulate* the existence of a continuous linear map from $\mathcal{L}$ into E^{m+1} with properties similar to those of the jacobian $\partial F(\hat{z})/\partial \hat{z}$, which we used in Chapter 2. The most convenient place for this stipulation seems to be in a modified definition of a conical approximation.

3 **Definition.** A convex cone $C(\hat{z},\Omega)$ will be called a *conical approximation* to the set Ω at $\hat{z} \in \Omega$, with respect to the functions $f(\cdot)$ and $r(\cdot)$, if there exist continuous linear functions $f'(\hat{z})(\cdot)$ and $r'(\hat{z})(\cdot)$ from $\mathcal{L}$ into E^1 and E^m, respectively, such that for any finite collection $\{\delta z_1, \delta z_2, \ldots, \delta z_p\}$ of linearly independent vectors in $C(\hat{z},\Omega)$ there exist an $\epsilon > 0$ and a continuous function $\zeta(\cdot)$ from co $\{\hat{z}, \hat{z} + \epsilon\,\delta z_1, \ldots, \hat{z} + \epsilon\,\delta z_p\}$ into Ω (with ϵ and ζ possibly depending on $\hat{z}$ and $\delta z_1, \delta z_2, \ldots, \delta z_p$) which satisfy

4 $$\lim_{\beta \to 0} \frac{1}{\beta} |f(\zeta(\hat{z} + \beta\,\delta z)) - f(\hat{z}) - f'(\hat{z})(\beta\,\delta z)| = 0$$

and

5 $$\lim_{\beta \to 0} \frac{1}{\beta} \| r(\zeta(\hat{z} + \beta\,\delta z)) - r(\hat{z}) - r'(\hat{z})(\beta\,\delta z)\| = 0$$

uniformly for $\delta z \in$ co $\{0, \epsilon\,\delta z_1, \epsilon\,\delta z_2, \ldots, \epsilon\,\delta z_p\}$. □

We are now ready to extend theorem (2.3.12).

6 **Theorem.** If $\hat{z}$ is an optimal solution to the Basic Problem (1) and $C(\hat{z},\Omega)$ is a conical approximation to Ω at $\hat{z} \in \Omega$ with respect to the functions $f(\cdot)$ and $r(\cdot)$, then there exists a nonzero vector $\psi = (\psi^0, \psi^1, \ldots, \psi^m)$ in E^{m+1}, with $\psi^0 \leqq 0$, such that

7 $$\langle \psi, F'(\hat{z})(\delta z)\rangle \leqq 0 \qquad \text{for all } \delta z \in \bar{C}(\hat{z},\Omega),$$

where we define $F'(\hat{z})(\delta z)$ to be $(f'(\hat{z})(\delta z), r'(\hat{z})(\delta z))$.

Proof. Let us introduce the notation $F = (f,r)$; that is, $F: \mathcal{L} \to E^{m+1}$. We shall now essentially duplicate the steps of theorem (2.3.12).

Thus let $K(\hat{z}) \subset E^{m+1}$ be the cone defined by

8 $$K(\hat{z}) = F'(\hat{z})(C(\hat{z},\Omega)).$$

The cone $K(\hat{z})$ is convex because $C(\hat{z},\Omega)$ is convex and $F'(\hat{z})(\cdot)$ is linear. Examining the statement of the theorem, we see that it implies that the cone $K(\hat{z})$ and the ray

9 $$R = \{y\colon y = \beta(-1,0, \ldots ,0), \beta > 0\} \subset E^{m+1}$$

must be separated by a hyperplane with normal $\psi = (\psi^0, \psi^1, \ldots, \psi^m)$ such that

10 $$\langle \psi,y \rangle \leqq 0 \qquad \text{for all } y \in K(\hat{z})$$
11 $$\langle \psi,y \rangle \geqq 0 \qquad \text{for all } y \in R.$$

To obtain a contradiction, let us suppose that $K(\hat{z})$ and R are not separated. Then the dimension of $K(\hat{z})$ must be $m + 1$ and R must be in the interior of $K(\hat{z})$. We can therefore find a simplex S in $K(\hat{z})$ with vertices 0 and $\delta y_1, \delta y_2, \ldots, \delta y_{m+1}$ such that

12 There exists a vector $\delta y_0 \in R$ which lies in the interior of S;

13 There exists a set of vectors $\delta z_1, \delta z_2, \ldots, \delta z_{m+1}$ in $C(\hat{z},\Omega)$ satisfying

$$F'(\hat{z})(\delta z_i) = \delta y_i \qquad i = 1, 2, \ldots, m + 1$$

for which the associated $\epsilon > 0$ in definition (3) may be taken to be 1.

Thus, with the choice indicated, there exists a continuous function ζ which maps co $\{\hat{z}, \hat{z} + \delta z_1, \hat{z} + \delta z_2, \ldots, \hat{z} + \delta z_{m+1}\}$ into Ω. [Note that the δz_i are linearly independent because the δy_i are linearly independent and $F'(\hat{z})(\cdot)$ is linear.]

Now for $0 < \alpha \leqq 1$ let $\Sigma_\alpha \subset S$ be a closed ball with center $\alpha\, \delta y_0$ and radius αr, with $r > 0$, where δy_0 is the point indicated in (12). To produce the counterpart of the map $G_\alpha(\cdot)$ in (2.3.22), we let X be the continuous linear map[1] from E^{m+1} into $\mathcal{L}$ defined by

14 $$X(\delta y_i) = \delta z_i \qquad i = 1, 2, \ldots, m + 1,$$

where the δz_i are the elements defined in (13). Then we define the map $G_\alpha(\cdot)$ from $\Sigma_\alpha - \{\alpha\, \delta y_0\}$ into E^{m+1} by

15 $$G_\alpha(x) = F(\zeta(\hat{z} + X(\alpha\, \delta y_0 + x))) - (F(\hat{z}) + \alpha\, \delta y_0).$$

[1] The continuity of X follows directly from the basic axioms defining a linear topological space.

Making use of (4) and (5), we find that

16 $$G_\alpha(x) = F'(\hat{z})(X(\alpha\ \delta y_0 + x)) - \alpha\ \delta y_0 + o(X(\alpha\ \delta y_0 + x)),$$

where $o(X(\alpha\ \delta y_0 + x))/\alpha \to 0$ as $\alpha \to 0$ uniformly for $x \in (\Sigma_\alpha - \{\delta y_0\})$.

Now, for any $\delta y \in S$, $F'(\hat{z})(X(\delta y)) = \delta y$, and hence (16) becomes

17 $$G_\alpha(x) = x + o(X(\alpha\ \delta y_0 + x)).$$

Since the composition $o \cdot X$ is continuous, we invoke the Brouwer fixed-point theorem, exactly as in the proof of theorem (2.3.12) following expression (2.3.24), to conclude that there exists an $\alpha^* \in (0,1]$ and a point $x^* \in (\Sigma_{\alpha^*} - \{\alpha^*\ \delta y_0\})$ such that

18 $$G_{\alpha^*}(x^*) = 0.$$

But (13), (15), and (18) imply that for $z^* = \zeta(\hat{z} + X(\alpha^*\ \delta y_0 + x^*))$

19 $$z^* \in \Omega$$

20 $$r(z^*) = 0$$

21 $$f(z^*) = f(\hat{z}) + \alpha^*\ \delta y_0{}^0 < f(\hat{z}),$$

where $\delta y_0 = (\delta y_0{}^0, \delta y_0{}^1, \ldots, \delta y_0{}^m)$. This contradicts the optimality of $\hat{z}$, and hence the cone $K(\hat{z})$ and the ray R must be separated. Consequently, there exists a vector $\psi = (\psi^0, \psi^1, \ldots, \psi^m)$, with $\psi^0 \leqq 0$, such that

22 $$\langle \psi, F'(\hat{z})(\delta z)\rangle \leqq 0 \qquad \text{for all } \delta z \in C(\hat{z},\Omega).$$

Inequality (7) now follows from the continuity of the linear map $\langle \psi, \cdot \rangle$. □

In the next section we shall see how to find functions $f'(\hat{z})(\cdot)$, $r'(\hat{z})(\cdot)$, and ζ in a particular case, a fixed-time optimal control problem with continuous dynamics.

B.2 THE MAXIMUM PRINCIPLE

We shall now explore the applicability of the theorem (B.1.6) by using it to obtain the *Pontryagin maximum principle* for fixed-time optimal control problems.

1 **The fixed-time optimal control problem.** Consider a dynamical system described by the differential equation

2 $$\frac{dx(t)}{dt} = h(x(t),u(t)) \qquad t \in [0,T],$$

where $x(t) \in E^n$ is the state of the system at time t, $u(t) \in E^l$ is the input, or control, of the system at time t, and h is a function from $E^n \times E^l$ into E^n. Given a cost function $h^0(\cdot,\cdot)$ from $E^n \times E^l$ into the reals, a constraint function $g(\cdot)$ from E^n into E^m, an initial state x_0, a constraint set $U \subset E^l$, and a final time $T > 0$, find a measurable, essentially bounded control $\hat{u}(\cdot)$ mapping $[0,T]$ into E^l and a corresponding trajectory $\hat{x}(\cdot)$, determined by (2) on the interval $[0,T]$, satisfying

3 $$\hat{u}(t) \in U \qquad \text{for all } t \in [0,T]$$
4 $$\hat{x}(0) = x_0$$
5 $$g(\hat{x}(T)) = 0$$

such that for all essentially bounded, measurable controls $u(\cdot)$ defined on $[0,T]$, with corresponding trajectories $x(\cdot)$ determined by (2) and satisfying (3) to (5),

6 $$\int_0^T h^0(\hat{x}(t),\hat{u}(t))\, dt \leqq \int_0^T h^0(x(t),u(t))\, dt. \quad \square$$

Let us make the following assumptions:

7 **Assumption.** The functions $h^0(\cdot,\cdot)$ and $h(\cdot,\cdot)$ are continuously differentiable in x and continuous in u. $\square$

8 **Assumption.** The function $g(\cdot)$ is continuously differentiable and its $m \times n$ jacobian matrix $\partial g(x)/\partial x$ has rank m for all $x \in \{x' : g(x') = 0\}$. $\square$

We shall now transcribe the optimal control problem (1) into the form of the Basic Problem (B.1.1). Let P_1 and P_2 be the $1 \times (n+1)$ and $n \times (n+1)$ projection matrices defined by

9 $$P_1 = [1,0,0, \ldots ,0,0]$$

$$P_2 = \begin{bmatrix} 0 & 1 & 0 & \cdots & \cdots & 0 \\ 0 & 0 & 1 & 0 & \cdots & 0 \\ \cdots & \cdots & \cdots & \cdots & \cdots & \cdots \\ 0 & \cdots & \cdots & 0 & 1 & 0 \\ 0 & \cdots & \cdots & \cdots & 0 & 1 \end{bmatrix}.$$

Thus, given a vector $z = (z^0,x)$ in E^{n+1}, with $x \in E^n$, we have, $P_1 z = z^0$ and $P_2 z = x$. Next let $\mathbf{h}(\cdot,\cdot)$ be a map from $E^{n+1} \times E^l$ into E^{n+1}, defined by

10 $$\mathbf{h}(z,u) = (h^0(P_2 z,u),h(P_2 z,u)),$$

where $z = (z^0,x^1,x^2, \ldots ,x^n)$.

In this notation problem (1) becomes:

11 **Problem.** Minimize $P_1z(T) = z^0(T)$ subject to

12 $$g(P_2z(T)) = g(x(T)) = 0$$

and to $z(\cdot)$ satisfying the differential equation

13 $$\frac{d}{dt}z(t) = \mathbf{h}(z(t),u(t)) \qquad t \in [0,T],$$

with $z(0) = (0,x_0)$, for some measurable, essentially bounded function $u(\cdot)$ mapping $[0,T]$ into U. □

Now let us define the functions $f(\cdot)$ and $r(\cdot)$ and the set Ω as follows:

14 **Definition.** $f(z) = P_1z(T), \qquad r(z) = g(P_2z(T))$. □

15 **Definition.** Let Ω be the set of all absolutely continuous functions $z(\cdot)$, from $[0,T]$ into E^{n+1}, satisfying (13), with $z(0) = (0,x_0)$, for some measurable essentially bounded function $u(\cdot)$ from $[0,T]$ into U. □

With these definitions, the transcription of problem (1) into the form of the Basic Problem (B.1.1) is complete except for the definition of the linear space $\mathcal{L}$ and a demonstration that $f(\cdot)$ and $r(\cdot)$ are continuous.

Since the set Ω consists of absolutely continuous functions, it might seem natural to take $\mathcal{L}$ to be the space of all continuous functions from $[0,T]$ into E^{n+1}. However, since we wish to use a conical approximation consisting of piecewise-continuous functions (first constructed by Pontryagin et al. [1] in the original proof of the maximum principle), we find it necessary to embed Ω into a larger linear topological space, which we now define.

Let $\mathcal{U}$ be the set of all upper-semicontinuous real-valued functions defined on $[0,T]$, and let $\mathcal{S} = \mathcal{U} - \mathcal{U}$. Clearly, $\mathcal{S}$ is a linear space. We now define the space $\mathcal{L}$ to be the cartesian product $\mathcal{S}^{n+1} = \mathcal{S} \times \mathcal{S} \times \cdots \times \mathcal{S}$, with the relativized pointwise topology [3], that is, the topology constructed from the subbase consisting of the family of all subsets of the form $\{z(\cdot) \in \mathcal{S}^{n+1}\colon z(t) \in N\}$, where t is a point in $[0,T]$ and N is an open set in E^{n+1}. With this topology, a net $z_s \in \mathcal{L}$, with $s \in A$ a directed set, converges to a function $z^* \in \mathcal{L}$ if and only if $z_s(t) \to z^*(t)$ for every $t \in [0,T]$.

To show that maps from $\mathcal{L}$ into E^{n+1} and from $\mathcal{L}$ into $\mathcal{L}$ are continuous, we shall need the following two simple results, which we draw from Kelley [3].

16 **Definition.** Let $t \in [0,T]$ be arbitrary. Then the *evaluation function* $e_t: \mathcal{L} \to E^{n+1}$ is defined by

17 $$e_t(z) = z(t). \quad \square$$

18 **Proposition.** For every $t \in [0,T]$ the evaluation function e_t is continuous.

Proof. Let z_s be any net in $\mathcal{L}$ which converges to a function z^*. Then $z_s(t) \to z^*(t)$, and hence $e_t(z_s) \to e_t(z^*)$, which proves that e_t is continuous. $\square$

19 **Proposition.** A function g mapping a linear topological space $\mathfrak{M}$ into $\mathcal{L}$ is continuous if and only if the composition $e_t \cdot g$ is continuous for every $t \in [0,T]$.

Proof. Suppose g is continuous; then, since e_t is continuous, the composition $e_t \cdot g$ is continuous.

Now suppose that $e_t \cdot g$ is continuous for all $t \in [0,T]$ but g is not continuous. Then there must be a net ξ_s in $\mathfrak{M}$ such that ξ_s converges to ξ^* in $\mathfrak{M}$ but $g(\xi_s)$ does not converge to $g(\xi^*)$. Hence there must be at least one $t \in [0,T]$ such that $g(\xi_s)(t)$ does not converge to $g(\xi^*)(t)$. But this contradicts the assumption that $e_t \cdot g$ is continuous for all $t \in [0,T]$. $\square$

20 **Proposition.** The functions $f: \mathcal{L} \to E^1$ and $r: \mathcal{L} \to E^m$ defined by (14) are continuous.

Proof. Since $f = P_1 \cdot e_T$, $r = g \cdot P_2 \cdot e_T$, P_1, P_2, g, and e_T are continuous, and the compositions of continuous maps are continuous, the proposition must be true. $\square$

21 **Definition.** We shall refer to the problem of minimizing $f(z)$ subject to $r(z) = 0$ and $z \in \Omega \subset \mathcal{L}$, with f, r, and Ω as defined in (14) and (15), as the *optimal control problem* in *basic form*. $\square$

Note that with the optimal control problem cast in basic form the control $u(\cdot)$ in (13) acts as a *parameter*, and therefore (13) is considered as a parameterized family of differential equations.

Let $\hat{z}(\cdot)$ be a given optimal solution to the optimal control problem in basic form, corresponding to the optimal control $\hat{u}(\cdot)$. We shall now construct a conical approximation at $\hat{z}(\cdot)$ to the set Ω defined in (15), with respect to the map $F = (f,r)$, where $f(\cdot)$ and $r(\cdot)$ are as defined in (14).

22 **Definition.** Let I be the set of all points in $(0,T)$, the interior of $[0,T]$, such that for every $s \in I$ and any absolutely continuous function z: $[0,T] \to E^{n+1}$

23 $$\lim_{\alpha \to 0} \frac{1}{\alpha} \left[\int_{s+\alpha p}^{s+\alpha q} \mathbf{h}(z(t),\hat{u}(t))\, dt - \alpha(q-p)\mathbf{h}(z(s),\hat{u}(s)) \right] = 0,$$

where p and q are arbitrary real numbers. □

It can be deduced from theorem 41.2 in [2] that the set $[0,T]/I \triangleq \{s \in [0,T]: s \notin I\}$ has measure zero, that is, that almost all points in $[0,T]$ are in I.

Now, let $\Phi(t,s)$ be the $(n+1) \times (n+1)$ matrix which satisfies the linear differential equation

24 $$\frac{d}{dt}\Phi(t,s) = \frac{\partial \mathbf{h}(\hat{z}(t),\hat{u}(t))}{\partial z}\Phi(t,s) \qquad t \in [s,T],$$

with $\Phi(s,s)$ equal to the $(n+1) \times (n+1)$ identity matrix, and $\hat{z}(\cdot)$, $\hat{u}(\cdot)$ the optimal pair under consideration. Then for any $s \in I$ and $v \in U$ we define the functions $\delta z_{s,v}$ by

25 $$\delta z_{s,v}(t) = \begin{cases} 0 & 0 \leqq t < s \\ \phi(t,s)\ [\mathbf{h}(\hat{z}(s),v) - \mathbf{h}(\hat{z}(s),\hat{u}(s))] & s \leqq t \leqq T, \end{cases}$$

and we claim that the set

26 $$C(\hat{z},\Omega) = \left\{\delta z \in \mathfrak{L}: \delta z = \sum_{i=1}^{k} \alpha^i\, \delta z_{s_i,v_i}\right\},$$

with $\alpha^i \geqq 0$, $s_i \in I$ and $v_i \in U$ for $i = 1, 2, \ldots, k$ and k arbitrary but finite, is a conical approximation to the set Ω defined by (15) at the optimal solution $\hat{z}$. The fact that this is a natural candidate for a conical approximation will become apparent from what follows.

To establish our claim, we must show that $C(\hat{z},\Omega)$ is a convex cone and then find functions $\zeta(\cdot)$, $f'(\hat{z})(\cdot)$, $r'(\hat{z})(\cdot)$, and $o(\cdot)$ which satisfy the assumptions of definition (B.1.3). We shall now carry out these steps.[1]

27 **Proposition.** The set $C(\hat{z},\Omega)$ defined in (26) is a convex cone.

Proof. Let $\delta z' = \sum_{i=1}^{k'} \alpha^{i'}, \delta z_{s_i',v_i'}$ and $\delta z'' = \sum_{i=1}^{k''} \alpha^{i''}\, \delta z_{s_i'',v_i''}$ be any two elements in $C(z,\Omega)$. Then, for any $\lambda \geqq 0$, $\lambda\, \delta z' \in C(\hat{z},\Omega)$, by inspection, and for any $\lambda \in [0,1]$, $\delta z_\lambda \triangleq \lambda\, \delta z' + (1-\lambda)\, \delta z''$ is seen

[1] The reader who is not interested in the details of this demonstration may proceed directly to (71), where the maximum principle is established.

to be of the form

28 $$\delta z_\lambda = \sum_{j=1}^{k} \alpha^j(\lambda)\ \delta z_{s_j, v_j},$$

where $k = k' + k''$, $\alpha^j(\lambda) = \lambda\alpha^{j\prime}$, $s_j = s_j'$ and $v_j = v_j'$ for $j = 1, 2, \ldots, k'$, and $\alpha^{j+k'}(\lambda) = (1 - \lambda)\alpha^{j\prime\prime}$, $s_{j+k'} = s_j''$, and $v_{j+k'} = v_j''$ for $j = 1, 2, \ldots, k''$. Hence $\alpha^j(\lambda) \geqq 0$, k is finite and δz_λ is in $C(\hat{z},\Omega)$; that is, $C(\hat{z},\Omega)$ is a convex cone. □

Let $\delta z_1, \delta z_2, \ldots, \delta z_p$ be any set of linearly independent elements in $C(\hat{z},\Omega)$, and let $C = \text{co}\ \{0,\delta z_1,\delta z_2, \ldots,\delta z_p\}$. We shall now choose an $\epsilon > 0$ and construct a continuous map ζ from $\{\hat{z}\} + \epsilon C$ into Ω. It will be seen that the choice of ϵ is closely connected with the way ζ is constructed.

First, each of the δz_j chosen above must be of the form

29 $$\delta z_j = \sum_{i=1}^{k_j} \alpha_j^i\ \delta z_{s_i^j, v_i^j} \qquad j = 1, 2, \ldots, p.$$

Now let us order the points s_i^j linearly. After renumbering the s_i^j and the v_i^j accordingly, we find that there are an integer k, points $s_1 \leqq s_2 \leqq s_3 \leqq \cdots \leqq s_k$ in I, corresponding points $v_1, v_2, \ldots, v_k$ in U, and nonnegative scalars β_i^j, with $i = 1, 2, \ldots, k$ and $j = 1, 2, \ldots, p$, such that (29) becomes

30 $$\delta z_j = \sum_{i=1}^{k} \beta_j^i\ \delta z_{s_i, v_i} \qquad j = 1, 2, \ldots, p.$$

Since the δz_j are linearly independent, every vector $\delta z \in C$ has a unique representation of the form

$$\delta z = \sum_{j=1}^{p} \lambda^j\ \delta z_j,$$

with $\lambda^j \geqq 0$ and $\sum_{j=1}^{p} \lambda^j \leqq 1$; that is,

31 $$\begin{aligned} \delta z &= \sum_{j=1}^{p} \lambda^j \Big(\sum_{i=1}^{k} \beta_j^i\ \delta z_{s_i, v_i}\Big) \\ &= \sum_{i=1}^{k} \Big(\sum_{j=1}^{p} \lambda^j \beta_j^i\Big)\ \delta z_{s_i, v_i} \\ &= \sum_{i=1}^{k} \delta t_i(\lambda)\ \delta z_{s_i, v_i}, \end{aligned}$$

where

32 $$\delta t_i(\lambda) \triangleq \sum_{j=1}^{p} \lambda^j \beta_j^i \qquad i = 1, 2, \ldots, k.$$

Let Λ be the simplex in E^p defined by

33 $$\Lambda = \left\{\lambda \in E^p \colon \sum_{i=1}^{p} \lambda^i \leqq 1, \lambda^i \geqq 0\right\}.$$

Then it is clear from the above that there is a one-to-one correspondence between the elements δz of C and the elements λ of Λ. Furthermore, it can be shown that this correspondence is bicontinuous. The continuity of the $\delta t_i(\lambda)$ is self-evident from their definition.

Now let $\gamma > 0$ be small but arbitrary; we shall fix an upper bound for γ later. As in [1], we shall construct the map $\zeta(\cdot)$ by solving differential equation (13), with a "perturbed" control which depends on $\delta z \in C$. First let us define these perturbations.

Let $\delta z \in C$, and let the corresponding δt_i be as defined in (32). Now let

34 $$l_i = \begin{cases} -(\delta t_i + \delta t_{i+1} + \cdots + \delta t_k) & \text{if } s_i = s_k \\ -(\delta t_i + \delta t_{i+1} + \cdots + \delta t_j) & \text{if } s_i = s_{i+1} = \cdots \\ & \quad = s_j < s_{j+1}, j < k, \end{cases}$$

and let

35 $$I_i = \{t \colon s_i + \gamma l_i < t \leqq s_i + \gamma(l_i + \delta t_i)\}, i = 1, 2, \ldots, k,$$

where $\gamma > 0$ is the scalar introduced above. It is clear that there exists a positive number γ' such that for all $0 < \gamma \leqq \gamma'$ the intervals I_i are disjoint and contained in $[0,T]$. (Note that I_i may be empty.)

For any fixed $\gamma \in (0,\gamma']$ we define the perturbed control $u_{\gamma,\lambda}(\cdot)$ on $[0,T]$ by the relation,[1] with v_i as in (31),

36 $$u_{\gamma,\lambda}(t) = \begin{cases} \hat{u}(t) & \text{if } t \notin \bigcup_{i=1}^{k} I_i \\ v_i & \text{if } t \in I_i. \end{cases}$$

37 **Definition.** For $\gamma \in (0,\gamma']$ and $\lambda \in \Lambda$ let $z_{\gamma,\lambda}(\cdot)$ be the solution of (13) corresponding to $u(\cdot) = u_{\gamma,\lambda}(\cdot)$ and satisfying $z_{\gamma,\lambda}(0) = (0,x_0)$. □

Since $u_{\gamma,\lambda}(\cdot)$ is an essentially bounded measurable function satisfying $u_{\gamma,\lambda}(t) \in U$ for all $t \in [0,T]$, it is clear that $z_{\gamma,\lambda}(\cdot)$ is in Ω.

[1] When some $s_i = s_{i+1}$ and $\delta t_i = \delta t_{i+1} = 0$, (36) defines $u_{\gamma,\lambda}(\cdot)$ almost everywhere (it may not be uniquely defined at some of the s_i). However, this is entirely adequate for our purposes.

Referring to a theorem on the continuous dependence on parameters of the solutions of a differential equation (theorem 69.1 of reference [2]), we find that there must exist a $\gamma'' > 0$ such that $z_{\gamma,\lambda}(t)$ is a continuous function of γ and λ for all $\gamma \in [0,\gamma'']$, all $\lambda \in \Lambda$, and all $t \in [0,T]$. Let $\epsilon = \min [\gamma',\gamma'']$, and let $\zeta(\cdot)$, mapping co $\{\hat{z}, \hat{z} + \epsilon\, \delta z_1, \ldots, \hat{z} + \epsilon\, \delta z_p\}$ into Ω, be defined by

38 $$\zeta(\hat{z} + \delta z) = z_{\epsilon,\lambda},$$

with λ defined by the relation

$$\frac{1}{\epsilon}\,\delta z = \sum_{j=1}^{p} \lambda^i\, \delta z_j.$$

Then, since the parameter λ is continuous in δz and $z_{\epsilon,\lambda}$ is continuous in λ (because of the continuous dependence of $z_{\epsilon,\lambda}(t)$ on λ for every $t \in [0,T]$ and because of proposition (19)), it is clear that ζ is a continuous map.

To complete our proof we have to exhibit the linear continuous functions $f'(\hat{z})(\cdot)$ and $r'(\hat{z})(\cdot)$ and show that relations (B.1.4) and (B.1.5) are satisfied. We shall do this by first showing that for $(\hat{z} + \beta\, \delta z) \in$ co $\{\hat{z}, \hat{z} + \epsilon\, \delta z_1, \ldots, \hat{z} + \epsilon\, \delta z_p\}$, with $0 \leqq \beta \leqq 1$,

39 $$\zeta(\hat{z} + \beta\, \delta z)(T) = \hat{z}(T) + \beta\epsilon \sum_{i=1}^{k} \delta t_i(\lambda)\Phi(T,s_i)[\mathbf{h}(\hat{z}(s_i),v_i) - \mathbf{h}(\hat{z}(s_i),\hat{u}(s_i))] + o(\beta\, \delta z(T)),$$

where $o(\beta\, \delta z(T)/\beta \to 0$ as $\beta \to 0$, and the $\delta t_i(\lambda)$ are determined by (31) and (32); that is,

40 $$\zeta(\hat{z} + \beta\, \delta z)(T) = \hat{z}(T) + \beta\, \delta z(T) + o(\beta\, \delta z(T)).$$

Obviously, this requires certain results in differential equations, which we now digress to consider.

41 **Lemma.** Let $u(\cdot)$ be any admissible control, i.e., a measurable, essentially bounded function defined on $[0,T]$ with range in U. Let $z(\cdot)$ defined on $[0,T]$ be the absolutely continuous solution of (13) corresponding to this $u(\cdot)$ and satisfying the "initial" condition $z(s) = z_s$ for $s \in [0,T]$. Let $z'(\cdot)$ defined on $[0,T]$ be the absolutely continuous solution of (13), also corresponding to this $u(\cdot)$ but satisfying the "initial" condition $z'(s) = z_s + \beta\xi + o(\beta)$, where ξ is independent of β and $o(\beta)/\beta \to 0$ as $\beta \to 0$. Then

42 $$z'(t) = z(t) + \beta\, \delta z(t) + o'(\beta,t) \qquad \text{for all } t \in [s,T],$$

where $o'(\beta,t)/\beta \to 0$ as $\beta \to 0$ uniformly for $t \in [s,T]$, and for almost all $t \in [s,T]$, δz satisfies the differential equation

43 $$\frac{d}{dt}\,\delta z(t) = \frac{\partial \mathbf{h}(z(t),u(t))}{\partial z}\,\delta z(t) \qquad \delta z(s) = \xi. \quad \square$$

The gist of this lemma is that the solutions of (13) are Frechet differentiable with respect to initial conditions. The proof can be found in [2], theorem 69.4.

44 **Lemma.** For any $\beta \in (0,\epsilon]$ and $\lambda \in \Lambda$ let $z_{\beta,\lambda}(\cdot)$ be defined as in (37), with $\epsilon > 0$ defined as for (38). Then for $i = 1, 2, \ldots, k$ and $t \in I_i$ [with $\gamma = \beta$ in (35)]

45 $$\mathbf{h}(z_{\beta,\lambda}(t),v_i) = \mathbf{h}(\hat{z}(t),v_i) + a_i(t,\beta,\lambda),$$

where $a_i(t,\beta,\lambda) \to 0$ as $\beta \to 0$ uniformly for $t \in I_i$ and $\lambda \in \Lambda$, and $\hat{z}$ is the optimal solution under consideration.

Proof. Using the theorem on the continuous dependence of solutions of differential equations on parameters (see [2], theorem 69.1), we can show that $z_{\beta,\lambda}(t) \to \hat{z}(t)$ as $\beta \to 0$ uniformly for $t \in [0,T]$ and $\lambda \in \Lambda$, and hence the lemma must hold. $\square$

We shall now finish establishing (39) in two steps. First we shall evaluate the increments in $z_{\epsilon,\lambda}$ over the intervals I_i, and then we shall make use of lemma (41) to compute the propagation of these disturbances.

46 **Lemma.** For any $0 < \beta \leqq \epsilon$, with $\epsilon > 0$ defined as for (38), and $\lambda \in \Lambda$, let $z_{\beta,\lambda}(\cdot)$ be as defined in (37). Then for any interval I_i for $i = 1, 2, \ldots, k$ [with $\gamma = \beta$ in (35)] the increment in $z_{\beta,\lambda}(t)$ on I_i is given by

47 $$z_{\beta,\lambda}(s_i + \beta(l_i + \delta t_i(\lambda))) - z_{\beta,\lambda}(s_i + \beta l_i) = \beta\,\delta t_i\,\mathbf{h}(\hat{z}(s_i),v_i) + o(\beta\lambda),$$

where $o(\beta\lambda)/\beta \to 0$ as $\beta \to 0$ uniformly for $\lambda \in \Lambda$.

Proof. This lemma follows directly from lemma (44) and the fact that for all $s \in [0,T]$, all p and q real, all $v \in U$, and every absolutely continuous function $z\colon [0,T] \to E^{n+1}$ we have

$$\lim_{\alpha \to 0} \frac{1}{\alpha}\left[\int_{s+\alpha p}^{s+\alpha q} \mathbf{h}(z(t),v)\,dt - h(z(s),v)\right] = 0. \quad \square$$

48 **Theorem.** For $0 \leqq \beta \leqq 1$ let $\beta\, \delta z$ be an arbitrary point in co $\{0, \epsilon\, \delta z_1, \epsilon\, \delta z_2, \ldots, \epsilon\, \delta z_p\}$, with $\epsilon = \min\,[\gamma',\gamma'']$ defined as before, and let $\lambda \in \Lambda$ correspond to δz according to (31). Then for $t \in [s_k,T]$

49 $$z_{\epsilon,\beta\lambda}(t) = z_{\beta\epsilon,\lambda}(t) = \hat{z}(t) + \beta\, \delta z(t) + o(\beta\, \delta z(t), t),$$

where $o(\beta\, \delta z(t), t)/\beta \to 0$ as $\beta \to 0$ uniformly for $\delta z \in$ co $\{0, \epsilon\, \delta z_1, \epsilon\, \delta z_2, \ldots, \epsilon\, \delta z_p\}$ and $t \in [s_k,T]$.

Proof. We begin by noting that δz must be of the form

50 $$\begin{aligned}\delta z(t) &= \epsilon \sum_{i=1}^{p} \lambda^i\, \delta z_i(t)\\ &= \epsilon \sum_{i=1}^{k} \delta t_i(\lambda)\, \delta z_{s_i,v_i}(t)\\ &= \epsilon \sum_{i=1}^{k} \Phi(t,s_i)[\mathbf{h}(\hat{z}(s_i),v_i) - \mathbf{h}(\hat{z}(s_i),\hat{u}(s_i)]\, \delta t_i(\lambda).\end{aligned}$$

We prove the theorem by induction on the integer k. Thus suppose $k = 1$. Invoking (47), we get

51 $$z_{\beta\epsilon,\lambda}(s_1) = \hat{z}(s_1 - \beta\epsilon\, \delta t_1(\lambda)) + \beta\epsilon\, \delta t_1(\lambda)\mathbf{h}(\hat{z}(s_1),v_1) + o(\beta\lambda),$$

and since (23) is satisfied by s_1,

52 $$\hat{z}(s_1 - \beta\epsilon\, \delta t_1(\lambda)) = \hat{z}(s_1) - \beta\epsilon\, \delta t_1(\lambda)\mathbf{h}(\hat{z}(s_1),\hat{u}(s_1)) + o(\beta),$$

where $o(\beta)/\beta \to 0$ as $\beta \to 0$. Consequently, we find that

53 $$z_{\beta\epsilon,\lambda}(s_1) = \hat{z}(s_1) + \beta\epsilon\, \delta t_1(\lambda)[\mathbf{h}(\hat{z}(s_1),v_1) - \mathbf{h}(\hat{z}(s_1),\hat{u}(s_1))] + \tilde{o}(\beta\lambda),$$

where $\tilde{o}(\beta\lambda)/\beta \to 0$ as $\beta \to 0$ uniformly for $\lambda \in \Lambda$. Hence, by lemma (41), for $t \in [s_1,T]$

54 $$z_{\beta\epsilon,\lambda}(t) = \hat{z}(t) + \beta\epsilon\, \delta t_1(\lambda)\Phi(t,s_1)[\mathbf{h}(\hat{z}(s_1),v_1) - \mathbf{h}(\hat{z}(s_1),\hat{u}(s_1))] + o(\beta\lambda,t),$$

where $o(\beta\lambda,t)/\beta \to 0$ as $\beta \to 0$ uniformly for $\lambda \in \Lambda$. Comparing with (50) and recalling that there is a bicontinuous one-to-one correspondence between $\delta z(\cdot)$ and λ, we find that for $t = T$ (54) becomes

55 $$z_{\beta\epsilon,\lambda}(T) = \hat{z}(T) + \beta\, \delta z(T) + o'(\beta\, \delta z(T)),$$

where $o'(\beta\, \delta z(T))/\beta \to 0$ uniformly for all $\delta z \in$ co $\{0, \epsilon\, \delta z_1, \epsilon\, \delta z_2, \ldots, \epsilon\, \delta z_p\}$. Thus for $k = 1$ and $0 \leqq \beta \leqq 1$

56 $$\zeta(\hat{z} + \beta\, \delta z)(T) = \hat{z}(T) + \beta\, \delta z(T) + o(\beta\, \delta z(T)).$$

Now suppose that (49) holds for $k = q - 1$ in (50), with $q > 1$. Let j be a positive integer such that $\cdots \leqq s_{j-1} \leqq s_j < s_{j+1} = s_{j+2} = \cdots = s_q$; that is, $s_i = s_q$ for $i = j+1, j+2, \ldots, q-1$ and $s_i < s_q$ for all $i \leqq j$. Then, by the induction hypothesis,

57 $$z_{\beta\epsilon,\lambda}(s_q + \beta\epsilon l_{j+1}) = \hat{z}(s_q + \beta\epsilon l_{j+1}) + \beta\epsilon \sum_{i=1}^{j} \delta t_i(\lambda)\, \Phi(s_q + \beta\epsilon l_{j+1}, s_i)[\mathbf{h}(\hat{z}(s_i),v_i) - \mathbf{h}(\hat{z}(s_i),\hat{u}(s_i))] + o(\beta\lambda, s_q + \beta\epsilon l_{j+1}).$$

Making use of (47) and the fact that the intervals $I_{j+1}, I_{j+2}, \ldots, I_q$ adjoin one another, we get

58 $$z_{\beta\epsilon,\lambda}(s_q) = z_{\beta\epsilon,\lambda}(s_q + \beta\epsilon l_{j+1}) + \beta\epsilon \sum_{i=j+1}^{q} \delta t_i(\lambda)\, \mathbf{h}(\hat{z}(s_i),v_i) + o(\beta\lambda).$$

Since (23) is satisfied at the points $s_{j+1}, s_{j+2}, \ldots, s_q$,

59 $$\hat{z}(s_q + \beta\epsilon l_{j+1}) = \hat{z}(s_q) - \beta\epsilon \sum_{i=j+1}^{q} \delta t_i(\lambda)\, \mathbf{h}(\hat{z}(s_i),\hat{u}(s_i)) + o(\beta\lambda),$$

where $o(\beta\lambda)/\beta \to 0$ as $\beta \to 0$ uniformly for $\lambda \in \Lambda$.

Expanding $\beta\epsilon\, \delta t_i(\lambda)\, \Phi(s_q + \beta\epsilon l_{j+1}, s_i)$ for $i = 1, 2, \ldots, j$ about s_q, we get

60 $$\beta\epsilon\, \delta t_i(\lambda)\, \Phi(s_q + \beta\epsilon l_{j+1}, s_i) = \beta\epsilon\, \delta t_i(\lambda)\, \Phi(s_q,s_i) + o(\beta\lambda),$$

where $o(\beta\lambda)$ is an $(n+1) \times (n+1)$ matrix such that $(1/\beta)o(\beta\lambda)$ tends to the zero matrix as $\beta \to 0$ uniformly for $\lambda \in \Lambda$. Combining (57) to (60), we obtain

61 $$z_{\beta\epsilon,\lambda}(s_q) = \hat{z}(s_q) + \beta\epsilon \sum_{i=j+1}^{q} \delta t_i(\lambda)\, [\mathbf{h}(\hat{z}(s_i),v_i) - \mathbf{h}(\hat{z}(s_i),\hat{u}(s_i))] + \beta\epsilon \sum_{i=1}^{j+1} \delta t_i(\lambda)\, \Phi(s_q,s_i)[\mathbf{h}(\hat{z}(s_i),v_i) - \mathbf{h}(\hat{z}(s_i),\hat{u}(s_i))] + o(\beta\lambda),$$

where $o(\beta\lambda)/\beta \to 0$ as $\beta \to 0$ uniformly for $\lambda \in \Lambda$. We now invoke lemma (41) to obtain, for $t \in [s_q,T]$,

62 $$z_{\beta\epsilon,\lambda}(t) = \hat{z}(t) + \beta\epsilon \sum_{i=1}^{q} \delta t_i(\lambda)\, \Phi(t,s_i)[\mathbf{h}(\hat{z}(s_i),v_i) - \mathbf{h}(\hat{z}(s_i),\hat{u}(s_i))] + o(\beta\lambda,t),$$

where we have used the fact that $\Phi(t,s_q)\Phi(s_q,s_i) = \Phi(t,s_i)$ and $o(\beta\lambda,t)/\beta \to 0$ as $\beta \to 0$ uniformly for $\lambda \in \Lambda$ and $t \in [s_q,T]$. Substituting from (50) into (62), we get, for $t \in [s_q, T]$,

63 $$z_{\beta\epsilon,\lambda}(t) = \hat{z}(t) + \beta\,\delta z(t) + o(\beta\,\delta z(t), t),$$

where $o(\beta\,\delta z(t), t)/\beta \to 0$ as $\beta \to 0$ uniformly for $t \in [s_q, T]$ and $\delta z(\cdot) \in \text{co}\,\{0, \epsilon\,\delta z_1, \epsilon\,\delta z_2, \ldots, \epsilon\,\delta z_p\}$, and where we have made use of the bicontinuous one-to-one correspondence between $\delta z(\cdot)$ and λ.

Since we have shown that (63) holds for $k = 1$, and that if it is true for $k = q - 1$, then it is also true for $k = q$, with $q = 1, 2, \ldots$, the theorem is proved. □

It now follows from the definitions of $\zeta(\cdot)$ [see (38)] and from (63) that for every $\beta\,\delta z(\cdot)$ in co $\{0, \epsilon\,\delta z_1, \epsilon\,\delta z_2, \ldots, \epsilon\,\delta z_p\}$, with $0 \leqq \beta \leqq 1$,

64 $$\zeta(\hat{z} + \beta\,\delta z)(T) = \hat{z}(T) + \beta\,\delta z(T) + o(\beta\,\delta z(T)),$$

where $o(\beta\,\delta z(T))/\beta \to 0$ as $\beta \to 0$ uniformly for $\delta z \in \text{co}\,\{0, \epsilon\,\delta z_1, \epsilon\,\delta z_2, \ldots, \epsilon\,\delta z_p\}$. Recalling definition (14), we find that for any $\beta\,\delta z \in \text{co}\,\{0, \epsilon\,\delta z_1, \epsilon\,\delta z_2, \ldots, \epsilon\,\delta z_p\}$ and $0 \leqq \beta \leqq 1$

65 $$\begin{aligned} f(\zeta(\hat{z} + \beta\,\delta z)) &= P_1 e_T \zeta(\hat{z} + \beta\,\delta z) \\ &= P_1(\hat{z}(T) + \beta\,\delta z(T) + o(\beta\,\delta z(T))). \end{aligned}$$

Since $f(\hat{z}) = P_1(\hat{z}(T))$, we find that

66 $$\lim_{\beta \to 0} \frac{1}{\beta} \left(f(\zeta(\hat{z} + \beta\,\delta z)) - f(\hat{z}) - \beta\,\delta z(T) \right) = 0$$

uniformly for $\delta z \in \text{co}\,\{0, \epsilon\,\delta z_1, \epsilon\,\delta z_2, \ldots, \epsilon\,\delta z_p\}$. Hence if we define $f'(\hat{z}) : \mathfrak{L} \to E^1$ by

67 $$f'(\hat{z})(\delta z) = P_1 e_T\,\delta z = P_1\,\delta z(T),$$

we see that (B.1.4) is satisfied, since the linearity and continuity of $f'(\hat{z})(\cdot)$ are obvious.

Similarly, for any $\delta z \in \text{co}\,\{0, \epsilon\,\delta z_1, \epsilon\,\delta z_2, \ldots, \epsilon\,\delta z_p\}$ and $0 \leqq \beta \leqq 1$

68 $$r(\zeta(\hat{z} + \beta\,\delta z)) = g(P_2(\hat{z}(T) + \beta\,\delta z(T) + o(\beta\,\delta z(T)))).$$

Since $g(\cdot)$ is continuously differentiable, (68) can be expanded as

69 $$\begin{aligned} r(\zeta(\hat{z} + \beta\,\delta z)) = g(P_2\hat{z}(T)) + \frac{\partial g(P_2(\hat{z}(T)))}{\partial x}\,\beta P_2\,\delta z(T) \\ + o(\beta\,\delta z(T)), \end{aligned}$$

where $o(\beta\, \delta z(T))/\beta \to 0$ as $\beta \to 0$ uniformly for $\delta z \in \text{co}\, \{0, \epsilon\, \delta z_1, \epsilon\, \delta z_2, \ldots, \epsilon\, \delta z_p\}$. Therefore if we define $r'(\hat{z})\colon \mathcal{L} \to E^m$ by

70 $$r'(\hat{z})(\delta z) = \frac{\partial g(P_2(\hat{z}(T)))}{\partial x} P_2\, \delta z(T),$$

we find that (B.1.5) is satisfied, since the linearity and continuity of $r'(z)(\cdot)$ are obvious.

Hence we have shown that the set $C(\hat{z},\Omega)$ defined in (26) is indeed a conical approximation to Ω at $\hat{z}$, with respect to the maps $f(\cdot)$ and $r(\cdot)$.

We can now establish the Pontryagin maximum principle for fixed-time problems.

71 **Theorem: maximum principle.** If $\hat{u}(\cdot)$ is an optimal control for problem (1) and $\hat{x}(\cdot)$ is a corresponding optimal trajectory, then there exist a scalar $p^0 \leqq 0$ and a costate trajectory $p(\cdot)$, from $[0,T]$ into E^n, with $(p^0,p(t)) \neq 0$, such that

72 $$\frac{d}{dt} p(t) = -p^0 \left[\frac{\partial h^0(\hat{x}(t),\hat{u}(t))}{\partial x}\right]^T - \left[\frac{\partial h(\hat{x}(t),\hat{u}(t))}{\partial x}\right]^T p(t) \qquad \text{for } t \in [0,T],$$

73 $$p(T) = \left[\frac{\partial g(\hat{x}(T))}{\partial x}\right]^T \psi \qquad \text{for some } \psi \in E^m,$$

and for every $v \in U$ and almost all $t \in [0,T]$

74 $$p^0 h^0(\hat{x}(t),\hat{u}(t)) + \langle p(t),h(\hat{x}(t),\hat{u}(t))\rangle \geqq p^0 h^0(\hat{x}(t),v) + \langle p(t),h(\hat{x}(t),v)\rangle.$$

Proof. Let us consider the optimal control problem (1) in basic form [see definition (21)]. If $\hat{z}(\cdot) = (\hat{z}^0(\cdot),\hat{x}(\cdot))$ is an optimal solution corresponding to an optimal control $\hat{u}(\cdot)$, then, by theorem (B.1.6), there exists a vector $\psi = (p^0,\psi)$ in E^{m+1} such that

75 $$p^0 f'(\hat{z})(\delta z) + \langle \psi, r'(\hat{z})(\delta z)\rangle \leqq 0 \qquad \text{for all } \delta z \in C(\hat{z},\Omega),$$

with $C(\hat{z},\Omega)$, $f'(\hat{z})(\cdot)$, and $r'(\hat{z})(\cdot)$ as defined in (26), (67), and (70), respectively. Substituting for $f'(\hat{z})(\cdot)$ and $r'(\hat{z})(\cdot)$ in (75) and choosing a $\delta z \in C(\hat{z},\Omega)$ of the form

76 $$\delta z = \delta z_{s,v},$$

with $s \in I$ and $v \in U$, arbitrary, we obtain for (75)

77
$$p^0\langle P_1^T, \Phi(T,s)[\mathbf{h}(\hat{z}(s),v) - \mathbf{h}(\hat{z}(s),\hat{u}(s))]\rangle + \langle \psi, \frac{\partial g(x(T))}{\partial x} P_2\, \Phi(T,s)[\mathbf{h}(\hat{z}(s),v) - \mathbf{h}(\hat{z}(s),\hat{u}(s))]\rangle \leqq 0.$$

Rearranging terms yields

78
$$\langle \Phi^T(T,s) \left\{ p^0 P_1^T + P_2^T \left[\frac{\partial g(\hat{x}(T))}{\partial x} \right]^T \psi \right\}, \qquad [\mathbf{h}(\hat{z}(s),v) - \mathbf{h}(\hat{z}(s),\hat{u}(s))] \leqq 0\rangle.$$

Now let $\mathbf{p}$: $[0,T] \to E^{n+1}$ be defined by

79
$$\mathbf{p}(t) = \Phi^T(T,t) \left\{ p^0 P_1^T + P_2^T \left[\frac{\partial g(\hat{x}(T))}{\partial x} \right]^T \psi \right\},$$

and let us write $\mathbf{p}(t) = (p^0(t),p(t))$, with $p(t) = (p^1(t), p^2(t), \ldots, p^n(t)) \in E^n$. Then, by inspection of (79), (24), and (10), we obtain

80
$$p^0(T) = p^0 \qquad p(T) = \left[\frac{\partial g(\hat{x}(T))^T}{\partial x} \right] \psi$$

and

81
$$\frac{d}{dt}\mathbf{p}(t) = - \left[\frac{\partial \mathbf{h}(\hat{z}(t),\hat{u}(t))}{\partial z} \right]^T \mathbf{p}(t).$$

Expansion of (81) in components yields

82
$$\frac{d}{dt} p^0(t) = 0$$

83
$$\frac{d}{dt} p(t) = - p^0 \left[\frac{\partial h^0(\hat{x}(t),\hat{u}(t))}{\partial x} \right]^T - \left[\frac{\partial h(\hat{x}(t),\hat{u}(t))}{\partial x} \right]^T p(t).$$

If we now substitute $p(t)$ into (78), we get (74). □

The maximum principle can also be extended to free-time problems and to problems in which the function h depends on t as well as on x and u. These extensions are quite simple and are left as an exercise for the reader.

This concludes our discussion of optimization problems in infinite-dimensional spaces.

REFERENCES

1. L. S. Pontryagin, V. G. Boltyanskii, R. V. Gamkrelidze, and E. F. Mishchenko: "The Mathematical Theory of Optimal Processes," Interscience Publishers, Inc., New York, 1962.

2. E. J. McShane: "Integration," Princeton University Press, Princeton, N.J., 1944.
3. J. L. Kelley: "General Topology," D. Van Nostrand Company, Inc., Princeton, N.J., 1955.
4. R. V. Gamkrelidze: On Some Extremal Problems in the Theory of Differential Equations with Applications to the Theory of Optimal Control, *SIAM J. Control*, **3**:106–128 (1965).
5. L. W. Neustadt: An Abstract Variational Theory with Applications to a Broad Class of Optimization Problems, I. General Theory, II. Applications, *SIAM J. Control*, **4**:505–527 (1964), **5**:90–137 (1967).
6. N. O. Da Cunha and E. Polak: Constrained Minimization Under Vector-valued Criteria in Linear Topological Spaces, in A. V. Balakrishnan and L. W. Neustadt (eds.), "Mathematical Theory of Control," pp. 10–25, Academic Press, Inc., New York, 1966.

Glossary of Symbols

I. GENERAL CONVENTIONS

1. E^n denotes the euclidean space of ordered n-tuples of real numbers. Elements of E^n are denoted by lowercase letters, and when it is necessary to show the components of a vector x in E^n, it is done as follows: $x = (x^1,x^2, \ldots ,x^n)$. When an n-tuplet $(x^1,x^2, \ldots ,x^n)$ is a vector in E^n, it is always treated as a *column* vector in matrix multiplications; i.e., it is transposed into an $n \times 1$ matrix, but the transposition symbol is omitted.

2. When a vector z or $\mathbf{x}$, in E^{m+1} is constructed from a vector $x = (x^1,x^2, \ldots ,x^m)$ in E^m by adding one component to the elements of x, and we wish to indicate this fact, then we depart from the notation in item 1, above and write the components of z or x as follows: $z = (z^0,x^1,x^2, \ldots ,x^m)$ or $\mathbf{x} = (x^0,x^1,x^2, \ldots ,x^m)$.

3. The scalar product in E^n is defined by $\langle x,y\rangle = \Sigma_{i=1}^{n} x^i y^i$; the euclidean norm is defined by $\|x\| = \sqrt{\langle x,x\rangle}$.

4. g or $g(\cdot)$ denotes a function, with the dot standing for the undesignated variable; $g(x)$ denotes the value of g at the point x. To indicate that the domain of a function g is A and that its range is B, we write $g\colon A \to B$. Assuming that $g\colon E^n \to E^m$, we write g in expanded form as follows: $g = (g^1, g^2, \ldots, g^m)$, so that $g(x) = (g^1(x), g^2(x), \ldots, g^m(x))$ is the image of x and is a vector in E^m. (The components of g are real-valued functions).

5. A function $g\colon E^n \to E^m$ is said to be *affine* if for all x in E^n $g(x) = b + \tilde{g}(x)$, where b is a fixed vector in E^m and $\tilde{g}\colon E^n \to E^m$ is a linear function.

6. $\dfrac{\partial g(\hat{x})}{\partial x}$ (or $\partial g(\hat{x})/\partial x$) denotes the jacobian matrix of g at $\hat{x}$. Assuming that $g\colon E^n \to E^m$, the jacobian is an $n \times m$ matrix whose ijth element is $\partial g^i(\hat{x})/\partial x^j$.

7. $\nabla f(\hat{x})$ denotes the gradient at $\hat{x}$ of a function $f\colon E^n \to E^1$. It is always treated as a column vector and is seen to be the transpose of the $1 \times n$ jacobian matrix $\partial f(\hat{x})/\partial x$. Consequently, for any y in E^n the scalar product of $\nabla f(\hat{x})$ with y satisfies $\langle \nabla f(\hat{x}), y\rangle = \dfrac{\partial f(\hat{x})}{\partial x}\, y$. For emphasis, we shall sometimes write the latter as $\left\langle \dfrac{\partial f(\hat{x})}{\partial x}, y \right\rangle$.

8. Superscript minus one (-1) denotes the inverse of a matrix, e.g., Q^{-1}.

9. Superscript capital T denotes the transpose of a matrix, e.g., R^T.

10. Superscript perpendicular $(\perp)$ denotes the orthogonal complement of a subspace, e.g., $\mathfrak{N}^{\perp}$.

II. GENERAL SYMBOLS AND ABBREVIATIONS

$A \triangleq B$	A equals B by definition; denotes
$A \Rightarrow B$	A implies B
$A \Leftarrow B$	A is implied by B
$A \supset B$	A contains B
$A \subset B$	A is contained in B; A is a subset of B
$A \cup B$	union of A and B
$A \cap B$	intersection of A and B
$A \times B$	cartesian product of A and B
$\{x : P\}$	set of x's having property P

$x \in A$	x is an element of A
$x \notin A$	x does not belong to A
$A + B$	$= \{x: x = y + z, y \in A, z \in B\}$ (linear combination of sets)
A/B	$= \{x: x \in A, x \notin B\}$ (difference of sets)
$\dot{A}$	interior of A
$\bar{A}$	closure of A if $A \subset E^n$; complement of A if $A \subset \{1,2,\ldots,m\}$
∂A	boundary of A
co A	convex hull of A
$\overline{\text{co}}$ A	closure of convex hull of A
rel int A	relative interior of A
(a,b)	open interval $\{t: a < t < b\}$
$(a,b]$	semiclosed interval $\{t: a < t \leq b\}$
$[a,b]$	closed interval $\{t: a \leq t \leq b\}$
$\langle\cdot,\cdot\rangle$	scalar product (dots stand for undesignated variables)
$\cdot\rangle\langle\cdot$	dyad (for $x \in E^n$ and $y \in E^m$, $x\rangle\langle y$ is the $n \times m$ matrix xy^T)
$\|\cdot\|$	euclidean norm
max (a,b)	max $(a,b) = a$ if $a \geqq b$, max $(a,b) = b$ if $b > a$
$\max\limits_i$	maximum over i
$x \geqq y$	for $x,y \in E^n$, $x \geqq y$ if $x^i \geqq y^i$ for $i = 1,2,\ldots,n$
sgn	signum function: sgn $x = 1$ for $x > 0$, sgn $x = -1$ for $x < 0$, sgn $x = 0$ for $x = 0$
sat	saturation function: sat $x = x$ for $\|x\| \leqq 1$, sat x = sgn x for $\|x\| > 1$
$\square$	end discussion (proof)

III. SYMBOLS WITH SPECIAL MEANING

$C(\hat{z},\Omega)$	conical approximation to Ω at $\hat{z}$
$IC(\hat{z},\Omega)$	internal cone to Ω at $\hat{z}$
$RC(\hat{z},\Omega)$	radial cone to Ω at $\hat{z}$
$TC(\hat{z},\Omega)$	tangent cone to Ω at $\hat{z}$
$TC_s(\hat{z},\Omega)$	sequential tangent cone to Ω at $\hat{z}$
f	cost function
r	equality constraint function
$F = (f,r)$	
q^0	cost function
q	inequality constraint function
Ω,Ω'	constraint sets
I	active inequality constraint index set
J	basis indicator index set
x_i	state of dynamical system at time i
u_i	system input at time i
f_i	dynamics function
f_i^0	incremental cost function
$\mathfrak{X}$	trajectory (of states)
$\mathfrak{U}$	control sequence

X_i, X'_i, X''_i	state space constraints at time i
U_i	control constraint at time i
$\mathbf{x}_i$	phase (augmented state) at time i
$\mathbf{X}$	trajectory (of phases)
q_i	inequality constraint function (state space)
g_i	equality constraint function (state space)
k	duration of discrete optimal control process

Index